ThE   UCAL

BOOK IV

Eternal Words

J. J. DEWEY

GREAT AD-VENTURES

P. O. Box 8011
Boise, Idaho 83707

Great AD-Ventures; P. O. Box 8011; Boise, Idaho 83707

ISBN: ISBN: 0-9665053-4-4

First Printing: June, 2006

Printed in USA

Dedicated to all the seekers of the world.

Enjoy!

Many thanks to my wife, Susan Carter and
Sharón Miller for their editing and suggestions.

Comments from Readers
From The Keys of Knowledge Internet Discussion group

"This is JJ Dewey's best book so far. I couldn't put it down. Just when you think he has taken you as far as you think you can go, he takes you even farther. It's a roller coaster ride, and the whole universe is your amusement park."
John Crane

"Sometimes it takes a great stretch of the imagination to reach new realms of experience and reality. Mr JJ Dewey certainly stimulates the reader and takes them on a journey into such profound possibilities. Very highly recommended."
Steven Meakin

"In 'Eternal Words,' author J.J. Dewey delivers once more an incredible journey of expansive thought on the nature of who we are as spiritual beings and our relationship to the One Great Life… Not until now have but a few individuals achieved such a beautiful crafting of words as Dewey has to explain for the "everyman" the deep meaning behind this phrase so it can be easily understood in its fullest of magnitude."
James Wong

"Read this book to discover the profound truth in the relationship between the life forces on the all levels of our universe. Where the journeys of such science fiction as Fantastic Voyage and Star Trek leave off, this book will pick you up and take you on the ultimate sojourn of science truth."
Adam B. Clayton

"This book contains a sequence, the communication between Joseph and the least and greatest consciousness in the universe, that, when grasped and explored by our scientists, will take us far beyond quantum physics and, ultimately, unite science and religion, by simultaneously answering the ultimate questions posed by each. Anyone that did not get this impression need only go back and re-read that chapter a few times."
Rick Audette, founder of "the Keys of Knowledge"

"Once again JJ takes us on an amazing journey that stretches our preconceptions of all that we believe we know, illuminates dark corners we didn't know existed, and reveals an unlimited horizon. These truly are Eternal Words!"
Olivia Weinbauer

"This book really stretches the imagination and answers so many questions in religion and science. This is better than science fiction. If you want to know who God really is and his role in the marriage between science and religion, then read this book. It's difficult to put down once you start reading it and when you're through, satisfaction is guaranteed."
Arit Efiong

"JJ Dewey adds another book to his growing saga of Joe and John, sharing with the reader his views of Aquarian Buddhism in an enjoyable fictional format. Dewey's views into consciousness and hermetic structuralism make one wonder how fictional this work really is, or if Dewey is merely a self-effacing genius with unique insights into Thothian philosophy and Builder sciences."
Woody Sanford

CHAPTER ONE
The Book

For some reason I had difficulty going to sleep. While I tossed and turned, my wife Elizabeth slept as soundly as a babe.

I usually have no problem going to sleep so I thought that perhaps I had too much on my mind. I decided to clear my thoughts and let my mind drift aimlessly. What happened next was surreal. I couldn't tell if I was entering a dream state, some out-of-body experience or an alternate reality.

I was transported to some type of large room, something like a courtroom, where I was sitting in a chair surrounded by a group of powerful entities or judges of some kind. There were several dozen of them. Each was wearing a blue robe with hoods like monks so I couldn't make out many of their features. Their robes were tied around the waist by cords of varying colors. I assumed this signified status of some kind.

One of them with a silver cord was walking back and forth in front of me as if he were pondering a question. Then he stopped, looked my direction and asked pointedly, "So, you are writing about the Keys of Knowledge?"

I looked around nervously, then back at him and answered, "Yes."

"And how do you justify the presentation of sacred truth mixed with fiction?"

I was startled and perplexed, "I didn't know I had to justify it. I am fulfilling an assignment given to me by John."

The man turned away as if he were scanning the group and then quickly looked at me again saying, "It matters not who gives you an assignment; it matters not whether the person is a God, an angel or a Satan. You must always justify your choice if you aspire to the Brotherhood of Light."

"Okay," I responded meekly.

"So, how do you justify your decision?"

"I don't see anything to justify. I'm writing a story that contains fact and fiction, but presents truth in an interesting way."

"But the fiction could distort the truth."

"And fiction can also enhance the truth," I countered.

"Enhance the truth?" he asked incredulously.

"Do you recall the book Uncle Tom's Cabin?" I asked.

"Of course."

"Harriet Beecher Stowe presented truth enhanced by fiction and changed the course of history, leading to the freeing of the slaves. What was the better course: to write a book of philosophy or to enhance the truth with fiction so it registered with the souls of men?"

The man stopped pacing and stood perfectly still. There was an uncomfortable period of about a minute of stone silence. The man then withdrew and took a seat.

Then a second person came forward, approached me and asked, "Why should you be the one to reveal the Keys when there are many others who are willing to take this position of glory?"

This was feeling more like an interrogation, making me uncomfortable. "I've asked myself that question," I said. "Maybe I should not be the one."

"But you volunteered to do this," he said authoritatively.

"I don't think so," I replied. "John gave me the assignment."

"But you have forgotten. Think back before your current life. You wanted to be the one to teach the Keys. Why do you think it should be you?"

I stood up and surveyed the group. "I'm not sure what this questioning is about, but if you are the ones who have custody of the Keys and one of you wants the job and are capable of doing it, then go ahead and replace me. If you want to call on another disciple who is more advanced than I, then go ahead. What matters is that the job gets done."

I then sat back down almost regretting what I had said, for if they replaced me I may not see John again in this lifetime. The thought saddened me.

I hardly dared to look up, but again there was silence. The second man with the green cord withdrew and sat down. A few seconds later a man with an orange cord approached me.

"Why do you consider yourself worthy to reveal the Keys to this age, when even the purest of men have not considered themselves endowed with the necessary righteousness?"

I looked around the room and sensed great interest in my answer. I wasn't sure how I was doing so I just blurted out my thoughts, "I'm not sure I am worthy of anything I have received. I'm not sure I am worthy to live in abundance in a free country. I'm not sure if I am worthy of my wife. And I'm really not sure if I am worthy to teach the Keys. All I know is that I do not feel unworthy of any gift from God. I honor my Lord by accepting that which I have been given."

After my answer the third man took his seat and I took the chance to survey the group. My eyes seemed to rest on one whose gentle smile graced his face. As my eyes fixed on his he arose and approached me. I noticed his robe, which first appeared blue, but started glistening into a robe of many colors tied by a brilliant gold cord. He came close and looked at me, but a rainbow of colors emanating from him obscured his face. All I caught was a glimpse of his penetrating eyes of fire which permeated me to the core. I felt so stirred inside I had to use all my self control to not cry like a baby in front of the group.

He placed his right hand on the crown of my forehead and said, "Go in peace."

In an instant I was back in my bed filled with spiritual fire and immediately sat up contemplating the vision, dream or whatever it was. Was this real or just a vivid dream? After thinking of the experience a few minutes, I was able to drift off into a very peaceful sleep.

The next morning I got up early and printed up the complete manuscript of the first book to give to Elizabeth for a final reading. As the printer was whirring out the pages I thought again of my experience with the Brotherhood. I decided to not tell Elizabeth until I had thought it through for a while.

After I heard Elizabeth stirring in the kitchen I took the completed manuscript and walked up to her. She was sitting at the

kitchen counter reading the paper. I tossed the manuscript in front
of her. It landed with a splat that startled her.

"It's done," I said.

Elizabeth composed herself and stared at the uneven pile of
sheets. "You mean the book?" she asked, thumbing through the
pages.

"Yep. That's the first volume. Only eleven more to go," I
added wryly.

"You plan on writing twelve books?" she asked.

"Actually it will be more than twelve. John once told me that
I will write at least twelve books revealing his teachings as well as
others giving my own philosophy."

"Well, you'd better get busy then because at the rate you are
going, you'll never get everything written," she said, showing her
practical nature.

"This business we started takes more time than I expected," I
added. "After working eighty to a hundred hours a week it takes a
lot of discipline to sit down and work on a book. At this rate it will
take a while, but when the time comes that we can make a living
from the book sales, I think I will be able to put out the writings
quite quickly."

"Let's hope so," she said. "Did you do a word count on this?"

"Yes," I said. "It's around 53,000 words."

"That's a fairly small book," she said. "Over 100,000 words
would be a lot better."

"We could publish it in big print," I mused, smiling.

She smiled but firmly stated, "That annoys me when publish-
ers do that. It makes me feel shortchanged."

"So what should we do then?" I said. "The book has a natural
ending where I left off. I don't think it would flow well if I added
some chapters."

"Perhaps the solution is to write a second book and combine
the two into one volume. Then a reader would have enough material to grab his attention."

I took in what she said and paced the floor. "This is crazy," I
said. "Here I was all ready to publish the book and within a minute's
time you've made me realize that I need to write another book
before we even get off the ground. That could take another year
with the limited time I have."

"Don't look at me," she said, looking deliberately innocent. "I'm just giving you my opinion."

"But your opinion is right," I admitted. "I think we do need more material before we publish. I've got an idea though."

"What's that?"

"We can place the first book on the internet and see what kind of feedback we get. This will stimulate interest in preparation for publishing books One and Two as one volume."

"Sounds good," she said. "Haven't you already placed some of the things John taught you in some discussion groups?"

"Yes, I put a few things out there to test the interest. I received some good feedback, but it seems there a lot more people interested in what some space alien or an exotic channeler has to say than in merely learning some true principles with no claim of authority."

"But if you told people that you've received keys from John the Beloved that would surely perk their interest."

"You know I can't do that. He told me that he can only be presented in story form as a possible fictional character. I am not to talk or write about him as a real person. There seems to be some danger involved if the world knew the truth about him."

"Well, it seems to be a big drawback for us that you can only present him as a fictional character. That means we are left with the teachings as the only proof that you are receiving them from a divine source."

"True," I agreed, "but don't you see? That's the way John wants it and somehow I sense that's the way it is supposed to be. If people believe me because I receive from John then they will believe because of John and not because of their perception of the truth. A seeker must learn to discover truth through the Oneness Principle no matter where it comes from, without needing a confirmation from some outer authority. The inner authority is what's supposed to count."

"You may be right," she said, "but the trouble is that most people need some type of outward authority. It's going to be difficult to get the attention of the public when we have to rely on people's inner sensitivity."

"But that's where the book, or should I say books, will come in," I said. "Because of John, the teachings will be so profound that those who are sensitive will know there is something special behind them."

"Let's hope so," she said. "Didn't John say he wanted to read the first book when you finished it?"

"Yes, he did. He didn't want to read a word while I was writing it, but did want to read it when it was completed."

"You'd think he would want to read it as you go along so he could make suggestions," she said.

"I think his waiting has something to do with some non-interference principle," I replied. "He once told me that in times past, the Brotherhood assisted humanity with what humanity could do for itself; problems were created and the work was ineffective. They apparently only assist us when absolutely necessary. You've probably heard the story of what happens when a human assists a butterfly emerging from its cocoon?"

"Yes, I've heard that story," she said. "If someone gives the butterfly too much help it will die; but if it goes through a great struggle breaking out of its cocoon, it will live and be strong and healthy." She paused a moment in thought and added, "So what happens next? Do you have some secret method of signaling John to let him know that you have finished Book One?"

"Not really, but he does seem to be able to tune into my thoughts quite accurately."

"So that could mean that he already knows you are finished and will be showing up to read it."

"Probably so," I said.

"So, I wonder when he will show up then," she mused.

The doorbell rang.

Elizabeth and I sat up in a jolt and looked at each other. We nervously went to the door and opened it. To our amusement we saw a cute little girl standing next to her mom. "Would you like to order some Girl Scout cookies?" she innocently asked.

"Uh yes, sure," I said as Elizabeth walked back into the kitchen smiling. I ordered three different kinds from the girl and retired to the kitchen table to nurse a cup of coffee.

"Didn't look much like John to me," she chuckled.

"I suppose not," I replied, tearing open a box of Samoan cookies. "She made my heart beat a little faster though. I was kind of disappointed it wasn't him."

"No reason to be disappointed," said a voice in the distance.

Again Elizabeth and I sat up in a jolt as we both looked in the direction of the voice. "I think he's in the computer room," I said.

"Sounds like it," she agreed. We walked down the steps into what was the family room; now used as a work room for our business. There was John staring at my computer screen, probing some of my files.

"Just checking to see if you have started Book Two yet," he said. "You can't let grass grow under your feet you know."

"Well, you've got to let me take a few breaths now I've finished the first book," I replied.

"Maybe," he said. "So, you have finished the first book?"

"Yes, I have. I have a copy for you upstairs. Come on up and we'll get something to drink. Since we don't have Dom Pérignon, coffee or tea will have to do. We also have three varieties of fine cookies to offer you."

"I think I'll go crazy and have coffee and a cookie this time," he said.

We went upstairs, got some coffee, an assortment of cookies and settled around the kitchen table. I handed him a computer print-out of the book. "Here she is," I said with some satisfaction.

John laid the manuscript in front of him on the table as we sat looking on in stoned silence. All three of us stared at it for about 30 seconds. I couldn't stand the silence. "I suppose you're going to tell me that you don't need to read it - that you can just take it in through some form of osmosis," I blurted out.

John looked up and smiled, "Not osmosis," he replied, "but a different kind of reading."

"What kind is that?" Elizabeth asked with great curiosity.

"Residual reading," he smiled.

"I've never heard of residual reading," she said.

"It's a little trick that I learned in the schools of the Brotherhood," he said. "A writing or book begins with thought. That thought is then crystallized into symbols, which are letters combined into words, combined into sentences, then paragraphs, then chapters and finally, the whole book. Behind each of the group symbols of writing is the residual energy of the thought of the writer. An adept can call forth the energy of this thought and direct it into the most basic of symbols and read an entire book in a few seconds."

"Wow! That sounds like quite a trick. Imagine how many books I could read if I could do that. I don't suppose you could teach me?" I asked.

"I could, but that's not a priority at present. I will, however, show you how the basic principle works and if you contemplate what you see here, you can use it to some degree."

"Sounds great," I said, expectantly.

"Hold hands for a moment," he instructed. After joining hands, he repeated a sequence of sounds that I am not supposed to put in writing. I felt a strange feeling of lightness as if I weighed only a few pounds. Then just as I felt we were about to float away, John dropped our hands and began to wave his own hands over the book, finally settling his palms, turned upward, a few inches above the manuscript. As he slowly raised his hands, something amazing happened. Suddenly, it appeared as if all the words and letters were rising off the page, passing through his hands and turning into symbols of light. They then began to form a circular motion about eye level and had the appearance of small complex symbols joining into greater, but more simplistic ones. Finally, they assumed something close to a Star of David within a circle and these were finally reduced to two golden triangles. One rotated counterclockwise and the other clockwise while oscillating and giving off some type of penetrating hum.

"What does this mean?" I asked.

"Focus," he commanded, not taking his attention off the triangle.

I attempted to focus to the best of my ability and noticed that Elizabeth was also. After a few seconds another strange thing happened. Suddenly, I felt the vibration permeate my body and spirit and in the same instant I began to understand the triangles as if they were living things merging with me. Within a few seconds I saw the book from beginning to end and more. I also took in the feelings, thoughts and experiences I had while writing the book. Every thought connected with the book was laid bare and absorbed.

After a few more seconds the triangle disappeared and John looked at me and said, "That, my friend, is residual reading."

"Wow!" I exclaimed again. "I know everything in the book and feel connected to it."

"You should. You wrote it," Elizabeth smiled.

"No. It's not remembering," I said. "It's like I just finished carefully reading the book all the way through again and then interviewed myself about all the missing details."

"I know," said Elizabeth. "I had the same experience."

"I assume that you saw the same thing we did?" I said, looking at John.

"That and more," he replied. "I know this process has amazed you but many who are sensitive already use it to a degree."

"How is that?" I asked.

"Have you ever been in a bookstore looking for a book to read and one particular book just seems to call to you for no particular reason?"

"Yes, several times."

"Many have had this experience and there is a reason for it. Your soul has the full capacity for residual reading, and, when it scans a book that is important for you to read, it will send a message to your lower nature about it. Those who are sensitive to soul impression will pick up an impression about the book and those who are wise will follow the impression."

"Most interesting."

John paused and changed the subject, "As I indicated earlier, the philosophy of the Brotherhood is to allow disciples and humanity to do as much for itself as possible. We only intervene when absolutely necessary or in the midst of a great crisis. I have followed this principle with you in that I have avoided unduly influencing you or even reading the book until it was finished."

"So, what did you think?" I asked, veiling my anxiousness.

His face turned more serious than normal as he replied, "Quite an interesting presentation. It is different than anything we have tried before. You've altered a number of things."

There was something about the way he said the word *altered* that disturbed me, almost as if he was inferring I had done something wrong. The thought made me reflect on my experience last night. "But you told me I was to use my judgment to alter details to make an interesting story. You even said I could alter your character or identity."

"Yes, I did, didn't I?" he said reflectively, glancing at the manuscript. "But there's been a new development since then."

"What new development? Does it have anything to do with the dream I had last night?"

"That was no dream," he said. "You were the center of a rift in the Brotherhood."

"What rift? What dream?" Elizabeth asked, looking back and forth at both of us.

I took a minute and related the experience to her.

John then continued, "When I gave you the mission to write the book, I did so after conferring with Joshua; but since then, a number of the Masters in the Brotherhood have developed reservations about the plan."

"Reservations?" I asked incredulously.

"Yes, reservations," he affirmed. "This is why you were brought to the conclave. You were questioned by the three who had reservations about the plan."

"Who *were* those three?" I asked. "I sensed they had not given their approval to the project. I tried to study them but they had their faces covered."

"They all had their hoods on because it is not yet time to reveal them. You do know, however, who the one is who touched your head?"

"Yes. I had a powerful impression about him."

"Hey, I'm out of the loop here," Said Elizabeth. "Who are we talking about?"

"Think a moment," said John. "Who comes to your mind?"

After a pause Elizabeth's countenance changed. "Oh yes, now I know. I don't know how I know, but I know it was Him."

John let the reality sink in and continued, "The situation has created somewhat of a rift in our deliberations. Some feel that disciples such as you should only present truth in its purest form, whereas others feel that the standard method has not worked in our last two attempts and a different approach is needed for a new era. We have used parables before to bring the truth to seekers, so most of the Brotherhood viewed the use of a story in novel form with some fictional events as a creative extension of what has been approved in the past. But not all feel this way."

"I was under the impression that the Brotherhood see eye-to-eye on all things of importance. Don't they all merely use the Oneness Principle through the soul and see as one?"

"As principles go you are correct, but as far as current decisions affect the future, there is not always complete harmony. Remember the visions you had of the future—that you saw a number of possible future outcomes, and that no outcome is completely certain?"

"Yes, I remember very clearly. I was surprised to learn that even the Masters cannot make completely accurate predictions all the time."

"Yes" he replied, "and that uncertainty is the basis of the current problem. The Brotherhood, when looking into the future, has seen the possibility that mixing some fiction with fact and true principles may do more harm than good."

"But didn't you indicate that Shakespeare had contact with the Brotherhood?"

"He did," John nodded, "but all his writings were presented as plays, not as teachings, even though they contained much wisdom."

"And how big is the possibility that the fictionalized books I write could do more harm than good?" I asked with my heart sinking.

"About twenty to twenty-five percent, but that is enough to be of concern, and some think the project is not worth the risk."

"It appears they are aware of the book, but have they read it?" I gasped.

"No. They have tuned into your vibration, but are in the same situation I was. They are waiting completion of the first book before they read and make a final judgment."

"That first person who questioned me seemed very concerned about using some fiction in the presentation."

"Yes," said John. "Of all the Brotherhood he is perhaps the most concerned, but your answer silenced him like I have never seen happen before."

"Really? I thought the *Uncle Tom's Cabin* reference was a good one, but not particularly a stroke of genius."

"Oh, but it was genius; if you only knew. You see this master took great interest in the slavery question and approached Harriet Beecher Stowe in the dream state and inspired her to write that book. Your answer touched the group to the core and made a couple of us smile."

"Wow," I replied. "I guess even I get lucky once in a while." Then I thought back on the book and asked, "And what happens if they decide against the book? Does this mean that we just forget the project?" I asked with some exasperation.

"Not exactly," he said. "All that you have written and will write is yours to promote as you will."

"So what would happen if they decided against the project?"

"If they decided against the project, you could still publish the book, but the Brotherhood would not give it their spiritual endorsement. It would basically have the power of an ordinary book."

"And what would the difference be if they did endorse it?"

"This book you have written along with the rest of the Keys would be endowed with a spiritual energy, a strong residual energy, which will affect the pure in heart beyond that of an ordinary book. Those who are ready will sense something different about the writings and will be moved by the Spirit of God. This was the plan from the time I approached you, and it is still my hope; but as with all good endeavors, it is difficult to get the needed support, even among the Great Ones."

"It never occurred to me there could be any disagreement among the Masters," I said, deflated.

"You've heard the story of the fall of Lucifer who dwelt in the courts of the Most High?"

"Yes."

"This is a symbol of the difficulty in making a plan and then gathering consensus. No matter how great the lives, no matter how wonderful the vision and understanding of principles, there is some uncertainly as to how those plans will play out. Disagreement periodically comes, even at the highest levels. Sometimes I think it is just God's way of keeping life interesting on an eternal basis."

"Why do I get the feeling that the ideas people have about God, angels, the Masters, Jesus, heaven and hell are all a lot different than people think?" I asked. "I don't think most envision Christ conducting a meeting with a bunch of Masters arguing with each other."

John smiled and replied, "The average believer would be shocked if he could compare his beliefs to that which really is, but let me say in support of the Brotherhood their most controversial meetings would seem very peaceful by human standards. If there is any disagreement it is usually very civil."

"So what's the next step?" I asked.

"The next step is to take the manuscript with me and present it to the Brotherhood, but first, I am going to do something I have not done in a long time."

"What's that?"

"I'm going to sit down and read it the old-fashioned way. Usually, residual reading gives me all I need to know, but I feel I need to actually read it word by word to get a better feel as to how it will affect the consciousness of the reader. This may also help me in my presentation to the Brotherhood."

"It will be interesting to see if you gain additional insights," I said, looking at the manuscript. "This problem with the Masters is a hurdle I never anticipated. A part of me is disappointed that the Masters are not perfect, but then another part of me realizes that what you're saying is true; humanity always believes in an ideal that never quite matches reality."

"Yet, the ideal pushes us ever onward until something greater than the original ideal is achieved," he replied. "Never be upset that reality differs from preconceived notions. The present is always a work in progress and the end is always glorious."

"And the in-between is sometimes a bitch," I half smiled, looking at Elizabeth.

"I can't disagree," John laughed.

Elizabeth spoke up, "You can tell the Brotherhood they'll have me to answer to if they reject the book after all we've gone through."

"I'll pass that along," he smiled. He then reflected a moment and added, "Have you reflected on the third Key of Communion?"

"Yes," I answered, "but will you still be teaching me if the Brotherhood decide against the book?"

"I expect so," he said. "If the plans of presentation change, that would not necessarily mean a change in the messenger."

"Necessarily?" I exclaimed. "Then a change is possible?"

"Anything is possible, but you have made no major missteps to warrant a change, so we will continue on the assumption the plan will continue."

"As Elizabeth said, after all we have gone through it only seems right to continue. I hope the powers-that-be know I am willing to do what I can."

"They know," he said, reassuringly. "Now let us begin the lesson on the next key."

CHAPTER TWO
Imperfect Gods

We refilled our cups with fresh coffee and moved on to the lesson. "Tell me what you recall of the hint towards understanding the Third Key," said John.

I reflected a moment and replied, "You said the Third Key was called *Communion*. I'm not sure if this is a key word or not, but apparently this is what the Key is named. A hint you gave us in understanding the Key is found in the parlor game *Chinese Whispers*. I've played it and it works well in a circle of eight to twelve people. The first person composes an easy-to-understand phrase such as *the cow jumped over the moon* and whispers it in the ear of the person next to him. The second person then takes what he has heard and whispers it to a third and the third person to a fourth until it reaches the last one in the circle. The final person then states what he has just heard. The final version may come out *the bow shot the broom* or something just as jumbled. The original person then gives the true phrase and everyone laughs and wants to try again. Time after time the final phrase is some muddled humorous reflection of the original. It's quite fun to play actually."

"It is entertaining to play as a game," John agreed, "but as the principle plays out in real life, many problems are created that are not so humorous. Can you tell me a couple?"

"I certainly can," injected Elizabeth. "I will tell Joseph something that is important to me and a short time later he will have either forgotten it or only be able to make a feeble attempt at repeating what I have said. With him the statement doesn't have to go around a circle of twelve, but a head of one!"

John laughed. "It's been a long time since I have been married, but your words certainly bring back memories of the male/ female banter over communication. But let's get back to the subject."

John paused a moment in thought and continued: "Decision is perhaps the most profound key. In the beginning I asked WHO/ WHAT ARE YOU? You are more than what you decide to be. The real you is the principle of decision itself. Without decision you would not even exist. Your very life principle is based on this power.

"Before you can make an effective and correct decision you must exercise the power of judgment, but before you can make a good judgment you must use the third key. The name of the third key is COMMUNION and it has another key word which removes veils between you and the truth. A hint that leads to this key is given in the game you mentioned. Now, *the cow jumped over the moon* is a simple enough phrase. What is the problem that causes it to be misunderstood after it is filtered through several people?"

"I've noticed two problems when I've played the game," said Elizabeth. "As the phrase is passed around the circle, the group gets a little light-hearted and the one whispering the phrase is often not very clear in enunciating his words. Sometimes he will even laugh when he's whispering it."

John replied, "So you are saying that even if the receiver is carefully listening there are times it is almost impossible to clearly make out the words?"

"Yes."

"And what's the second problem?

"The second problem is with the receiver. Sometimes he will not hear correctly even if the sender is fairly clear."

"And why does he not hear correctly?"

"I suppose it is because he is not paying enough attention," she said.

"And that brings us to a third problem," I added. "Sometimes there is so much background noise and laughter that you can't hear the whisper because it is drowned out by other sounds."

"Well spoken," said John. "So we have three causes of distortion here. First, there are times when the message is not clear at the time of sending. Second, the receiver is not focused and third, the message is obscured because of background noise. What do you suppose this has to do with the Third Key of Communion?"

"Let me think out loud for a moment," I volunteered. "The word *Communion* implies a communication. It is also the name of the sacrament where bread and wine are taken in remembrance of Christ in an effort to commune with God. The game we are talking about is also a game of communion or communication. Perhaps the person who originates the message can be compared to God. Maybe the first person to hear it is like a prophet or spokesman for God who passes the message along, but the content is changed and misunderstood along the way. I suppose this has happened with Christ's message on love. It was clearly spoken at first, but each generation has distorted it until much of his message has been altered and misunderstood."

"Very good," said John. "But the principle illustrated in the game applies whether the originator is God or man. We want to ask two questions here. What causes the distortion of the original word; and secondly, how can this distortion be corrected? The first part you partially answered, but what is the key to correcting or even preventing such distortion?"

"I think the key is to pay attention," said Elizabeth. Then her eyes lit up as she continued, "Say, I just had a thought. Does this mean that when my husband learns this key, he will be able to listen and understand everything I say?"

"Probably not," smiled John, "but you may see some improvement."

Elizabeth looked like the cat that swallowed the bird for her observation.

After taking a moment to think I added, "I would say that the key is to not distort that which you pass on to others. You've got to make sure that you communicate correctly. For instance, sometimes Elizabeth starts talking to me when my mind is on something else. I'm so deep in thought that I'm sometimes not even aware she is speaking. Then she'll ask me to repeat what she said and I'm in big trouble. What she should have done is to make sure I was listening in the first place."

"You wouldn't think that would be necessary when I'm only a couple feet away," said Elizabeth defensively.

"Good points, all," said John. "Now I want you to take these seed thoughts and think on them until we meet again. Contemplate what the key word must be and the principle behind it."

"Are you leaving already?" I gasped.

"I've given you all I can for the moment on the third key. My job is done and I have much to do."

"But you haven't even finished your coffee," Elizabeth whined. "Can't you just stay and visit for a while?"

"I don't have the luxury of extra time for small talk at the moment," John said. "There would have to be some higher purpose served for me to stay longer."

"No problem," I countered. "I think you will have to agree that when you reviewed the book that your teachings made interesting reading whether you were discussing the Keys or some other topic. The extra teachings you have given out added to the quality of the book. Give us some more teachings now and I will incorporate them in a future book. This can only make it more interesting. Isn't that serving a higher purpose?"

John smiled and leaned back, "I can't resist strong reasoning. Okay, ask me one question."

I hadn't mentally prepared for this response. Over the past couple weeks I had dozens of questions whirring through my mind to ask John, and now that he opened up to one question I found myself temporarily tongue-tied.

"If you don't ask him something then I will," said Elizabeth.

"What did you have in mind?" I said.

"Well, maybe he'd tell us winning lottery numbers," she grinned.

I glanced at John and from the look on his face and the slight shaking of his head back and forth I figured that would be a wasted question. "Maybe I'd better ask," I said.

I reflected over a number of possible questions and finally asked, "Life, creation, man, the universe, what's the purpose of it all? More specifically, what is our ultimate purpose? What does God want out of the whole scheme of things?"

"I guess that if you are going to ask a question, it might as well be the ultimate one," he smiled. "Tell me. What have you heard taught as to the purpose of man?"

"The most popular one is that God made us to please him."

To this John replied, "And according to these teachers, how

many people actually please God?"

"Not too many," I said. "It seems that God is pretty frustrated because of the numbers who disobey him."

"Yet they maintain that God is all powerful, do they not?"

"Yes."

"Tell me then. Why would an all-powerful God create so many who displease him?"

"I guess it doesn't make a lot of sense when you think about it," I said.

"Yet, there are many who rebel against what is seen as God's will. Since God is supposed to know all things, why did he create a plethora of rebels just so he could either destroy them or send them to hell?"

"I've thought about that before," I said. "If I were perfect and all-powerful, I certainly wouldn't have the majority of my creations endowed with such flaws that I would be angry and destroy them all. This has never made sense to me. If I were all powerful I would create the good and useful and avoid making flawed creations. Why would I make a computer that drives me crazy?"

"Your thinking makes sense," he said. "Now let us look at the reality of what you just stated. All creation has the good mixed with the bad. We have life and death, disease and health, beauty and ugliness, pain and pleasure and so forth. Put away all preconceived notions and tell me why this would be so."

I reflected a moment and replied, "Well, many philosophers and eastern thinkers have written much about duality. They say that good and evil are two sides of the same coin that there is no such thing as evil or a bad thing."

"And don't they also say, there is no such thing as a good thing?"

"Yes, I suppose so."

"So, if this coin with two sides is neither good nor evil, then what quality does it possess?"

"They say it is something like Nirvana, a state of ultimate peace where there are no dualities."

"But doesn't this sound like a good end that is to be achieved?"

"It seems to be, but when I have had discussions with people who think this way, they maintain that this peaceful state is not good but just IS, or something to that effect."

"Yet, they speak about it as if it is the ultimate good to achieve, do they not?"

"Yes, they do," I laughed. "They say this ultimate state is neither good nor evil, but they certainly want it more than a good candy bar."

"Indeed," smiled John. "If Nirvana, or the Kingdom of Heaven, did not have a quality we would consider good, then why pursue it? If it truly is *no thing* and it is neither good nor evil, we would have no impulse to travel that path.. Tell me, who in his right mind would travel a strenuous path toward a goal that leads nowhere and rewards one with nothing? Would you?"

"Not really," I said. "I travel the path, despite the hardships, because I believe the end to be a better condition than that which I enjoy today. I suppose that would be a good thing. I certainly would not call it evil, or even a *no thing*."

"If we use logic that even a child can understand, we can reach solid conclusions. Now let me ask again. Put away all pre-conceived notions, including what you have learned of duality and tell me why there is so much imperfection?"

"Okay," I said. "I might sound sacrilegious here, so I'll just let it out. Logically, it would seem that there is so much that is undesirable in creation because everything is created by an imper-fect, rather than a perfect Being. Why would a perfect God create a world and life on it with so many flaws?"

"And what is the standard answer to this question?" he asked.

"Christians say that God did create everything perfect, but the Fall that was caused by man changed everything to an imper-fect state."

"Does this make sense to you?" he asked.

"Not really."

"Why not?"

"According to scripture, the serpent existed before the Fall and he was not perfect. In addition, man could not have been per-fect either because he made an imperfect decision that led to the Fall."

"So, even if we take the Bible literally we must conclude that perfection did not exist before the Fall," John said.

"That seems logical," I said.

"Does the Bible say anywhere that this world or the universe was ever in a perfect state?"

"Not that I recall."

"What does your logic tell you about perfection on the earth millions of years ago?" John asked.

"Well," I said, gathering thoughts, "scientists tell us that the dinosaurs, as well as much life on earth were wiped out by a large meteor or some other major catastrophe. If everything was perfect before man came along, then why would God allow his creation to be destroyed?"

"So, you would agree that since the beginning of this planet there has been much change?"

"Yes, of course."

"And change is still taking place?"

"Yes."

"But if there ever was perfection, no change would be occurring would it?"

"I don't suppose so," I said. "Logically speaking, if we were in a state of perfection which is then followed by change, the perfection would no longer exist."

"Good," he replied. "So if you changed the Mona Lisa by putting a big grin on her face, the painting would lose its perfection, would it not?"

"Yes. Where are we going with this?"

John gave a slight smile, "You are in the process of answering your own question and solving the riddle of existence."

"You're becoming more like Socrates all the time," I observed. "Okay, I'm game. Let's continue."

John replied. "Let us look at what we know. We know that mankind is not perfect now; neither is the earth or the other lives on it. Man also was not perfect before the Fall, for he was an imperfect decision-maker. Then too, all Bible believers accept that the serpent was not perfect. In addition, science tells us that the earth has been far from perfect for millions of years. What does this tell us about God who created it all?"

"At the risk of sounding blasphemous, it would seem that God would also be imperfect. If he were perfect, as the religions teach, then his creations, including humanity and even the serpent would have to be perfect."

"Unless we are perfect and don't know it," injected Elizabeth.

"But you can argue for or against anything using Orwellian doublespeak," I said.

"True," said John "There are those who argue that one plus one equals three through the use of convoluted reasoning. In pursuing the truth it is important to stick to basic reasoning a child can understand. Those who stray from this, venture off into the land of illusion, and have difficulty returning to the basics of truth. So let us stick to basic understandable reasoning. If we then use such reasoning, you are correct that not only is the earth and humanity imperfect, but so is the one who created them. If we approach the meaning of existence from the view that neither God nor man has yet arrived at a point of perfection, what does this tell you about the purpose of creation?"

"Maybe God is lost and just trying to find his way home as the song says," added Elizabeth.

"Maybe," said John. "What do you say, Joseph?"

"Either the purpose of existence is not perfect, and therefore still evolving, or..." I paused in thought.

"Or what?" asked Elizabeth.

"Or perhaps there is a perfection that we are headed toward, but no one, not even God knows exactly what it is yet. This would explain why, in the present, there is so much imperfection yet we feel within our hearts that perfection is possible," I conjectured.

"Your last statement is well spoken and contemplation upon this leads to the understanding of a great mystery," said John.

"Doesn't the Bible tell us to be perfect even as our Father in Heaven is perfect?" injected Elizabeth. "It sounds like Jesus thought that God is perfect now."

"Sounds that way, doesn't it?" said John. "But if you read this scripture in the Greek an entirely different meaning appears. The Greek for the verse Elizabeth quoted from Matthew 5:48 is the word TELEIOS. The adjective form TELEIOO is also used in reference to the perfection of Jesus as in Heb 5:9, which reads, *And being made perfect, he became the author of eternal salvation unto all them that obey him.* This word does not really mean perfection as we think of perfection today, but more literally means *to finish, accomplish, or complete.* Let me; therefore, translate these two verses, as they were understood by the people of that day.

"The verse in Hebrews more correctly should read, *And after finishing his work he became the author of eternal salvation.*

"In the King James Bible the verse that Elizabeth quoted reads: *Be ye therefore perfect, even as your Father which is heaven is perfect.* Instead, it should read, *You shall finish your work even as your Father which is in heaven completes His.*

"To put it in simple modern English we could give this injunction. *Do your job well, even as God does His.*

"The average person has many steps to go before he is as advanced as Christ or his Father, but you are doing your job as they are if you merely take the next step in your progression. When you complete that step and finish your particular work, you are being perfect as God is perfect."

"So did they have a different concept of perfection back then?" I asked.

"There are several Greek words that are translated as *perfect* in most Bibles," he said, "but the word *perfect* of today which implies precision and exact correctness is most correctly represented by the Greek word AKRIBELA. AKRIBELA was used in reference to those who were striving to keep the law and the commandments with exactness and was used in reference to the enemies of Jesus who were very demanding about following the letter of the law. The ironical thing is that those who idealized perfection, as we see it today, saw Jesus as a very imperfect being. As they saw it he was far from exacting in keeping the Sabbath and they accused him of being a glutton, a drunkard, and a party animal who mingled with the low lives."

"Where in the world does it say that?" said Elizabeth.

John smiled, "Much is lost in translation but check out Luke 7:33-34 and you'll see what I mean."

"So why are so many deceived into thinking that God has a perfect plan in place?" I asked.

"Why do you think?" he replied.

"I suppose it is comforting to believe that a higher power cannot make a mistake and that we can depend on Him," I said. "I have to admit that I like the idea of there being a higher power much wiser than myself."

"And of course, there are innumerable higher lives than you. From our vantage point they seem one hundred per cent reliable and all knowing. If we take into account the principle of relativity, then those who represent God in the higher worlds seem perfect to us; but when we look at the wholeness of things, including the imperfections around us, they reveal that even the Creators have not yet achieved perfection."

"So what is the purpose of the imperfect Creator in creating man?"

John paused and replied, looking at us both, "What makes you think you were ever created?"

I was taken back by this, as was Elizabeth, and after a few seconds of absorption I responded, "All the sacred writings of the world say that God created man."

"Not exactly," he said. "All the creation accounts relate the creation of the body of man. Genesis, for instance, describes the creation of Adam's body and adds that God gave him breath that brought him to life, but what is that life that breathes within the body? This is the real question. To answer it let us go back to the lessons of the first Key. Are you your body?"

"No."

"What else are you not?"

"You taught me that I am not my body, neither my emotions nor even my mind."

"So what are you?" he asked.

"I am Decision, the first Key," I said confidently.

"Decision is the first Key word, but not the Key. Let me ask again, what are you?"

"Sorry, I misspoke. You taught me that I am the actual power that is behind the principle of decision."

"Correct," said John. "Decision is the key word because the power behind it is the source of your Eternal Self. Tell me this; can a life be created if it is eternal?"

"Logic would have to say no."

"What logic?"

"Well, if we were created this would mean there would have been a beginning to us; and that which is eternal has no beginning."

"But the churches seem to define eternal life as life that had a beginning on this earth, but will never end," added Elizabeth.

"But does this make sense?" asked John. "Can there be a thing with a beginning and no end?"

"I'm not sure," said Elizabeth.

"See if you can think of something," he challenged.

Elizabeth thought a moment and responded, "I could shine a flashlight into the sky. The light would have a beginning but travel in space forever."

"Good try," smiled John, "but there is a flaw in your reasoning. Most of the photons, which compose the light, will eventually land somewhere and have an end as light. The remaining photons will, in the end of things, be attracted to a black hole and cease to be light. Now from another angle, we can say that the essence of the light is eternal. Its essence was an eternal form of energy before you shined your flashlight and will continue in some other form after it is transmuted. So we can see how the form that the light takes has a beginning and an end, but the essence is eternal. But is there any aspect of the light that has a beginning but no end, or an end with no beginning?"

Elizabeth put her hand to her chin, "Hmmm. I'm not sure."

"The principle of eternity is illustrated by the circle," he continued. "Let me see your ring."

Elizabeth slipped her ring from her finger and handed it to John. He then held it up and said, "Where is the beginning or end to the form of this circular ring? Can you point to the spot?"

"I suppose not," said Elizabeth. "You can't really say where a circle begins or ends."

"Now, suppose I take this ring and cut a piece out of it. Can you then find a beginning and end?"

"Yes," she said. "You then have two ends. One could be a beginning point and the other an end."

"Now for the key question," he said, with a knowing look in his eyes. "Can you shape this ring so it has a beginning with no end or an end with no beginning?"

"I might be able to," she said mischievously.

"When you come up with something let me know," he said handing the ring back to her. She then held the ring for a moment, looking at it like it was a Rubik's Cube.

"I've got a possibility," I said, probably sounding like some eager student in a classroom. "How about a thought? A thought has a beginning, but then never ends. Once a thought is out there, it can't be destroyed." I considered I might have the best of him.

"That is one of the best possibilities I have been presented over the years, but your reasoning has a flaw. Again, let us go back to the lesson on the first key. We concluded that you are not your vehicles. This means you are not your body; neither are you your feelings. We also concluded you are not something else. What was that?"

"You said we are not our thoughts," Elizabeth recalled.

"And why are you not your thoughts?" he asked.

"Because our minds are also a vehicle, just a higher vibration than our physical bodies," I replied.

"Correct," he said. "A thought originates from the eternal world of principles, which has no beginning and no end. The vibration of thought matter then gives it clothing so it can have a beginning to form and manifest in the lower worlds. When the lower worlds collapse and go back to their eternal essence, the body of manifestation for the thought will also end; but the principle behind it never had a beginning and will never end. In addition, in between creations there will be no manifestation of thought as we have it today."

Interesting," I said. "I'll take your word for it that all things in existence are either eternal or transitory, but nothing has a beginning and no end. Where does this take us?"

"It takes us back to the point that you are either created and will have an end or you are uncreated, eternal, and will never have an end."

"If I had to choose between the two, I'd pick the eternal idea. I don't like the idea of coming to an end and ceasing to exist as an entity," I said.

"So if you are eternal and never had a beginning, where does God enter in?" he asked.

"That's just what I was thinking," I said. "What's the difference between me and God if we are both eternal and uncreated?"

"Perhaps less than you think," he said smiling. "Have you not heard that you are in the image of God?"

"Of course"

"And have you not heard the scripture that Jesus is one with God?"

"Yes."

"But perhaps you are not as aware that you are also one with

God. Dust off your Bible and turn to Philippians 2:5-6.

I retrieved the Bible and turned to the passage and read: *"Let this mind be in you, which was in Christ Jesus: who being in the form of God, thought it not robbery to be equal with God."*

"So what state of mind are you supposed to have?"

"The same as Christ," I said.

"And what mindset is that?"

"To think that it is not robbery to be equal with God."

"Wow!" exclaimed Elizabeth. "That's something I never heard preached in church. You seem to be saying that the Bible tells us that we are supposed to see ourselves as equal with God!"

"That seems to be what Paul was saying, does it not?"

I silently read over the passage again and said, "It does seem to be saying that."

John continued, "Arrogant young Jesus angered the Jews by teaching this oneness of God and man. As they tried to stone him he asked them what he had done wrong. Turn to John 10:33-36 for the dialog.

I found the verse and read, *"For a good work we stone thee not; but for blasphemy; and because that thou being a man, makest thyself God. Jesus answered them, Is it not written in your law, I said, Ye are gods? If he called them gods, unto whom the word of God came, and the scripture cannot be broken; Say ye of him, whom the Father hath sanctified, and sent into the world, Thou blasphemest; because I said, I am the Son of God?"*

"Who were called gods by Jesus?" he asked.

"Regular people like you and me."

"Why this is true is taught in John 17:20-22, which records a prayer of Jesus."

I turned the pages and read, *"Neither pray I for these alone [the twelve apostles] but for them also which shall believe on me through their word; that they ALL MAY BE ONE; as thou, Father, art in me, and I in thee, that they also may be ONE IN US: that the world may believe that thou hast sent me. And the glory which thou gavest me I HAVE GIVEN THEM THAT THEY MAY BE ONE, EVEN AS WE ARE ONE."*

John then added, "So regular mortals are to be one in what way?"

"We are to be one even as Jesus and the Father are one," I

replied.

"So if we are gods, how many gods are there?" John asked.

"It would seem that there are many gods."

"But if man and God are one, then how many gods are there?"

"Since you put it that way, there could be only one God?"

"Obviously, we are many lives, and if we are gods then there are many gods," said Elizabeth.

"To put it simply," John continued, "all the lives in the universe make up the body of God just as all the cells in your body make up the life which is you. Each of the cells in your body that realize they share the life of the whole body can say *I am Elizabeth*. Even so, can all who realize they are one with the life of God say with Jesus that it is *not robbery to be equal with God*, or to say *ye are gods* or even *I am god*?"

"This is all very fascinating," I said. "But my original question has to do with the purpose of creation and what God's motive is."

"I may seem to be going off the question, but I am very much on subject," he said. "We have thus far concluded that you, me and everyone else is one with God and are even called gods, have we not?"

"Yes."

"If we are truly one with God and are gods, then what is the purpose of God?"

I laughed and said, "Just as I think you are wandering off subject you throw the core of the principle right back at me with the weight of all that seemed to be off subject, but was really very much on subject. Every time you teach us, my faith in you is increased."

"That's all well and good," he said. "Now how about answering my question?"

I reflected again on the question, *If we are truly one with God and are gods, then what is the purpose of God?* "Very interesting question," I said. "Dare I say that if we are one with God, then our purpose is the same as God's purpose, and God's purpose is also our purpose?"

"But how can that be when we are imperfect and often do not know what we are doing?" asked Elizabeth.

"This takes us back to my earlier statement," said John. "All creation is imperfect, showing us that God is imperfect. If we are one with God and we are not perfect, this is the final evidence that all the creator gods are not perfect either. God manifests through many imperfect lives that assist in imperfect creation, but with the idea that the end of creation will achieve some type of ultimate beauty and perfection. After the consummation, all creation will collapse and the life of God will rest and prepare to create again. Then it will again go through cycles of imperfect creation until the final perfection is achieved."

"Fascinating," I said. "So what is the purpose of this one great life? Why is it creating to begin with and why is it bothering to continue to create?"

"Why do you work and create, and why do you continue with your life?" he countered.

"I continue because I just find myself here in the center of my own universe, and I create because it gives me satisfaction."

John gave a slight smile and replied, "And God merely finds himself in the midst of His universe and works on a creation that will give Him the greatest possible joy. You are in the image of God. Examine your purpose and you will know the purpose of God. Know your own imperfections and you will have a hint of the limitations of God. Look ahead as an eternal being and you will see through faith a perfected end of all things as the eyes of God sees them."

"So what's the original purpose of all things then?" I asked.

"There is no original purpose as humanity understands the term, yet the energy of Purpose is behind all creation. The universe goes through cycles of creation and then disintegrates into an undifferentiated state. When a new cycle of creation begins the life of God senses this Purpose and directs it toward new creation. It seeks to find a new perspective of Purpose never seen and then bring it to perfection. From the beginning of Purpose to the end of perfection, however, there will be many long cycles of imperfection as the new cycle of creation moves forward.

"In the beginning of all conscious life each entity like you, reflecting the life of God, finds himself in the midst of a universe. When purpose can then be understood, the life of God seeks it and creates to have purpose. Conscious understanding of Purpose is a byproduct of creation rather than the reason for it. Those who refuse to go to work and create have no purpose. Even so it is with God and so it is with you."

"I must echo the words of Elizabeth here," I said. "This is certainly something we will not learn in church. So if I am not created, how did I get to where I am today?"

"Your essential self was not created, but assisted by others who were farther along than yourself. Just as you are more advanced than lower life forms, even so there are many higher than you are. Just as I am assisting you, others assist me and still others higher assist them. From our point on the ladder of spiritual evolution the Ancient of Days would seem like a perfected God; but, from his own eyes, he is a limited imperfect being seeking to find his next step. He seeks to add to his purpose, which will bring a greater joy than he ever felt."

"From my eyes you are pretty close to perfection," I said. "I do not believe I have ever seen you make a mistake."

"That's because you do not see all that I see," John replied. "For instance, I thought that all the Brotherhood would support the book without much deliberation, but I was wrong. Now I must read it again carefully, word for word, and present the case to my brothers hoping for unanimous support. I have a feeling I will have a battle on my hands."

"Maybe you should have picked a more experienced author," I said.

John looked me straight in the eye and gave me an assuring look. "We have the right man. It is the presentation that raises the prime question. Let us arise and say the Song of the 144,000. Then I must go."

We arose, placed our arms on each other's shoulders, and repeated the Song together.

We thank you Father that you have revealed to us your protective universal light; That within this light is complete protection from all destructive forces; That the Holy Spirit of Your Presence permeates us in this light, and wherever we will the light to descend.

We thank you Father that you fill us with your protective fires of Love; That within this love is complete protection from all

destructive thoughts and feelings; That the consciousness of
Christ is lifted up in us in this love, and wherever we will the
love to be enflamed.

We thank you Father that you are in us and we are in you;
That through us Your Will is sent forth on wings of power;
That Your Purpose is accomplished on earth as it is in heaven;

That through us Your Light and Love and Power is manifest to all
the Sons and Daughters of Mankind.

After the intonation we stood silently for a few minutes, absorbing a great and powerful peace. Finally, John broke away,
grabbed the manuscript, bid us goodbye and walked out the door,
shutting it behind him. Elizabeth and I felt too overwhelmed to
move because of the residue of the spirit. We just looked in the
direction of the closed door, knowing that our thoughts were exactly the same. We felt sad that there was a division in the Brotherhood and somehow sensed the great burden John had taken on to
defend the book before his band of brothers. We had faith that he
would prevail and wished him well. That was all that we, as imperfect souls, could do.

CHAPTER THREE
Close Encounters of a Strange Kind

The next week I placed *Book I* on the web for people to download for free. It was in 1997 when the web was still young and emerging. I thought it would be a good test of public interest. I sent e-mails to all good contact names I had accumulated suggesting they check out the book. I searched the web for e-mail addresses I thought were good leads and e-mailed a letter, briefly telling them about the book and offering it to them free. Since e-mail was just catching on, many were happy to receive e-mail of any kind.

I received quite good results, so I started accumulating as many e-mail addresses as I could and sent out a link to Book One.

"How's the experiment on the web going?" asked Elizabeth over a cup of morning coffee.

"Not bad," I said. "I sent information on the book to my e-mail list and received some very positive responses. Then I downloaded several thousand additional e-mails and sent them information about the book and also received a good response. Even with random names I am receiving a five to ten percent response rate. With responses like this we should be able to turn this into a best seller in no time."

"Except we have nothing to sell until you finish Book Two," she said.

"Correct, but I've decided that we can give away Book One which will capture their interest. When Book Two is complete we will publish both books in one volume and offer it for sale to those who liked the first book."

"And what are people saying about the book?" she inquired.

"It's very positive," I said. "Some are saying it is the best book they have ever read. Others are saying it changed their life and still others just seem curious and ask a lot of questions about John."

"Let me guess," she said. "They want to know if he is real."

"Yes, they really do."

"I seem to recall that John told you to not reveal the truth of his identity. So what do you tell them?"

"It's kind of an awkward question and I handle it the best I can. I just tell them that the story contains elements of fact and fiction and I do not reveal which is which. I tell them to read by the light of their soul and to accept that which registers with them and reject that which does not."

"I guess that's all you can do," she said. "Are you getting any negative feedback?"

"Virtually none on the book, but one in maybe a thousand recipients are agitated that I sent them an unwanted e-mail and a couple complained to my provider. The provider threatened to kick me off the service if I did not stop sending unsolicited e-mail. He called it SPAM. Funny name, don't you think?"

"SPAM, like the canned meat I ate as a kid? Yes, that is a strange thing to call it. So how are you going to continue sending e-mail then?"

"I called another provider and explained what I wanted to do. I told the guy I talked to that I was only mailing each e-mail address one time and that I wasn't selling anything, but offering to give away a free book. I would include my true identity and return address and everything would be done in total honesty."

"And what did he say?"

"He seemed to think this was an interesting idea as no one on his service had done this previously. He said that this would be fine as long as he did not get too many complaints."

"So are you going to switch over then?"

"I suppose," I said. "It's the only way I can continue advertising."

Elizabeth reflected for a moment and added, "The word SPAM keeps going through my mind. I get a bad feeling about it."

"I don't like the term either. Why do you suppose you get a negative feeling about it?"

"I'm not sure," She responded. "Did you say that this e-mail is free to send?"

"Yes."

"Then it's only a matter of time before this SPAM thing catches on fire and becomes abused."

"Its possible," I said, "but then the providers can just kick the abusers off the service."

"Perhaps," she said, "but imagine how much mail we would get if the postage and printing were free. Instead of getting three or four pieces a day, we'd be getting hundreds."

"That would be weird to get a hundred unwanted e-mails a day. That would spoil e-mail for everyone. Right now I only get a couple of unsolicited e-mails a week and I usually read them because they are quite a novelty."

"But that could change," she said, revealing her feminine intuition.

"We'll cross that bridge when it comes," I replied.

During the next week I continued to receive some very favorable e-mails from across the world. Only a couple seemed offended because it went against their religious paradigm. Overall, those heavily into dogma seemed to avoid it all together. Three that caught my interest came from my local area. They all seemed so excited that they wanted to meet me in person. The first was a female named Sylvia.

One day, when I was in the office waiting on an old customer, she showed up. I was taking an order from Ed and Edna, who were opening up a new location and needed some signs - Sylvia came in and just stood in the distance, looking intensely in my direction. Since I had never seen her before now, I was quite curious about her somewhat adoring stare. She was blond, maybe five foot seven, about thirty, perhaps a little above average in looks. As I finished waiting on the couple I couldn't help being distracted by the attention she was giving to me.

Finally, I wrapped up the order and Ed and Edna turned to leave. Just as they took a step or two toward the door Sylvia rushed forward and gave me the biggest hug I had received for some time. Edna turned and looked at me with raised eyebrows, "A friend of yours and Elizabeth, I assume."

"I hope so," I said somewhat embarrassed as they exited.

Sylvia let go, stepped back and exclaimed, "It's me!"

"You?"

"Yes, me. You do know who I am, don't you?"

"You wouldn't be Sylvia, would you?"

"I knew you would know me. I knew it!" She then gave me another big hug.

I gently backed off and moved toward a chair. "Have a seat and we'll talk."

I pulled up a chair for myself and we sat down facing each other. "So what brings you here?"

"John," she smiled.

"John?"

"Didn't he tell you?"

"Tell me what?" I asked.

"Tell you I have been chosen."

"Chosen?" I gasped.

"Surely John told you that I am to be his voice to the world?"

"Voice?" I said, finally realizing I was sounding like an echo.

"Maybe John hasn't had time to tell you. I have been chosen to be his voice, to be a teacher and to help you with your mission."

Something didn't register correctly, but I was curious about her story. "And who chose you?"

"Why John, of course," she smiled. Then she added, "Under the direction of Jesus himself."

"Did John appear to you?" I asked.

"Many times," she exclaimed.

I thought I would test her and asked, "What is unusual about his right hand?"

She paused a moment in an awkward silence and said, "That's not the way he appears to me. His spirit comes into me and talks through me. In fact I sense that he wants to speak right now. Do you mind?"

"I suppose not," I replied, interested in seeing where this was going.

She threw her head back and was perfectly still for a few seconds. Then her body came to life, she sat up and whispered in a strange voice I had not heard previously, "I am your servant John speaking through the chosen one, Sylvia. How may I help you?"

I had witnessed a number of voice channelers in my life and have not been that impressed with the material received. Even so, I thought I would satisfy my curiosity. "Do you claim to be John the Beloved speaking through Sylvia?"

"I do not claim. I am," he said fairly authoritatively.

"What color of shirt did you wear the last time we met?"

There was a short silence as if he did not expect such a question. Then he replied, "Joseph, Joseph. Do you not know me? Why must you attempt to test me? Where is your faith?"

"The John I know would expect me to test you," I replied. "Now what color was your shirt?"

"Oh, Joseph. I do not pay much attention to my clothes. To be honest I do not remember for sure but I think I wore the blue one."

"It wasn't blue. It is possible you may not remember what shirt you wore, but unlikely. The John I know has amazing abilities of recall. Let me ask you another question. What color is John's earring?"

"Joseph, you know what color it is."

"What color?" I demanded.

"Gold, of course," he said, looking slightly downward.

"The only problem is that John does not wear an earring," I said, figuring I had him cornered.

"Not so fast," he said. "I have several gold earrings. I just have not worn them in your presence."

"Hmmm," I muttered reflecting. I did not quite have him yet. "What did you teach us the last time we were together?"

"I taught you about the Keys, of course," he replied.

"And what was the name of the Key?"

"Oh, Joseph. Do I need to repeat that which you already know? Now can we cease these games and let me give you the message?"

Even though I was not satisfied I was curious about his message. "What message?" I asked.

"You must listen carefully. I have chosen Sylvia to be my messenger to the world. From now on I will speak through her and teach you through this vessel."

There was a short silence and the voice continued, "The keys

you have received so far are blinds. In other words, they are not
the real keys but hide behind the real keys that Sylvia will reveal.
Sylvia has the true Keys of Knowledge that she will teach to you.
Together you will teach them to the world."

"So what's a real Key of Knowledge?" I asked, testing again.

"These are not just given out to anyone, even a teacher such
as yourself. Before you can obtain the real keys you must commit
yourself to follow my voice as it comes through my servant."

"And why should I follow your voice? You give me no evidence you are John. You could be anyone."

"Joseph!" the entity exclaimed. "Are you saying you do not
know me after all this time and effort I have put into you? Either
I have failed you or you me. Which do you think it is?"

"Neither, because I do not believe you are John."

"Then perhaps you are not ready for any future keys. If you
can't accept me now... if you cannot recognize me, then perhaps I
should sever our relationship. Unless you make a covenant with
me now you will never see John again."

I decided to reflect a moment. I felt fairly certain that this
was not John speaking, but I have made it a habit to always consider all things even if the point is very improbable. This has worked
well for me in the past. Several times the unbelievable turned out
to be the real thing. Even so, I could not be held hostage by a John
that did not seem like John. I decided to analyze the situation on
the odd chance this was John or some test.

First, he could not give me any evidence he was John. Second, he did not sound like John. Third, it did not make sense that
I was given false keys, and most importantly, I attempted to pick
up this entity's vibration. What I found was a low vibration and it
felt nothing like John's. This last item removed all doubt so I felt
quite confident in my reply. In fact there seemed to be something
quite familiar about this energy.

"You would like that wouldn't you Philo?" I responded, trusting what I had gotten. "You'd be happy if I never saw John again."

"You call me Philo?" he replied with a raised voice. "Why
do you call me by a strange name?"

"Because I smell a strange putrid smell that can only come
from you, Mr. Philo."

Poor Sylvia I thought, as I watched her possessed face turn beet red as the entity's wrath seemed to make her blood boil. Suddenly he shouted with an alarming voice that seemed to make the building shake, "You'll wish for sweet oblivion when I get through with you!"

Suddenly Sylvia's body fell forward completely limp. After a few seconds I thought she may be dead and became concerned about the repercussions. I grabbed her hand and held it, looking at her, repeating her name. After a minute or so she came around and sat up.

After regaining her consciousness I asked, "Are you okay?"

"Yes. I think so," she said. "My head aches though." After a pause she asked, "So did you talk to John? He's unbelievable, isn't he?"

"He's unbelievable all right," I said. "The truth is you have not been channeling John, but an evil entity named Philo. It is of utmost importance that you do not let him have your body again."

Again her face turned red, but this time it was caused by her own emotions and not Philo's. "You of all people should recognize John the Beloved Disciple! To call him evil is a sin that will bring you eternal damnation. John told me earlier that if you rejected him it would be a sign that you have now chosen the dark path and would be an enemy to the light. How wise he was. You wrote a great book, but like many teachers your ego has gotten the best of you and you have fallen from your mission."

"That's not your judgment to make," I responded. "I implore you to listen to my warning. That entity is not John and is very dangerous. You must distance yourself from him."

Sylvia got up, raised her right hand toward my head and shouted, "Get behind me Satan!" She started backing toward the door, uttering curses as she opened it and disappeared.

I was curious as to what happened to Philo since my last encounter with him, so I thought I would call my friend Lance in California who may know something. He told me that the last he heard Philo was in a hospital recovering from some kind of coma oscillating between semi-consciousness and apparent unconsciousness. "There was one really curious thing though," Lance said. "When he comes to semi-consciousness he shouts out your name with intense anger. I know you two did not hit it off, but that doesn't explain this phenomenon."

I warned Lance to stay away from Philo, but wasn't sure he took me seriously. I concluded that even in his unconscious state Philo was still dangerous. Apparently he is capable of some type of astral travel where he can work through the bodies of some unsuspecting mediums.

The second person I encountered was a man named John. A couple of days after meeting Sylvia he called me on the phone, introduced himself and insisted we meet in person at the Denny's Restaurant mentioned in the book. I wasn't too excited about this as I had little free time, but he was too enthusiastic to turn down.

He told me that I could recognize him because of his long brown beard and long hair. He described himself as fortyish, fairly tall, and thin. "Think of how Elijah probably looked," he said.

As I walked into Denny's he was easy to spot sitting alone at a booth sipping a cup of coffee. I sat down opposite him and introduced myself.

His eyes lit up. He grabbed my hand and said, "My name is John. John Elijah Michaels."

"That's quite the name," I observed.

"Glad you noticed," he said with enthusiasm. "They are three Bible names just like yours - Joseph John Dewey. As your book says, Dewey comes from David, giving you three Bible names as I have.

"I suppose so," I said.

"Want to hear how I got my name?" he grinned.

"Sure."

"From God."

"God?" I asked.

"Yep, the Big Guy himself. After I read John's comments about the science of names in your book I felt uneasy about my own name, which was Perry. Perry just didn't seem to describe the real me so I sought God in mighty prayer and asked what my real name was. You know what God revealed to me?"

"Must have been something about your current name," I replied.

He looked at me in silence for a few seconds, giving me the impression he was expecting me to know all about his revelation. I felt I was downgraded a couple points in his eyes somehow because I was not told from on high all the details of his revelation.

After the silence his enthusiasm seemed to return. "Actually, it was about who I was. I was shown that in a previous life I was John the Baptist, who prepared the way for our Lord, and John the Beloved was one of my disciples who I prepared for his mission."

"I see," I said. "Since you think you were John the Baptist then you changed your name to John."

"There's no thinking," he frowned. "I *was* John the Baptist."

"Okay," I said with enough skepticism that I was sure I dropped a couple of points on his scorecard. "And I assume your middle name is Elijah because you were incarnated as Elijah before you were John."

"Exactly," he said. "Jesus clearly said that John the Baptist was previously Elijah - so that was a no-brainer."

"And how about *Michaels*? Does your last name have anything to do with Michael the Archangel?"

His eyes brightened and I could see I gained back a couple of points on his scale. "You got it!" he exclaimed. "After I received my first two names I sought God again for my final one and a vision of Revelations chapter twelve appeared before my eyes. I saw that I not only participated in the War in Heaven but was Michael the archangel, the same who cast Satan out of heaven."

"He must be pretty mad at you then," I said with a slight smile.

"You're telling me," he said very seriously, missing the humor. "Satan has been on my heels attempting to frustrate or destroy me all my life. At least now I know why I've had so many problems."

"That would seem to explain it if it were true," I said.

"What do you mean, *if*?" he asked sternly. "There is no if. John should have made this clear to you."

"Sorry," I said, "John has told me nothing about the current whereabouts of John the Baptist or any of the archangels." His eyes glared at me and I knew I was dropping a few more notches in his mind. I decided to add, "Let us suppose I was to accept that you were all these entities – then what?"

"You should already be aware of the next step. Jesus called John the Baptist the greatest prophet who ever lived. Peter, James and John the Beloved were his disciples even before Jesus came along. Now you need to think about what this means. John is your teacher, right?"

"Yes."

"And I, as John the Baptist, was John's teacher. What does that tell you?"

"You tell me."

"I think you see the point. If I am John's teacher then that places me in a supervisory position over you. If I am over John then surely I would be the one to guide you when John is not present."

"And how do you think I need guidance?" I asked.

"Actually, we can help each other," he responded.

I said nothing but waited for his response. In a few seconds he continued. "You see God has entrusted to me a plan to bring in the new order of the ages to which even Christ himself will give allegiance to when he comes. I have attempted to share the plan, but because I am not rich or famous no one will listen. This is where you enter the picture. I think your book has the possibility of attracting a large following. Just as my mission as John the Baptist was to attract students and then turn them over to Christ, your mission is to do the same. You must gain a following and turn them over to me. I know this will be difficult for you as it was for me two thousand years ago, but this was the main reason that Jesus called me, as John the Baptist, the greatest prophet who ever lived. It is very rare to find a teacher with enough humility to turn his students over to one greater than himself. You must now show that humility and do the same for me."

"And I must do this because...?" I inquired.

The man looked a little impatient, "Because it is the will of God!"

"That may or may not be," I replied, "but before I seek the will of God I first use my common sense and the discerning power of my own mind. Now John the Baptist had great powers of persuasion, had a significant following and was well known as a great leader, even by his enemies. The same was true of Elijah. If you are these same entities reincarnated, then why haven't you brought these same talents with you? By your own words you have not been able to get anyone to believe you."

John Elijah looked as if he did not appreciate being challenged. "These are different times," he said. "The people's minds are darkened and it is more difficult for them to see the light."

"I personally believe the average person is more enlightened in this age," I said. "It is true that each age has its own particular problems though. Now if you were John the Baptist and Elijah, you should now possess wisdom even greater than they possessed since you have had thousands of years to progress. Can you give me a piece of original wisdom or a new principle that you have to give to the world that would reveal the wisdom of an Elijah or a John?"

"Of course," he responded. "My plan for the New Order of the Ages reveals the wisdom you are seeking."

"So what's new in your plan?" I asked.

"The plan is not new but has been here from the beginning," he said. "What is new is that the time has arrived to implement it so the true prophets can lead mankind into an age of peace."

"And I take it that you are the main prophet to do this?"

"That is what God has revealed to me," he said, bowing his head.

"Do you have anything you have written?"

From a knapsack he pulled out a notebook, opened it and handed it to me. "Here is a collection of revelations I have received from God. If these do not convince you, nothing will. Here, read this one from the other day."

"Okay," I said taking the notebook. I took it and noticed that everything was written in his own handwriting with pains being taken to make sure it was legible. Being an experienced handwriting analyst I couldn't resist checking out this character. I noticed that the writing revealed only about average intelligence, strong emotion and the high idealism found in the writing of many fanatical believers.

I started reading the revelation, which went as follows:

Thus saith the Lord to My servant John Elijah Michaels. Blessed are you for heeding my words, though you are shunned by your brethren even as Joseph of old. There is a path of deliverance so the words I give you may shine in the light of day. Seek out my servant Joseph who has written the book <u>The Immortal</u> *and is in touch with my Beloved.*

He owes you much because of your service in past lives. Now is the time of payment. You must reveal to him that it is now his

*turn to be a spokesman and forerunner of the light, even the light
that I have placed within you. Explain to him that which he must
do to assist you. I will witness to him by the power of my Spirit. If
he accepts then you will be two witnesses preceding the glorious
coming of the Lord. If he rejects this message then he will forfeit
his mission and I will turn him over to the evil one to suffer the
buffetings of Satan, worlds without end.*

*Now is the time of his decision. He must choose either eternal
life on one hand or eternal death on the other. He must choose
correctly or he will never see my Beloved again.*

"Wow," I said. "You're in contact with a pretty harsh god."

"We're in the last days," he replied, "and there's not much
time left. We are in the hour of decision and you must decide for
or against God. As you can see by the revelation you must choose
correctly or you will not see the Beloved again."

I moved forward and responded, "The God I worship does
not use fear as a motivation, but love. John the Beloved reflects
the love of God and has also used light and love to motivate me
and never tried to force my hand with fear. You are welcome to
think of yourself as any past entity you want, but that gives you no
authority over my destiny. You must impress people with who
you are in the present, not who you may have been in the past. I
thank you for your time, but I receive no impression to work with
you."

He looked stunned and said, "So your decision is no? You're
saying no to a revelation from God?"

"Not to God, but to you. I wish you no harm. I am just not
going to be your spokesman."

He rose up and pointed his finger at me and yelled, "You
have fallen from grace even as Judas of old. You will go to the
bottomless pit and never return. You are of the Antichrist!"

I looked around, a little embarrassed. Fortunately we were
fairly isolated from others in the restaurant, but several had turned
their heads. "Whatever you say fella," I replied.

I left some money for the coffee, got up and started walking
toward the door. He grabbed me by the arm and said, "Not so fast.
We're not done yet."

I pried his fingers away and turned toward him. "I'm going
now," I said.

Unexpectedly, he then drove his fist into my stomach. I bent over, caught by surprise. As I caught my breath and looked up I was amazed to see John Elijah with some type of vile of liquid in his hand throwing it in my face and speaking in some type of foreign tongue that I did not recognize.

"Ooom Coomo Soomo Droon," he chanted.

When he saw I was catching my breath he ran for the door and went outside. I ran to the door and watched him in the distance. He was laughing, shouting, "You have not seen the last of me. I will watch you die and the vultures shall eat flesh from your bones. You are cursed henceforth and forever."

"Good Lord," I thought, wiping the liquid off my face. "If people like these are my supporters, what will my enemies be like?"

Was this the beginning of people coming forward to help me? I wondered what the future would bring.

CHAPTER FOUR
The Twelve Communions

The next morning as we finished dressing Elizabeth and I discussed my encounters.

"After meeting two such strange people who approached you with the idea of helping you, I'm hesitant to tell you about another person who called yesterday," she said frowning.

"I understand completely," I said. "But everyone can't be weird. There has to be some normal seekers out there. How did he sound?"

"He's young," she responded. "His name is Phil and he's only twenty-one. He seemed fairly charming and was very enthusiastic."

"Did he claim to be Moses, Napoleon or some great sage?"

"Not so far," she said.

"Did he hint that he was channeling John or some other wise entity?"

"Nope. He just talked about how much he enjoyed the book and he wants to help you with your mission."

"I don't know how much help I can stand," I said. "I'll have to think about this one for a few days."

Elizabeth rose from the bed and walked to the closet, "Have you put much more thought into the Third Key?" she asked over her shoulder as she grabbed her shoes.

"A little," I said.

"Maybe you could get some stimulation from Wayne. He called and wants to go to breakfast with you tomorrow."

"Good idea," I said, stretching out on the bed. "It'll be good to talk to someone who thinks for himself and is not seeking to control me."

"By the way, he said he read the book you printed out for him." she teased.

"It'll be interesting to see what he thinks," I said.

The next morning Wayne and I met at a restaurant called *The Trolley House*, known for their generous-portioned breakfast. I got there first and was half way through my first cup of coffee when Wayne walked through the door. I noticed he had on a new cowboy hat. By *new* I mean one that I had not seen. I don't think I've ever seen him in a really new anything. Everything he wears and owns has a weathered look that seems to compliment his personality.

He spotted me, ambled to my table and pulled up a chair. "Nice hat," I observed, half-joking. "Looks like it still has a few years wear left."

He took it from his head and looked at it. "It does indeed," he said smiling.

"You get it from an auction or something?"

"Not this time. My mom gave this to me the other day when I was paying her a visit."

"Your mom?"

"Yep. She told me it was in my grandfather's belongings before he died and he got it from his father." He turned the hat over and revealed the inside hatband. "Tell me what you see here," he said, handing it to me.

"It says Stetson," I observed. "That's a good brand."

"But it's not just any Stetson. What's different about the writing?"

"Outside of being somewhat worn it looks gold in color."

"Right you are. This hat was stamped in real gold leaf by John B. Stetson himself. My mother told me that my great grandfather bought this from Stetson shortly after he went into the hat business. Not many of these around."

"It might be worth something to a collector," I said. "Want me to check it out?"

Wayne proudly put the hat back on his head and sat back, tipping his chair. "Nope. I don't even want to know what its worth.

Might be tempted to sell it if I knew, and I want to keep this one."

"Like you say, it's still got a few good years left in it," I added.

"Maybe more than you think," he said. "They don't make 'em like this any more. This hat will probably outlast me and the next guy who wears it."

"Maybe so."

Wayne placed the hat carefully on an empty chair. "I read your book. Quite a yarn I must say. First time I've been a character in a story."

"So, what did you think?"

"I think you could have embellished me a bit more. You could have told your readers I reminded you of Clint Eastwood or John Wayne, for Pete's sake."

"You're lucky I didn't go the other direction and tell them you look like Slim Pickens."

"No. You're lucky you didn't go in that direction," he chuckled.

"I made you out to be pretty smart though," I added soothingly.

"But not smart enough to get the key word," he shot back.

"Well, even though you never got the key word you were a big help."

"What was the key word?" he asked. "The book left the readers hanging."

"You'll find out in the beginning of Book Two," I said. "So outside of being disappointed that you didn't come across like Clint Eastwood, what did you think?"

Wayne sat back, taking a moment to reflect, "I think you have a great imagination," he said. "Coming up with this John character was a stretch even for you. You have always been creative, but this one takes the cake." He paused a moment and then added, "What is fascinating about John is that he is a real character from history, and Jesus indicated he may not die, but might wind up wandering the earth. That idea is enough to make some think the John character is real. But there's only one problem."

"What's that?"

"I think you need to develop your writing skills a bit. Your John character wasn't that believable. If you're going to make up a fictional person you need to give some more description and reveal a little more of his character."

"So if you didn't know me and just came across the book, what would you think?" I asked expectantly.

Wayne took a breath and replied, "I'd think the writer had a good imagination, but was having some difficulty in making the main fictional character seem real."

"Interesting," I said. "Let me throw this by you. I've placed the book on the internet and have received hundreds of letters. Guess how many believe John is real?"

"You tell me."

"All of them."

"That's kind of hard to believe," he said giving a look of disbelief.

"I'll tell you what is interesting," I said. "I've given the book out to some friends and family, maybe about a dozen copies, and guess how many of them believe John is real?"

"Probably not as many," he said.

"You're right," I said. "But the difference is astounding. Zero percent of those who know me thought John was real, and all those who don't know me think he is."

"Well, you remember what Jesus said, don't you?"

"What's that?"

"A prophet has honor except among his own people."

"Yea," I laughed. "There must be some type of true principle described there." After a pause, I added, "Tell me. What would you say if I told you John were real?"

Wayne laughed and said, "Both you and I know he is a product of your imagination – so you're not going to tell me he is real, are you?"

I was tempted to tell him the truth about John, but then thought back to John's instructions to not reveal the truth about him so I replied, "I guess I'm not, but you never know."

"Hey. It's your friend Wayne you're talking to here. We both know you made him up. Let's stay real here."

"Whatever you say," I said, grinning. Suddenly, out of the corner of my eye an individual at another table caught my attention. I turned my head and looked and was astounded to see that it was John. He smiled at me and gave a slight acknowledgement with his index finger. Suddenly it occurred to me that it would be great to prove John's existence to Wayne by introducing the two and the instant I thought this I noticed that John's index finger was wagging back and forth, as if signaling a no.

"You okay?" Wayne asked. "You look a little pale."

I caught myself, turned back to Wayne and added, "Yea, I'm fine."

"Why do you keep glancing at that empty table?"

"Empty?"

"Yes, that one there," he said, pointing in John's direction.

I turned and looked again and sure enough it was empty. "It's nothing," I said, a little nervous. "You ever get the feeling that someone is behind you and you turn and nothing is there?"

"Several times," he said. "If that's your problem I can understand."

I decided to change the subject. "So, I've been working on the third key for a future book."

"I've got to admit that the Keys, as you call them in the book, are interesting. So, what's this third key going to be about?"

"It's called Communion," I said.

"That have anything to do with the Catholic Eucharist?"

"No, not directly," I laughed. The waitress came by to take our order.

"So what's good on the menu?" he asked.

"You can't go wrong with the Trolley Omelet," I said. "That's what I'm ordering."

"Two Trolley Omelets it is!" said Wayne, decisively. "And bring me a big glass of water."

"More coffee for me," I said. "You're drinking an awful lot of water," I said. "Is it helping you to lose weight?"

"Helps some," he said. "After you drink a lot of water for a while you get to really have a thirst for it. It leaves much less space in your stomach for food."

"Interesting," I said. "I have never drunk much regular water except when I was working in the heat."

As Wayne gulped down a half glass of water I continued my train of thought, "Now about communion. Think how important accurate communication is in the entire scheme of things. The principle even filters down to you and me right here. If we couldn't communicate with reasonable understanding, we couldn't even be

friends; also there could be no marriage and even civilization itself could not exist."

"True," said Wayne. "Communication is important all right,
but that's no secret. It's common knowledge that without it we're
toast. You've got to come up with some new angle if you want to
get the attention of your readers."

"When you think about it, communion, or accurate communication, is a deeper subject than most people realize." I grabbed
a napkin and pulled out a pen. "Let's make a list of all the levels,
or areas where communication is used by all us human beings." I
wrote a number one. "The first is what we are doing now. Let's
call it *person to person*." I wrote it down as the first entry. "I
suppose we could say this includes both vocal and written communication as well as more subtle things such as body language.
Can you think of another type of communion affecting humanity?"

Wayne thoughtfully responded, "When you use the word *communion* my mind drifts back to the Eucharist—you know, the symbol of communion between God and man."

"I'll put that down as number two," I said. I wrote down
God-Man.

Wayne sat back, closed his eyes for a moment and replied,
"Of course, a lot of people think there is no God who communicates with us, or if there is He just ignores us."

"Then there are many believers who feel they have communicated with some type of higher power." I said. "Can you think
of a third item?"

"It's your turn."

"Okay. Let me see. How about the communication that goes
on within us, such as the communion of the heart and the head, or
we could say the emotions and the mind."

"Do you really think the head and heart communicate?" he
asked suspiciously.

"I think so; let me give you an example." I said. "Suppose
you were to fall in love with a woman, but your mind told you she
was absolutely not compatible. Wouldn't the mind be trying to
tell the heart to hold back and the heart trying to impress on the
mind to go for it? That's a form of communication isn't it?"

"Quite a bit different from what we're having, but I suppose it is a communication of sorts. You know, several times I've met a female who pulled on my heart strings, but I've never met one my heart and mind agreed upon, except my daughter; but that's outside the romance category."

"Yea, I've been waiting for you to fall head-over-heels in love since we were kids." I teased. To see Wayne in love with heart and mind would be a sight to behold.

Wayne laughed, "I think I'm getting too old and set in my ways. That's about as likely to happen as it would be for your John to walk in and sit at that table you were staring at so intently."

I laughed with him, but not for the reason he thought. "Okay, now it's your turn to add to the list."

Wayne put his hand to his chin, creating a studious look and replied, "How about communication between humans and the animals? It's kind of like God and man, but on a lower level."

"I've heard it said that we are like gods to the animals," I said. "Take your dog, for example. He looks at you with total faith as if you were his god, or final authority, and there's nothing more delightful to him than to be in your presence or fulfill your will, kind of like we imagine it would be if we had access to God."

"Now, if I could just find a female who had the same attitude as my dog I might just fall crazy in love as you mentioned," Wayne grinned mischievously.

I chuckled, this time for the reason he thought. "So what's the difference between human and animal communications and human to human?"

"Animals don't generally understand our actual words, but react to the tone of our voice and gestures. Sometimes I think the women in my life are the same way," he grinned.

"You'll risk your life if you let any female hear you talking that way," I laughed. "So, after your dog makes a mistake and you shout his name and hold up your hand as if to strike, the basic message that he screwed up is communicated, true?"

"Basically," he agreed. "The animal doesn't understand as we do, but he gets the message."

"How about the lower kingdoms – the vegetable and mineral, or nature itself? Do we communicate with them?"

"Now you're getting into the esoteric," he said. "I have read experiments though, where they played music and also prayed for plants. When they played loud acid rock the plants grew away from the sound, and when they played classical music the plants grew toward the sound. The plants that were prayed for grew larger and healthier than those that were ignored. One could say that this indicates that plants are capable of rudimentary communication. But perhaps others would say that is just a reaction to stimuli." Sometimes Wayne sounded like a scientist.

"On the other hand, we could say to the skeptics that even our communication right here is response to stimuli. Instead of responding to pleasant music you are responding to my actual words," I countered.

"Except I am responding because I understand your meaning whereas a plant responds more like a computer program," he rejoined.

"But maybe we're like a complex computer program and a plant is like a simpler one. Perhaps we both respond with some type of consciousness, but on different levels."

"Who knows for sure?" said Wayne, throwing up his hands.

"Whatever the case, I'm listing number five as *human-nature*. Can you think of another one?"

The waitress brought us our omelets. "This looks great," said Wayne. "I think we'll have to come here again."

"Sounds good to me," I said, taking my first bite.

Wayne took a bite, too, "Mmm. We really will have to come here again."

"Glad you like it. Don't lose track of what we're doing here though. Have you thought of another item for the list?"

"Well," he replied, chomping away, "we seem to receive communication in our dreams. Sometimes we receive knowledge we are unaware of in the waking state. This could come from a higher or subconscious part of us, or it could sometimes come from outside of ourselves. Whatever the case, some type of communication is involved."

"That's good," I said. "How shall I word it? Let's see, number six, *human-subconscious* or possibly *human-dream state*."

"*Human-dream state* sounds better," said Wayne. "We get some communication from our subconscious even in the waking state."

"Good point," I said. "Then for number seven we can add

human-subconscious-Higher Self. Like you say, we receive numerous impressions from our subconscious in the waking state. Any more ideas?"

"It's your turn," he said.

"Hmmm. Many believe there are higher lives such as resurrected beings, masters and angels that communicate with humanity. I suppose we can call number eight *humanity-higher lives.*"

"There's no hard evidence on that one, but I suppose it's only logical that higher lives do exist." Wayne was showing his logical side here. He had always been resistant to blindly accepting anything that has little or no proof behind it. Even so, he is far from being the typical skeptic for he is open to some unusual and unproven possibilities that the skeptic usually dismisses.

"Your turn again," I said. "Anything else you can come up with?"

"I suppose we could say there is animal to animal communication."

"You're right, of course," I said. "There are lots of non-human communications. Scientists are now saying that there is even a form of communication between atoms, molecules and the cells in our bodies. I think we need to keep this discussion within the sphere of communication that affects humans or the field will be much too broad for me to cover in a future book."

"Probably," he said. "I think we've covered all the easy ones. Now you're really making me work the old gray matter to come up with more. Let me see." He poked through his hash browns for a moment and finally his countenance came alive. "I think I have another one. How's this? We have a communication between our consciousness and our own bodies. It is as if the body attempts to give us information about its condition. If all in the system is completely healthy, we have a sense of well being, but if something is amiss there will be a signal, or a communication of some type. Sometimes the signals are so subtle they're difficult to pick up. For instance, I always feel a slight, almost unnoticeable sense that something is wrong before I come down with the flu or a cold. It's almost as if my body is trying to warn me in advance so perhaps I can prevent the illness or at least diminish its effects."

"Great point," I said. "For number nine I'll write *Human-Physical Body.* You're right about the body signaling to us about illness. I know there have been times I felt like I was coming down with something and was able to prevent it by eating light, taking extra vitamin C or something like that. Then there are other times I ignored the warning and suffered for it."

"Then there are times you do all you can and still get the flu," he smiled.

"On the other hand, maybe we didn't get the correct communication from the body when that happen," I shot back enjoying the repartee..

"Then we have the hypochondriac who thinks he's received bad news from the body when he's only imagined such things," said Wayne.

"He's like the false prophet who thinks God is talking to him when it's only his overactive imagination. There are times, however, when a person will be warned of a serious illness, like cancer or something, and it will save his life if he listens," I added seriously.

I paused a moment in thought. "You mentioned the communication between the heart and the mind, but just as our consciousness communicates with the body, it also registers impressions from the feeling nature and the mind, and sometimes higher."

"Like what?"

"The soul, the spirit... mystics believe there are seven planes of existence all together. They teach that above the mind are four additional planes that are possible for us to contact, but few even contact the first above the mind, which is the source of intuition."

"Communication with emotions, mind and higher realms... You've named more than one new category here," Wayne responded impressed.

"I suppose you're right," I said. "Let's see, we have *human-emotions* for number ten; *human-mind* for eleven and for twelve, let's just sum up all that is above the mind with the word *spirit*."

"So humans contacting the spiritual worlds, however many there may be, is number twelve then," Wayne added. "Twelve seems to be a number of completion. Maybe we've covered the gamut of communication here."

"Perhaps. There may be other subtle communications, but you're right. Twelve is a good number to end our list"

"So does this help you arrive at the Third Key you are going to write about?" he asked.

"It helps to lay the foundation for understanding. I think the key is related to what goes wrong with communication, not communication itself, but I'm not sure yet."

"What do you mean?" he asked.

"Have you ever played the game *Chinese Whispers* where you begin with a phrase, whispering it around a circle?"

"You mean where the last guy gets the message and it's all distorted?"

"That's it."

"We played that at a Christmas party when we were in college. It was fun. So what does this have to do with your key? Sounds like you're creating this material by the seat of your pants and you expect to find some key when you're not even sure it exists."

"It exists all right."

"What makes you so sure?"

"Higher communication," I responded. "I know there is a Key of Knowledge here and that we can find it."

Wayne looked at me for a few seconds as if he were debating interrogating me on this point and then replied, "Okay. Let's operate on the assumption that there is a Third Key and maybe more. What does it have to do with *Chinese Whispers*?"

"Let's look at what happens in the game," I said. "The first guy formulates a phrase to communicate to the guy next to him, which is then passed around the circle. Each time the phrase is repeated the meaning has deteriorated until the original is as good as lost. Do you think this principle would apply to the twelve types of communication that we concocted?"

"Makes sense," said Wayne. "You don't need a circle of twelve people to see it happen. Sometimes I'll give the simplest of instructions to my employees and they'll totally get it wrong. Just the other day I sent Jim to trim the bushes at 1224 Franklin Avenue and he went to 1224 Franklin Street. Now everyone in Boise knows the difference between Franklin Street and Franklin Avenue, don't they?"

"I know because I lived in the area most of my life, but a lot of people don't," I said.

"Right, but he should have had the common sense to see that

I wrote *avenue* and not *street*."

"So what happened? Did he trim the wrong bushes?"

"Sure did."

"So was the guy glad or mad to have his bushes trimmed?" I started to chuckle.

"Don't know," said Wayne, looking down at the table.

"What do you mean you don't know? Oh, let me guess. The homeowners were gone when Jim did the work, and when you found out about the mistake you decided to let dead dogs lay."

"That's pretty close," Wayne replied. "I thought about telling him, thinking that I may even be able to bill him if he was happy, but then if he was angry I could be open for another law suit."

"So the guy comes home from his work and sees his bushes all neatly trimmed. I wonder what he thought." I started to really laugh at the scene in my mind.

"Yes. It's kind of amusing to think about," he conceded. "At least I'm getting a little entertainment value out of the deal."

"Maybe God designed us to ineffectively communicate to add a little humor to our lives," I chortled.

"I don't know," he said. "I've lost a lot of money because my guys didn't understand instructions and screwed up. Most of the time there is no humor to be found."

"Sorry," I said wiping the grin off of my face. "Your problem basically illustrates the *Chinese Whispers* principle. Each level of communication brings a deterioration of the original meaning. Do you ever give instructions to a foreman, who then passes them along to another?"

"Of course."

"And I'll bet that with two levels of communication the percentage of error is even greater."

"I'm afraid so, but with a dozen guys working for me I can't work with them all individually."

"The point is that each level of communication creates a loss or distortion of the original message, just like in the game. Let's operate on the assumption that God spoke to great men such as Moses, Isaiah, Peter, Paul, Mohammed, and Krishna and so on. They in turn spoke to their disciples. Already we have two degrees of corruption. First we have the messenger who receives from God, some archangel or higher life. Do you think the messenger understands the message exactly as God did when He gave it to him?"

"Assuming it was a real revelation from God, one would think that the prophet has a much lesser understanding of the message than the one who gave it," Wayne replied.

"Then, after the messenger gives the teaching to disciples, he eventually dies and then the disciples lose another portion of the vision."

"I see where you're going," Wayne said. "What you say reminds me of something I read about the New Testament. It used to be written on scrolls and if you wanted a copy of it you had to reproduce it by creating another handwritten scroll. They say that when a scribe would make a copy, he would sometimes find a passage, with which he disagreed and alter it to make it sound more palatable. Then there were other times that the scribe would come across a passage that he thought was obscure so he would write in a note of explanation. Then when the next copy was made the new scribe would add in the note and the alterations as if it were part of the original. Some scholars feel that many such notes and alterations are now part of the canon and seen as actual words of Jesus, Paul, and John and so forth. I've heard that the nearest copy we have to an original gospel is a twelfth copy. Now it takes about twelve people to make a good *Chinese Whispers* game and based on how twelve people can pulverize an original idea, you have to wonder how many mistakes are in the New Testament or the entire Bible itself."

"You realize you're speaking blasphemy here, don't you?" I said, feigning shock. "For some reason, the fundamentalist thinks the Bible is word for word the infallible word of God," I said.

Wayne laughed. "That's me all right, the blasphemer. Which version of the Bible do you suppose they think is infallible?"

"Well, the hardcore usually go strictly by the King James, but the more orthodox and traditional Christians realize that this old standard is not perfect and are using more modern versions."

"So, do they think these modern versions are infallible, where the King James is not?"

"I think they see the original Greek as infallible, but they fail to admit that the twelve duplications that you mentioned could have produced any errors. For some reason they assume twelve different scribes could have made twelve different copies without making any alterations or notes."

"Anyone who has played *Chinese Whispers* knows it is impossible," said Wayne.

"So in the instance of the Bible, we have the original writers giving out a message that is already one step down from God. Then it's finally transmitted to this generation, which is twelve additional whispers, or steps, from the messenger. It's no wonder there are hundreds of Christian religions. I think there is a key or a major hint about a key in this principle."

"It's interesting conversation," he said. "So are you telling me that the Key of Knowledge you will be writing has to do with the fact that each layer of communication has imperfection in it?"

"I haven't got the key figured out yet, because I think there is more to it than that. Imagine what the world would be like if each communication made was transmitted without distortion and with complete understanding?"

"Maybe men and women would finally stop fighting and accept each other," Wayne laughed.

"And maybe nations would understand each other and cease fighting also," I added. "When you think of it, many wars are started through a simple misunderstanding or a series of bad communications that end in an impasse."

"On the other hand," Wayne mused, "some wars are begun because of something that is understood. When the Japanese bombed Pearl Harbor we received a definite communication that we had to fight or lose our freedom."

"But the leaders of Germany and Japan were deceived in the beginning through corrupt communication from politicians, spiritual leaders and philosophers."

"Perhaps, and that may be an interesting topic to explore next time," he said looking at his watch. "I have an appointment with some bushes and have to go. I'll be interested in seeing what you come up with next. If it's good enough maybe you'll convince me John gave it to you," he said, putting on his hat with a grin.

"I think the best is yet to come," I replied.

That evening, after dinner, I was working on the computer in our work room, waiting for Elizabeth to bring me a cup of tea, when I heard a terrifying scream as she came down the stairs of our tri-level. She fell to the floor in exactly the same location she did the first time she took ill. My hands started to shake and the pit of my stomach started to churn as I relived the cruelty of MS and how it struck her down before.

"Sweetheart, are you okay?" I ran to her and lifted her. There was some blood trickling from her nose, evidently from the concussion of the fall. I picked her up and carried her upstairs to our bed, washing off her face with a damp cloth.

Just as I was about to call 911 she started coming around. "Are you with me?" I asked shakily.

She struggled to lift herself up and replied. "I'm not sure."

Fearing a repeat of her illness I asked, "Can you walk?"

"I'm afraid to try." She looked very worried.

"You must try. Here, take my hand."

She nervously took my hand and I pulled her up. It seemed a struggle for her to get to her feet, but then the instant I let go she started to fall. I caught her just in time and laid her back on the bed. Tears streamed down her face as she said. "It's back. The disease is back. I feel just like I did earlier!"

It was indeed our worst fear that her MS would come back, but since she had seemed to have a complete recovery we hadn't even been thinking of the possibility as of late.

"This couldn't happen out of the blue without a conceivable reason," I said, forcing myself to be logical. "There have to be dark forces at play. I sensed a complete recovery in you."

"There are indeed dark forces," she said while wiping her tears, giving me a very serious and fearful look that greatly troubled me. "The particular dark force is Philo."

"Philo!" I gasped, leaping to the bedroom door. Has he been here in the house?"

"Worse," she said.

"What's worse than that?" I said kneeling by her, holding her hand again.

She seemed to greatly struggle just to speak. "He's here. Not in the house, but..." her voice grew faint, "he's in me... He's with me now."

Her voice faded until she lapsed into unconsciousness.

I felt a chill in the room that went to the bone. I was so very alone.

CHAPTER FIVE
An Extra Hint

I called her name over and over and nothing happened. I attempted to speak the sacred word as I did once before, but it wasn't given to me to speak correctly; it has to be spoken with the permission of the mind of God to wield its power. I concluded that it was expected that I handle the situation with my limitations and learn from the experience.

But the question was what was I to do? My wife was unconscious through the power of an astral roving dark disciple, and I seemed to have no power to rouse her. I dared not take her to a hospital, at the moment, for that situation could play into Philo's hands.

There was only one thing I could think to do. I picked her up, laid her on the bed, sat beside her and said the Song of the 144,000. Then I held her and prayed for her with all the power of my soul. As I began praying it was as if we were both engulfed with dark clouds. I attempted to picture light dispelling the darkness and prayed with great fervor.

After a few moments she weakly came to consciousness. I helped her sit up on the bed and asked anxiously, "Can you speak?"

"I think so," she said softly.

"You must concentrate and tell me what you know about Philo. Why did you mention his presence?"

She looked at me weakly and spoke, "When I was coming down the stairs I suddenly felt overwhelmed by some evil presence. Then when I lost consciousness I sensed this entity attempting to communicate with me."

"And was this being, Philo?"

"I'm afraid so," she said, almost apologetically. "He told me again that I was his in a previous time and I am still his; that if I do not yield to him my disease will return and I will be alone because you will be destroyed. He said that you have no chance against the forces arrayed against you, and that even some of John's brotherhood does not want you to succeed. He said that if I yield and let him use my body from time to time, I will have radiant health and you will be spared to live a normal life."

"And did you respond?" I asked a little nervously.

"Yes. I told him I would never cooperate with him."

"Good girl," I said, squeezing her hand. "I'm proud of you."

She looked at me with great feeling and said, "But next I felt overwhelmed with his anger and I sensed he was trying to destroy me. I felt as if I was wandering in thick darkness. It seemed hopeless, like I was in some bottomless pit. Then I saw a point of light and attempted to move toward it in consciousness and I woke up in your arms." Tears streamed down her face as she said, "I'm afraid he is right. This disease is back. And what will I do if something happens to you?"

"Nothing's going to happen," I said, hoping I was right. Suddenly, my eyes lit up. "There's a permanent solution to this problem. Remember what John told me when I first met him?"

"A lot of things."

"But there's one thing in particular that is of great importance to us now."

"Didn't he say something about me being healed if you solved the first three keys?"

"Yes! That's it," I said enthusiastically. "Because you seemed to be completely healed I almost forgot about it, but now I can see that this may be the most important key of all. Can't you see? All we have to do is solve the Third Key and John will be bound by his word to heal you. This time it will be for good and the disease will never return."

"I feel very weak, as weak as I ever have," she said, closing her eyes. "You need to solve the key soon or I sense you will lose me." Opening her eyes again she asked, "When is John going to show up so you can work on the key again?"

"I'm not sure. I had the feeling that he would just come when I'm ready to learn more."

"Then you need to get ready."

"But I've done all the talking and thinking about it I can until I get another hint. I don't know what more to do now other than wait."

"Maybe you could call out to him or something," she said.

"Maybe," I replied. "It worked once."

I stood and looked upward. "John, wherever you are, please, come to us. We need you." I said this several times with Elizabeth joining in, but nothing happened. "I guess it's not time yet," I said, "or maybe he is just busy."

Elizabeth reached out her hand to me and said, "Take my hand and let's say a prayer that he will come to us."

I sat next to her on the bed and we prayed together for several minutes. Afterwards we felt a sense of peace but John still did not show.

"Maybe you just have a temporary weakness," I said. "Try and walk again." I stepped back and held out my hand.

She looked a little nervous, but hopeful, and lifted herself up to her feet and attempted to take some steps. After one weak step she faltered and started to fall. I moved to catch her, cursing myself for being so far away from her in a weak condition. Because she was falling away from me I feared I may not catch my dear wife in time. Suddenly it looked as if an invisible force caught her and held her upright.

"What is that?" she gasped, turning her head around. "Something is holding me."

"Something lifted you up," I said with cautious relief. "Whatever it is, I hope it's on our side."

Suddenly, a familiar form became visible and a welcome voice said, "Of course I am on your side."

Elizabeth turned and hugged him tightly, "John! Thank you so much for coming."

"Just out of curiosity, how long have you been here?" I asked.

"If you are wondering if the Brotherhood peeks in on private moments you have nothing to worry about. We are only present when requested or for the sake of great work. My presence has been requested, has it not?" John queried, his eyes twinkling.

Elizabeth sat on the bed and said, "You are a sight for sore eyes! We have been praying for you to come."

"It looks like we have a little problem here," he said, patting Elizabeth's shoulder.

"No. It's a big problem," she said with pleading eyes. "My disease has come back with a vengeance."

"Apparently Philo is in and out of consciousness," I said, "but that doesn't seem to stop him from making mischief. In his unconscious state he seems to be working through other people's bodies and now he attempted to possess Elizabeth. Somehow he managed to bring her illness back."

"Yes," John replied. "But even more troubling than Elizabeth's problem is the course of the dark disciple. They have absolutely no remorse or concern for the distress they cause to others. Their only motive is to satisfy their selfish will. If they could only see and understand the whole picture, and the end of their works, they are the ones who would tremble in fear much more than their victims do."

"I suppose so," I said, "but I have a hard time feeling sorry for them." I paused to change the subject, "Can you help Elizabeth?"

John looked at her and said simply, "I can help her temporarily."

"But I know she can be restored to health like she was earlier," I pleaded.

"You are correct," he nodded, "but just as you were constrained from saying the sacred word, even so am I constrained from healing her at this time. There is a purpose to every crossroad that comes into our lives. There is knowledge for you to learn by working through this problem just as there is for most of the problems we face."

"You said you would heal her if I solved the Third Key," I said nervously. "Does that still stand?"

John looked at me with his penetrating blue eyes and replied, "What do you think?"

"I think and hope yes," I said.

"A Brother of Light does not give his word unless he has power to fulfill it. This is one of the great distinctions between the Dark Brothers and us. Their word to their disciples is only good as long as they are needed. We keep our word no matter what the circumstances, and every statement we make is as true as word can be."

"So when I get the Third Key you will permanently heal Elizabeth then?" I asked more sure of myself.

"Yes. I am bound by my word. Please realize this about us and then you can have a trust in the Brotherhood which is unshakeable."

"You mean to tell me that none of the Brotherhood ever slips up or misses on a commitment or states something that is not exactly true?"

"You're asking something that has never been revealed," he said. He paused a moment, as if considering whether or not to answer. Then, as if he received some internal answer, he replied, "There is no such thing as perfection in this world of form and dualities. Yes, even the Great Ones make mistakes. The typical mistake of a Master would not be understood by the average student, but the principle of speaking truly is understood by all self-conscious beings. It is a mistake for all to violate. And yes, even the members of the Brotherhood slip up and speak something that is not exactly true from time to time. It is rare, but it does happen."

"What happens to them when this occurs?" I asked, curious.

"They suffer a loss of power and must incarnate on the earth again as a baby. The Master must then prove again that he can keep his word in difficult circumstances as well as pass through all his states of enlightenment until he arrives back where he was previously. When he does this he is readmitted to the full ranks of the Brotherhood."

"That's fascinating," I said. "Most people, who believe in the existence of Masters, or resurrected beings, seem to see them as pretty much infallible."

"There is a principle at play that works out in the stairway of lives," he said. "Even though it may seem to the lower lives that the higher lives live in perfection and are carefree, the truth is just the opposite. The higher have even greater problems to solve and make more far-reaching mistakes than do those in lesser kingdoms.

"As an illustration, take the example of a pet such as a dog. In his consciousness it seems that his master has all the problems of existence solved. His command must be obeyed and he appears infallible. Best of all, he has an unlimited supply of food that just seems to be there as if it materialized out of thin air. The pet owner seems to have the problem of food and shelter solved. What else is there to worry about for the animal?"

"I think I see what you are getting at," I said. "Many of our problems and mistakes are beyond the consciousness of the pet to even grasp. Even so, the Brotherhood has problems and makes mistakes that would not even be understood by the average human."

"Correct," he said taking Elizabeth's hand. "I can restore you for the moment, but Joseph must solve the Third Key before you can be permanently healed." He looked in her eyes and said, "Depart."

Suddenly, her body shook and she would have fallen backward if John weren't holding her steady. I thought I saw a gray shadow leave the room, but wasn't sure if I imagined it or not. Elizabeth then composed herself as John spoke again, "Stand up," he commanded.

Elizabeth looked at him with hope in her eyes and cautiously stood. When she found that she had her strength again she started walking back and forth. "Oh. This feels so wonderful to have my strength back! Tell me this can be permanent."

"There is nothing more I'd rather do at this time," he said, "but the Spirit within constrains me so a higher purpose can be fulfilled. If I were to go contrary to the communication I receive, I would be making one of those mistakes I was explaining to Joseph."

"And have you ever made such a mistake or not spoken truly since you've had this unusual mission?" I asked.

"Two major ones," he replied. "The last one was over a thousand years ago."

"Were you then reborn as a baby instead of being restored as an adult?" I asked curiously.

"Yes," he said, not volunteering any additional information.

"And were you born in any time period or situation I would know about?"

"Perhaps."

"Can you tell us what it is?"

Again, he seemed to contemplate whether to give an answer

and finally replied, "I was born around the time period referred in legend as Camelot."

"That's amazing," I said with some awe in my voice. "You must have been one of the main players then like Merlin or King Arthur. Which one were you?"

"That's not for me to tell you at this time," he said. "The standard story only gives hints at the real truth, but if you reflect and discover your own past you will discover the mystery and more fully understand the secret of Excalibur."

"I guess it wouldn't be a normal visit with you if you did not leave us with unanswered questions," I said, laughing.

"Come," he said. "Let us go downstairs, sit at the table, and drink some tea and talk."

I happily noted that Elizabeth seemed to have her strength back as we walked downstairs and found myself not wanting to think about her situation after John's leaving. After we made some tea and settled around the dining room table, we continued our conversation.

"As you might guess, I'm pretty anxious to solve the Third Key," I said. "Since we have the promise that Elizabeth will be healed when it is solved, we are ready to go to work."

"I understand," he smiled. "Unfortunately, this process cannot be rushed, but if it means anything to you, you have my full confidence. Now tell me what you have gathered from your reflections."

"Apparently you know some of the things already. After all, I did see you in the Trolley House, didn't I?"

"Yes. I caught the gist of your conversation through the Oneness Principle and decided to listen more carefully."

"So you were actually there then?"

"Yes and no," he replied. "What you saw was not my physical body as you are viewing now, but an energy body created by my thought. Its purpose is to be a vehicle of my consciousness, allowing me to be in two places at one time."

"Sounds like quite a trick," said Elizabeth.

"So why couldn't others see you?" I asked.

"The thought form you saw was adjusted to the frequency of your physical brain. Only you and one other person were able to see me. The other person was a child with a similar wavelength to yours."

"That makes sense," said Elizabeth, her eyes twinkling. "Sometimes my husband is just a big kid."

John smiled and replied, "Now let us move on to where we left off in the last discussion. Let us briefly review. First, what is the problem that causes a communicated message to be misunderstood when it is filtered through two or more people?"

I reflected a moment and replied, "In our last discussion we concluded that a natural distortion occurs because of error by the sender or receiver. Such error seems impossible to eliminate."

"You use the word *distortion*. There is another word that better describes this, and is the name of the principle involved. This is the key word for understanding that which hinders the Third Key."

I turned to Elizabeth. "What's another word for distortion?"

"I don't know, maybe perversion."

"I have a feeling that's not it. Mind if I get the Thesaurus?"

John nodded his approval.

I retrieved the Thesaurus, opened it and read, "Synonyms of *distort* are *to color, twist, load, warp, wrench, belie, falsify, misrepresent, pervert, deform, gnarl, misshape, garble, mangle, slant and misstate*. Are any of these the preliminary key word?"

"What do you think?"

"I don't know. It seems to be a pretty thorough list. Most of them seem to describe what happens in the *Chinese Whispers* game."

"Do they?" he replied.

I glanced again at the list. "Well, maybe not exactly, but they give the general idea."

"But we want a word that gives the specific idea of the principle involved here."

"Then are you saying that not one of these synonyms, or even the word *distortion*, accurately describes the principle?"

"What do you think?"

"I'm guessing by your reaction the answer is no. I'm just trying to figure out why and also why it would be left out of the Thesaurus."

"Let me give you a hint. The words you have given so far describe the process that takes place as well as effects behind the principle, but not the principle itself."

I looked at Elizabeth. "Can you think of anything Sweetie?"

"I'm not sure. It seems that the word *distortion* best describes the problem that occurs with communication in *Chinese Whispers*. We've covered every synonym I can think of." She looked at John and asked, "Is this some type of trick question where the word is not strongly related to the distortion that occurs in the game?"

"The key word is exactly related," he replied. "Distortion is the closest word so far, but there is another that more precisely describes the principle and is important to grasp in understanding it."

"Could you give us another hint?" I pleaded.

John reflected for a moment and said, "You have both used copy machines many times, have you not?"

"Yes," we replied in unison.

"What happens when you take an original and make a copy, then you take the copy and make a copy of that, and finally make a third copy from that copy?"

"Each copy removed from the original loses some of its quality. This is the same principle that Wayne and I were discussing when we were talking about how copies of the Bible were passed down."

"Exactly," he agreed. "Now what word describes the principle involved?"

"Well, the second, third and fourth copies are distortions of the original, but you say there is another word." I glanced again at the list of synonyms. "I guess we could say the copies are perverted, deformed or garbled."

I looked into John's eyes for his reaction and said, "But I take it they do not accurately describe the principle, do they?"

"No they do not," he agreed. "Now you must reflect within your soul, for this principle was of great concern to you in your recent past lives and you have been an exponent of it."

"Really?" I exclaimed. "Then I feel all the more foolish for not getting it. Let me reflect a moment."

I took a moment of silence and attempted to grasp the key word. Finally I said, "My mind's a blank. It's hard to concentrate when all I can think of is helping Elizabeth."

"I understand," John nodded, "but you must retrieve it or we cannot continue. If you cannot grasp it then I must leave you for another week to contemplate."

"I can't afford to waste another week," I said standing up starting to pace. "It could mean life or death for Elizabeth. Can you give me another hint?"

"It's highly unusual for me to do this. I've already given you two tonight."

"Please," I said, grabbing his arm, "this once, give me one more."

John sat back, "I will only give you a hint that may stimulate your intuition. In fact, you may not consider it a hint at all."

"I'll take anything," I said, sitting back down.

John put his hands on the table, rubbed his index fingers together and softly said, "The word is in the Bible."

"What kind of hint is that?" said Elizabeth. "There must be a million words in the Bible."

"It may be more of a hint than you may think," he said. "Contemplate, my friends, on all we talked about and then reflect on the Bible and see what words come to your mind."

"It sounds like a long shot to me," I replied, "but at this point I'll try anything."

I sat back, closed my eyes and reflected on the conversation thus far. Apparently the word *distortion* is close. The key word has to describe the changes in meaning that happen when copies are made or words are passed around a circle. The word is not in my Thesaurus, but it is in the Bible. Where in the Bible could it be? He said reflect on the Bible. Okay I thought to myself. *In the beginning God created the heaven and the earth.* No. That can't be it.

"This is frustrating," I said. I can't review the whole Bible in my mind."

"You don't have to review the whole Bible," he said. "You just have to retrieve a verse with the key word. Relax and see what comes."

"All right," I said with some disbelief, but sustaining a little hope. I closed my eyes again and decided to just think of the scriptures and see if any of them popped into my mind or stood out. After a few moments reflection I had about a dozen stories, Bible characters and verses that passed through my mind until it seemed scriptures I hadn't thought of or read for a long time just flowed by me. When this began to happen I decided to take the position of an observer and just watch the scriptures until something seemed to register. As I was doing this, one finally came into my consciousness that caught my attention.

"I think I have something," I said.

John responded with a simple, "Okay."

I continued, "Here is a scripture that came into my mind that seems to register strongly with me at this time: *this corruptible must put on incorruption, and this mortal must put on immortality.*"

"And does this bring a key word to mind?" he asked.

"The word *corruptible* or *corruption* is similar to *distortion* and does seem to accurately describe what happens in *Chinese Whispers* as well as the effect of making a copy of a copy. The original is corrupted."

"So is this the word you are settling on for today?"

I turned to Elizabeth, "What do you think?"

"It seems to fit," she said, "and it is not in the Thesaurus."

"It seems to register with our souls," I said. "I think this is the word."

"Now think upon this word and tell me what comes to your mind?"

"Okay," I said. "First, the more I think of this word the more I see that it describes the principle of deteriorating meaning in communication, distortion in making copies or any type of duplication. All things in motion change and produce corruption when compared with the original."

John took a shiny new quarter out of his pocket and handed it to me. "How old would you say this quarter is?"

"It looks brand new, like it was just minted," I said.

"And what do you suppose it will look like in a hundred years?"

"Probably worn, scratched and dull," I replied.

"And what will your body look like in thirty years?"

"Probably worn and weathered also."

"Notice that the scripture tells us that the body is corruptible. But we see that not only organic lives suffer corruption, but so do objects such as coins. Even great mountains, planets and galaxies undergo change from their original state of creation."

"And if we play *Chinese Whispers*, the original statement undergoes corruption as it passes through the circle," added Elizabeth.

"Yes," said John. "But there is an important point to consider. If we start the game by saying *the cow jumped over the moon* and the last guy hears *the bow shot the broom,* we seem to see corruption at work. But does this mean that the original phrase no longer exists or cannot be retrieved?"

"No," said Elizabeth. "At the end of the game it is retrieved. The first person in line reveals it."

"And after it is revealed, then the corrupted phrase is instantly replaced by the original, is it not?"

"Yes."

"And what does the scripture say about our bodies?"

Elizabeth thought a moment and replied, "It calls our bodies corruptible and says they must put on incorruption."

"Now you understand how the phrase *the cow jumped over the moon* became corrupted but later put on incorruption by merely being revealed by the original player. But how can the body put on incorruption?"

"I don't see how it can, unless there is some type of eternal resurrection as the religions teach," I said.

"So why can even an average human restore an original phrase, but not his own body?" he asked.

"Because the two are different," I replied. "The phrase is easy to restore. It merely has to be revealed. Restoring the body is much more complicated. We can work to keep it healthy, but we can't return to our youth by speaking a word."

"Maybe the two are not as different as you think. Pick up the quarter I gave you and look at the date."

I picked it up and examined the date, "Good grief! This quarter is forty years old and is in mint condition."

"I have had this quarter with me since it was minted. Why do you suppose it still looks new when the much newer ones in your pocket are dull and aged?"

"I have no idea," I gasped.

Then John reached in his pocket and pulled out another coin and handed it to me. "How old does this quarter look?"

I took it and examined it. It had a draped bust of a lady on one side and an eagle on the other. "It says *United States of America* on it, but I have never seen a coin like this. It looks freshly minted."

"Check out the date."

"Wow! It says 1796. You're not going to tell me that you've been carrying this around since it was minted?"

"Not unless you ask," he smiled mischievously.

"Are you telling me that you are able to keep these coins from corruption by using the same principle that the guy in the game used by revealing that the original phrase was *the cow jumped over the moon?*"

"You're getting the idea," he grinned. "Now if a coin can become incorruptible through this principle, then can't we do the same with our physical bodies?"

"It makes sense," I said, "But it's hard to believe it is as simple as you say. It looks like we are talking apples and oranges. Restoring a word or phrase and restoring a body are two entirely different things."

"Are they?" He asked. "What is the first verse I wrote in the gospel of John?"

I reflected back on the famous scripture and replied, "*In the beginning was the word.*"

"Exactly," he said. "In the beginning of the game *Chinese Whispers* is *the word*. The word seems to be corrupted, but in reality it was neither corrupted nor was it lost. The first cause, or player, merely revealed it and all was restored. Now is your body also not a word that operates on the same principle?"

"I'm not sure," I said, a little overwhelmed.

"And that's why my quarters are new and shiny and yours are not," he said matter-of-factly. "Let's have another round of tea. We have a ways to go yet."

CHAPTER SIX
Creation Room

"So what is the principle that keeps your coins from aging and can even make our bodies incorruptible? What word can I speak to restore a physical thing?" I asked.

"To understand that let me ask this question," said John. "What is a word?"

It seemed to be a very simple question, but one that I found difficult to find words to answer. Finally I answered, "Well, a word is a thing spoken that identifies something."

Elizabeth grabbed a dictionary opened it and added, "It says here that *a word is a sound or combination of sounds that symbolizes and communicates a meaning.*"

"Now we're getting somewhere," he said. "A word is a sound. What is a sound?"

"Since I play the piano perhaps I can answer that," said Elizabeth. "The notes on the piano are sounds and each note has a different frequency or vibration."

"So a word is a sound, which is, in turn, vibration," I injected.

"And what does the vibration represent?" he asked.

"Whatever the meaning behind the word is, I suppose."

"Pick a word," he commanded.

"How about *coin*?"

"And when you speak the word *coin,* isn't a certain combination of vibrations sent forth to reach the ears of others?"

"Yes."

"And these vibrations represent an idea?"

"Agreed," I said, trying to follow his thought.

And, in between the thought and the idea, what force acts as the bridge between the two?"

"I'm not sure."

"Suppose you are reading a magazine and see a picture of a new car. The idea or concept of a car enters your mind. What has to happen within you before you will act and do what is necessary to get the car?"

"I suppose I would have to want the car enough to spend the money."

"Very good," he said. "In other words, you first have the idea of a thing in your mind, which is followed by want or desire, which in turn is followed by the materialization of the physical object."

"Makes sense," I said.

"Now a word, as you generally understand the term, starts with an idea. It is followed with a desire to communicate, which is materialized into a vibration that symbolizes the thing, which is, in this case, a car."

"But there is a big difference between saying the word *car* and actually having a new Porsche in my front driveway."

"You think so," he said with a knowing look.

"I take it you don't think so," I replied.

He pulled out the shiny 1796 quarter again and set it on the table. "This is a coin, is it not?"

"I would think so," I said.

"Now does the word *coin* refer only to this coin or to the idea of coins in general?"

"The idea of coins in general."

"What word then refers to this specific coin?"

"I don't know," I said, thinking. "I guess we could call it John's coin."

"But there are many who are called John and many coins. What word refers to this coin?"

"How about John the Beloved's 1796 quarter?" added Elizabeth.

"But I could have two such quarters," he replied.

"I know you well enough to know you're leading us to a conclusion that is beyond the obvious," I said. "You're not looking for a set of regular words are you?"

"Then what am I looking for?"

"You said you are looking for the word that identifies your coin."

"Yes." He nodded. "Now what word could it be?"

"Well, I've concluded it is not a regular word, but you agree that a word is a vibration that represents a thing. Perhaps the coin's word is some type of vibration peculiar to itself."

John smiled and replied, "You're finally headed the right direction. Now let us probe what you know before we reveal the unknown." He picked up the coin and continued, "This coin is made of matter, mostly silver with a bit of copper. What are these metals made of?"

"Atoms," I said hoping I was saying the right thing.

"And what are atoms made of?"

"Protons, electrons and neutrons," I answered, almost sure I was giving the right answer.

"And what are protons and neutrons made of?"

"They are made of even smaller particles called quarks. That's as far as we can go."

"And what are electrons made of?"

"From what I understand, they now think they may be made of waves."

"So, have they discovered any particle yet that they can identify as being solid matter?"

"No," I replied. "All they can find is smaller and smaller particles or waves."

"So they do not know if there is a solid particle, but they do know there are many waves and wavelengths at play in the microcosm of the atomic world?"

"I suppose that is correct," I said.

"And what is sound again?"

A light began to go off in my head as I replied, "Sound is vibration and vibration is composed of waves!"

"And what is the word which is this coin?"

"This is getting interesting," I mused. "I think I see where you are going. This coin is made up of vibrations, and since vibration is sound, then this coin is made of sound. If we could somehow hear the fine vibrations we could hear the word which is this coin."

"You start off a little slow, but you usually come through," John smiled.

"This is interesting, but I think we are talking about a word which cannot be sounded. In your coin are billions of atoms of two elements blending in billions of wavelengths. Now, it's quite simple to sound some note like Middle C, but how would you either hear or sound the word which is as complicated as this coin?"

"Quite simple," he responded. "All creation, which appears complex when divided into its many parts, always evolves toward the greatest of simplicity. The element silver is composed of billions of tiny sounds, but the many tiny voices blend in a great choir to make one master sound. To speak the word which is silver, I merely make the one sound instead of the many."

"But you said the coin is made of two elements, which is copper as well as silver. Is it composed of two words?"

"No. The sound which is silver blends with the sound which is copper to make one sound just as two voices blend to create harmony."

"So does every coin composed of copper and silver have the same word?" I asked.

"Not quite. There is a word for formless copper and silver, but an individual coin introduces other factors. You have the weight which is 6.74 grams and the diameter which is 27.6 millimeters. In addition, you have the etching on the coin. All of these factors have an influence on the sound just as the addition of notes to a basic chord affects the sound on a piano."

"So is every quarter of that year represented by the same word?"

"Not quite," he replied. "Two forms that seem to be exactly the same, such as two coins of the same year and mint, will be very similar in sound, yet with a slight variation. The words which are forms are tempered by the slight differences in the atoms themselves and by the thoughts of the creators of the form, as well as those who use the form."

I again picked a quarter out of my pocket. "So are you telling me that this weathered coin is altered somewhat in sound because I have been carrying it around?"

"Yes. You have altered the sound and have actually contributed to its corruption from its original form and sound. You are not alone, though, for many have had that coin before you and have influenced the corruption of the original sound."

"So, could we sound the original word for this coin and restore it?"

"We could," he affirmed.

"So, how in the world do we find the original word and sound it?" I asked, somewhat puzzled.

John smiled as if he were dealing with a child learning in the first grade. "The sound to be learned does not exist on the physical plane. You must first learn sound as it originates and is held on the highest levels of the mind, and bring it down to the physical in order to produce the manifestation of which we are talking."

"And how are we to make a sound on the higher planes?" I asked with great interest.

"Oh, Joseph. You have forgotten much, haven't you?"

"You mean I once had this knowledge?"

"In a former time and place. You must seek more than knowledge from me. Seek within the realms of your own soul and much will come back to you, or perhaps I should say knowledge will come which your soul feels you will need for your mission."

"That's all well and good," I said, "but I think I'm a ways from remembering how to make sound on the higher planes. You've got to satisfy my curiosity."

"Very well," he said. "All those who have permanent access to the New Jerusalem have a room there where the art of creation is practiced. I will show you a portion of my room."

He then touched both Elizabeth and I on our foreheads and after a couple of seconds pointed to the wall and said, "Look!"

We anxiously did so and saw a point of light that grew brighter until some type of vision appeared before us. To our amazement we saw a portion of a very large room, most of which seemed to be hidden from us. The portion we saw had a large piano surrounded by beautiful plants and flowers.

"You see the piano?" he asked.

We both nodded yes.

"Notice anything different from a regular piano?"

"It's longer and has more keys," responded Elizabeth.

"Very observant," he said. "Your piano has fifty-four white keys. This one has ninety-two. Does this number mean anything to you?"

"That's the number of naturally occurring elements," I said, almost sensing I was reading his mind. "Are you telling me that this piano somehow plays the sounds of the elements?"

John smiled, "Exactly. Keep tuning in and many truths will come to you."

"I see that it has black keys like a regular piano," observed Elizabeth. "What do they do?"

"They create bridging sounds that blend and fuse the elements into isotopes, compounds, molecules and more complex substances."

"So do you have to go to the New Jerusalem to be able to play this piano?" I asked.

"My consciousness is already in the New Jerusalem," he replied. "The consciousness of the adept is not limited by his physical body. Even so, I have temporarily blended your consciousness with mine so you can see one of my creations in the realm of mental energy."

"Interesting," I pondered thoughtfully. "So how can you produce sound from your piano there, when we are here?"

"The piano player would be happy to assist," he replied. Immediately a piano player in an immaculate tuxedo stepped forward and sat at the piano. "Which element would you like him to play?" he asked.

"Well, since we're talking about coins, how about silver?"

"Silver it is," he said, motioning to the piano guy to play.

The player then pressed on one key near the right end of the keyboard, holding his finger down on the key. "Do you hear the sound?" John asked.

"I hear nothing," I said. I then looked at Elizabeth and asked, "Do you hear anything?"

"Not a thing," she said, shaking his head.

The player lifted his hand from the keyboard as John shook his head gently back and forth, "That's because you are listening for physical sound. Come up higher my friends and listen for the sound on the spiritual plane."

I meditated a moment and still heard nothing and I could see by the look on Elizabeth's face that she was not successful either. "We're trying, but we hear nothing," I said.

John then took his hands and clapped them together, making a fairly loud sound. "Did you hear that?"

"Yes, of course," I said.

He then clapped a second time, but this time we could barely hear the sound. "Did you hear that?" he asked.

"Yes, but if was hardly audible," I said.

"Keep listening and tell me when the clapping sounds normal." He then continued making a strong clap every couple seconds.

"When I pay attention the clapping seems to be getting louder."

"Then continue to pay attention," he replied.

As we both paid close attention the clapping sound seemed to get louder. Finally, I told him that the sound seemed to be like normal clapping. Elizabeth added her agreement.

"Very good," said John. "You are hearing that which you have never heard in this life. Listen again."

He continued clapping and again we could barely hear the sound. "What do you hear?" he asked.

"It's like a far away sound, something like last time but a little different," I said

"Then pay attention, like you did last time," he said.

We both paid close attention and again the sound became more discernable. "The sound of your clapping is very clear now," I said, "but it is different and very penetrating."

John continued clapping saying, "It's very penetrating because you are hearing on three levels at one time. You are hearing sound on the physical, the emotional and the mental levels."

"I like it," said Elizabeth. "It's very soothing."

"Perhaps you are ready to hear the pianist play then?" he said.

"Let's try again," she said.

John made a motion and the player again pressed the same key. This time we did hear something. It started as an indescribable hum in our minds causing us to see numerous geometric forms. This was followed by a feeling of a strong emotional vibration, the likes of which we have never before felt. This vibration produced an emotional feeling that is impossible to describe, except that it felt good and interesting. How would you explain the taste of an apple to someone who had never eaten fruit? The only thing I can describe that has any meaning is that it had a metallic feel to it and was followed by a strange metallic taste.

"Creation," he said, "has taken place on two planes, the mental and the emotional. To bring it down to the physical, you must place the attention of your mind on the sound and your feelings upon the vibration."

We attempted to do this.

"Focus, with greater intensity."

This we also attempted.

"Greater still," he said.

We put all we had into it.

"Now hold out your right hands and increase the intensity," he said.

We held out our right hands, palms up and concentrated with all the energy we had. Suddenly, just above my hand was a point of silver light and from this point it appeared that pixie dust was materializing and falling into my hand. Elizabeth took note and started to drop her hand in amazement.

"Don't lose focus," said John to Elizabeth. "Continue as you were and focus all the more."

She then raised her hand back up and focused with renewed faith. Shortly thereafter the silver point appeared above her hand and the magical dust appeared for her also.

After our minds adjusted to the miracle, I moved my hand with the dust toward John and asked, "What is this?"

"What does it look like?" he returned.

"Could it be silver?" I asked hefting it. "It has a silver color and has a weight like it."

"It's silver my friend," he said decisively. "And this is not 99.9% as you stamp on your purest bullion. What you are holding is 100% pure."

"Amazing," I said. Thinking quickly, I got a small jar out of the cupboard and Elizabeth and I poured our silver into it. "So what happened when your piano player plays other keys?"

"You've witnessed the playing of one key and the creation of one element. By playing many keys and chords most anything can be created."

I then pulled out a worn 1967 quarter from my pocket and asked, "Can he restore this quarter and make it new even as your quarters are?" "'"

"Are you not afraid you are asking the impossible?" he asked amused.

"Normally I would, but I have a feeling that part of your plan was to provide us with a demonstration."

John smiled and replied, "You know me too well Joseph John. Hand me the quarter."

John took the quarter, held it in his hand and said, "Just as the silver you held has a sound, every form have a sound. Listen to the sound of this lowly quarter."

"What do you mean?" I asked. "I've carried quarters around all my life and never heard a peep out of any of them"

"Neither have I," said Elizabeth, sounding amused at my attempted humor.

"Maybe you never listened," he retorted, holding the quarter closer to our view. "This coin is singing away. If you have ears to hear, use them now."

If it had been anyone but John, I would have immediately dismissed such a suggestion, but this man was not one to ignore. "All right, I'll try," I agreed.

I focused my attention on the coin and attempted to listen. I began to see geometric shapes and be effected as I was last time. I realized that John's clapping or some other trick he had up his sleeve had increased my sensitivity. "I think I am picking up something," I said.

"I think I am too," said Elizabeth.

"Now continue to focus with your mind and see the image of the coin a few inches above the physical coin."

"I see it!" Elizabeth and I both exclaimed simultaneously.

"Now listen to the sound of both coins."

We listened and the clarity of the geometric shapes increased along with a hum. This time the vibration seemed a little lower than last time. I noticed the piano player also seemed to be paying attention. After a moment he then played two white keys and three black ones. The piano then produced a hum along with the geometric forms exactly as we were hearing from the coin.

"What's he playing?" I asked John.

"He is playing the sound of the coin. The two white keys are for copper and nickel, the elements that compose the coin, and the three black keys are to blend in the shape, size and weight."

"Fascinating," I said. "So how do we restore the coin to its original luster?"

John looked in the direction of the coin and replied, "The original thought behind the creation of this coin still exists in spiritual matter. Look one step higher above the coin and see."

We both looked above the floating coin and attempted to see yet another image. I knew that in normal circumstances this would be near impossible, but I felt a heightened sensitivity due to John's presence and made the attempt. After a few seconds we saw yet another image. This time, instead of a duplicate of a worn coin, we saw a shiny new one.

"I see it!" said Elizabeth. "It looks like it just came from the mint."

"Now hear the sound of the original coin," he directed.

Without any reservations this time we followed instructions. Again we saw geometric shapes and heard a hum.

"What is the difference between the sound of the worn coin and the sound of the original?" he asked.

"The sound was similar to the first except there seemed to be greater crispness and purity in the shapes and the hum of the second." I said.

"And if you had to describe the difference between the first and second sound, what word would you use?"

I thought a moment and then it hit me. "I know the word," I said. "It's *corruption*. The sound of the worn coin is like a corrupted version of the sound of the new coin."

"Excellent!" said John. "Now we're making progress. Next I want you to focus entirely on the sound of the new coin and ignore the sound of the old."

Again we followed instructions and slowly the first image began to fade. As it began to fade my attention shifted from the new image to the worn image and it seemed to come back into view again.

"Keep your attention on the new coin," John instructed. "You must completely ignore the worn one."

As I focused on the new one with greater attention, the old one disappeared completely, leaving only the image and sound of the new coin lingering above the physical coin.

"Much better," said John. "Now the player, who is listening

to the sound, will play the full sound of the original coin."

The entity then played the same two white keys and about a half dozen black ones. We then heard the sound of the original coin from the piano blending with the sound coming from the image of the coin.

"It is done," said John. As soon as he pronounced this statement I felt as if the vibration of the whole room was lowered and the images of the piano player and the phantom coin immediately disappeared, and silence replaced any sound.

"That was quite an experience," I said. "It seems that everything is as it was before."

"Not quite," said John. "Examine your coin."

I picked up the coin and to our amazement, it no longer showed the signs of any wear. It was shiny and new. "Wow, this is amazing," I said. "Will you teach me how to do this?"

"I just did," he said.

"Yeah, but you helped us out. When you clapped your hands and did your magic you increased our sensitivity. Without you we could have never restored the coin."

"Why do you limit yourself so?"

"It's just reality," I said. "Look at us now. Without your help we can't even see or hear the spiritual duplicate of the coin."

"Can't you?" he challenged.

I laid the coin on the table and looked at it. "No, I can't," I insisted. "I am staring away and see only the physical coin."

"Well, that's your problem right there," he said. "You don't stare at the coin; you *see* the coin. I want you both to repeat something after me. Are you ready?"

We both nodded.

"What Christ can do, John can do; and what John can do, we can do. What we can do, all can do."

We repeated the phrase.

"Now repeat again and sound as if you believe it."

We repeated it again, attempting to sound more positive.

"Not good enough," he said, challenging again. "Repeat it like you mean business."

We repeated the phrase one more time with all the energy we had, sounding as positive as we knew how to be.

"Much better," he said.

"So is believing we have these spiritual powers some type of key to obtaining them?" I asked.

"Belief precedes all attainment," he said, "but there are a number of important ingredients. The first two keys you have learned are of prime importance. To advance in your spiritual powers you must decide to move ahead. Before and after this you must use good judgment to be assured you stay on the path of progress. Then the third key is also of importance, but, of course, you do not yet have this. The bottom line is that you are not as far away from these spiritual manifestations as you think. A lack of initial belief in God working through us is a great stumbling block."

"I'll tell you this," I said, "Since we have met you, a lot of our unbelief has faded away. The statement that all things are possible used to be a cliché, but now it is more like a statement of fact."

"Then you made a good first step," he said.

"I have a couple of questions about your room in the New Jerusalem. What's the story behind that?"

"No big story," he smiled. "One of the main purposes of the New Jerusalem is to provide space and spiritual opportunity for the inhabitants to learn and use their natural powers of creation. The first thing a regular visitor acquires is his own private creation room."

"So once you become a regular, someone assigns you a room?"

"Not quite. After a few visits a seeker discovers that the atmosphere and vibration enhance his powers of creation and he begins to naturally experiment. He then discovers there is a time to mingle and blend with the inhabitants, and a time to be alone. Now, of course, for the disciple there is no such thing as truly being alone because he is always in communion with others of his group through the Oneness Principle. Even so, to avoid distraction, it is advantageous to have a room of your own where you can be by yourself as far as form is concerned. No one gives you a room. Instead you create it yourself using the power of your thought."

"So what about the piano player and the piano?" Elizabeth queried. "Were they real or did you create them?"

"They are as real as any form can be, and yes, I created them," he replied. "You should also realize that you saw into only a tiny portion of my room. After many centuries it is very vast in size and is made to assist me in manifesting all my needs as I go about my mission."

"Except for money," I assume. "You told us that even though you can produce wealth out of thin air that you cannot use it if it takes away from the wealth of others, like counterfeit money for example."

"Good remembering," he observed. "Yes. Injecting wealth into the system without the advantage of labor is like purchasing with counterfeit money. The real power behind money is labor, for without labor there is nothing of value to purchase. This is why your silver dust will return to its source upon my leaving."

"You say that your creation room assists you in manifesting all your needs, yet you cannot use your powers to replace money," said Elizabeth. "It seems that the use of these spiritual powers is pretty limited."

"Here on the earth we place much too much value on money, John reasoned. This makes us overlook the many things that may bring joy that are beyond the reach of money. The first thing to realize is that there are no restrictions on creation in the New Jerusalem. If you want to create a great feast there that would cost a lot of money here on earth, there is no problem because your use of products there never creates a shortage for anyone else. All are free to create to their heart's content and there is no want. On the other hand, we must be careful as to what we materialize on the physical plane, else we take on negative karma and become subject to rebirth against our will."

"So what powers can you bring down to the earth plane?" asked Elizabeth. "Can you give us an example?"

John placed his hand to his chin as if thinking and said, "I'll tell you a couple of things. One of my most useful creations is my great library. Over the centuries I have added thousands of scrolls, books, plates, everything of interest that I have found over the millennia with writing on them. You may be impressed with the internet, but this library puts it to shame. Many of the books and manuscripts there are lost to history, but not lost to me."

"And how do you use this library?" I asked.

John clapped several times and this time our vibration was

raised quite quickly. When we looked at the wall again we saw the inside of a great library with such vast corridors that we could not see the end of them. Sitting on a desk was a lone elderly librarian.

John looked at him and caught his eye, "Retrieve my first book," he commanded.

The man, though elderly, spryly got up, seemed to disappear for an instant and quickly reappeared with an ancient scroll. Suddenly the piano player appeared again. "Play the sound," John directed.

The piano player looked at the scroll and began to play. I noticed that when he hit a note it continued to sound after his finger was lifted. He seemed to hit about twenty notes altogether and the sound of all of them blended together in great beauty and power. The sound even affected me emotionally and made me choke up with a sense of inner joy. I sensed that Elizabeth was similarly affected. Then John held out his right hand and in it materialized the same scroll that was retrieved by the librarian.

John handed it to me. It looked like an ancient scroll, but showed no signs of wear. It was as if someone had just finished writing it. "What is this?" I asked. "It appears to be written in Greek."

"The Gospel of John, the same one that was written by my own hand as a disciple of the Lord."

"Wow. I feel privileged indeed," I said. "I wish I could read it."

"I suppose this will also evaporate after you leave," added Elizabeth.

"*Evaporate* is not the word I would use," smiled John, "but yes, I cannot leave it here."

"Speaking of money, it's probably worth a zillion dollars," I said. "I can see why the Brotherhood has rules about financial gain. A couple of you could upset the financial systems of the world."

"Indeed," he agreed, laying the scroll on the table. "Now to retrieve some information I do not need to materialize a book, but merely have to direct my librarian to get it for me. He turned again to the librarian and said, "Caesar, get me my copy of Hamlet."

"Caesar? You call your librarian Caesar?"

John chuckled. "Yes, I named him Caesar. After all the trouble the Roman Caesars caused me, I enjoy having a Caesar for a servant."

"Makes sense," I said. "I see that Caesar has your book. Looks like some kind of hand bound edition. I suppose it is another original."

"Now I can retrieve information from the book in several ways. As you have already seen, I can manifest it on the physical plane. I rarely do this except when I have extra time to relax and read the old-fashioned way. Instead, I can project the words I wish to read in front of me."

Then suddenly we all saw an expanded page from the book suspended in the air for us all to read. "I see you have it opened to Hamlet's famous words – *To be or not to be*," I said.

"A third way to use the library is to retrieve the original thoughts of the writers the way I did when I read your book. This gives me the impressions I usually need to formulate knowledge. A lot of the criteria of how I use the library depend on the time factor. As you know, I usually have a lot on my plate and have to make the best possible use of time."

"I must admit that this library idea could be very useful," said Elizabeth. "Can you show us another example of something usable from your creation room?"

John paused a moment in thought and replied, "I have something that I am sure you will agree can be extremely useful. He pointed to the wall again as the vision of the library faded and a new unexpected image came to view. Elizabeth and I looked on in amazement. I was surprised but Elizabeth was so startled she about passed out.

She caught her breath and said, "I never expected this! Of what use would this creation be?"

"I will explain," he said. "First another cup of tea."

CHAPTER SEVEN
Eternal Words

Elizabeth nervously prepared another round of tea as we anxiously awaited further explanation from John. As John took a sip she demanded, "Okay, I'm looking in your library and see an image of myself. What does it mean?"

As we all looked toward the projected image of John's library we saw a hovering duplicate of Elizabeth. We were both extremely curious.

"I'm sure you remember my promise to you that when you solved the first three keys I would heal Elizabeth."

"Yes, of course," I said.

"To insure that this would be the case I absorbed and sounded the Word which is Elizabeth when I first met her. Just as the shiny new coin has an uncorrupted word, so do we. The image you see of Elizabeth is the result of her Word sounded in a healthy state. Having this image of her in my room gives me power to restore her to health on either a temporary or permanent basis. It seemed as if she was healed for a period of time and this vibration of hers would not be needed, but thanks to Philo and your karmic connection with him this is no longer the case."

"Are you sure you cannot heal her permanently at this time?" I asked.

"Unfortunately, I am restrained by law at the moment," he responded. "But be of good cheer. When the needed lesson is learned she will be healed permanently from her disease."

"Or when we complete the Third Key," I reminded him.

"Either way a lesson will be learned," he observed.

"You can understand that we are anxious to solve the Third Key," I said. "Can you take us any further at this time?"

"I can leave you with an additional hint, but first let us review what you have learned tonight. We saw in the game of Chinese Whispers that the originating communion was changed through what principle?"

Elizabeth jumped in, "Through the principle of corruption."

"And after the word was corrupted what did the group have to do to restore the correct phrase?"

"They had to go back to the source, the first person who originated the statement."

"And then I demonstrated the truth of this for you in applying it to form. All form is the result of sound, or a word, and all form goes through the process of decay or corruption. But the sounding of the original word on all planes restores the form just as sounding the original phrase in the game restores the meaning."

"But in Chinese Whispers you only have to sound it on one level. To restore the coin you had to sound it on three. That's a little different."

"Not really," said John. "The principle is still the same; the playing field is merely expanded."

"So I take it that corruption is not the key word, but a hint on the way to the key," I noted.

"That is correct. Now, for your additional hint I leave you with this question. The key to communion is to negate corruption. How is this done?"

"Haven't you already told us? You just go back to the source."

"And what are the ways to go back? And if you are the originator of the word, how do you prevent your words from being corrupted? If you are the first receiver, how do you make sure you hear and pass it on properly? All of these are ingredients in the principle of communion and must be understood to negate corruption."

"It sounds like the solution does not always involve going back to the source," I observed.

"That is not always possible for the average disciple. For instance, the world does not have the original manuscripts of the Bible. The ones available have been altered to some degree, going through a dozen or more in the copying process. Now someone with my knowledge may be able to go back to the source, but humanity is unable to. They, therefore, must plow with the horses they have. In order to move forward in the principle of communion, the disciple must understand the whole principle and apply it to his situation."

John paused a moment and added, "This is all I can give you on this point at this time. You must now go through a period of gestation where you think upon what you have learned and contemplate the new hints."

"But we'd be willing to keep at this with you without a break until we understand the Key," I pleaded.

"I know you would," he smiled. "But some things cannot be rushed. You need time to reflect so in the end you will fully understand. Let me remind you that the key word is never the key, but a symbol of the key. The true Key of Knowledge lies in its understanding. A key word can be given in a second, but the understanding must be acquired."

"You can't blame him for trying," added Elizabeth.

"I would expect no less," he said, smiling tenderly at Elizabeth.

"So what can we do to keep both Philo and the disease at bay?" I pleaded.

"To handle Philo, Elizabeth must not give him energy from which to feed," he replied. "This involves the Principle of Attrition that you so painfully learned. You must now coach her on using it. As far as the disease goes, you must follow the highest you know. Consider that the Principle of Corruption is behind the disease itself. What caused the corruption and how can it be eliminated?"

"We'll think on what you say," I said. "So have you had time to physically read the book or present it to the Brotherhood?"

"I have," he said.

"What did you think?"

"Ingredients of your writing style could use a little polish, but overall I found myself quite taken with the book as a whole. It is definitely much more engaging for the average seeker than a direct and sometimes dry presentation of new teachings."

"How about the Brotherhood's reaction? Did they read the

physical copy?"

"Several who had doubts did and the rest have read it residually."

"And what did they think?" I asked, anxiously.

John paused a moment and replied, "Those who have doubts about the plan indicate they will support you on certain conditions. One of them is that you must pass the great test of the Third Key."

"So, what is the test?"

"I'll tell you when the time is right," he said.

"I'm ready to do anything at any time and in any place to help Elizabeth," I said with some eagerness, while looking at her.

"I know," he said smiling. "I know. But now you must contemplate the hints I have given you and prepare for our next meeting. In the meantime, look after Elizabeth. She'll need your strength."

At that John arose and said, "It is time for me to leave."

As he arose I almost panicked inside. I felt I had to garner as much information on the Key as possible so I could solve it in time to save Elizabeth. I grabbed John's arm and pleaded, "I feel there's something more you can give me."

John looked at me as if he were reflecting on whether or not I was correct.

I studied his face and took advantage of his hesitation. "There is something else isn't there? There's something else, you can give me."

John sighed and sat back down. "The parable of the Master applies to you here."

"What parable?" asked Elizabeth.

"I see that you have a New English version of the Bible. Turn to Luke 11:5-10 and read."

I did have a version of the New English Bible in my library. How he knew this was just one more mystery to me. I retrieved it and read:

Then he said unto them, Suppose one of you has a friend who comes to him in the middle of the night and says, 'My friend, lend me three loaves, for a friend of mine on a journey has turned up at my house, and I have nothing to offer him.'

And he replies from, the inside: 'Do not bother me. The door

*is shut for the night; my children and I have gone to bed; and I
cannot get up and give you what you want.'*

*I tell you that even if he will not provide for him out of friend-
ship, the very shamelessness of the request will make him get up
and give him all he needs.*

*And I say to you, ask, and you will receive; seek, and you will
find; knock, and the door will be opened. For everyone who asks
receives, he who seeks finds, and to him who knocks, the door will
be opened.*

After reading I looked up and said, "So you're going to give
me more, not because I am your friend, but because I am shame-
less like the guy in the parable?"

John chuckled and replied. "If the truth be known, it's more
because you remind me of myself when I was with the Master. I
often shamelessly put pressure upon him to tell me things. I know
there were times he taught me more to shut me up rather than because of any affection."

"I guess I don't feel so bad then," I said. "I think that if I
follow in your footsteps, I am on solid ground."

"That may be open to debate," he smiled, "but you can pat
yourself on the back for bringing me back to the table to give you
more information."

"I'll honor your valuable time," I said. "Just give me one
more thing."

John looked at me with great intensity and finally spoke.
"Now turn to Matthew 24:35 and again read the Masters words.
Your King James is as good as any here."

I turned and read, "Heaven and earth shall pass away, but my
words shall not pass away."

"Now visualize this," he said. "In the game of Chinese Whispers, a person begins with an original phrase, but by the time it
goes around the circle, what happens?"

I was about to answer that it was something to do with corruption when another thought came in my mind that I felt was
inspired. "The original phrase passed away," I said.

"Exactly," he said. "Most words, phrases and thoughts that
undergo layers of translation lose their meaning, but there are ex-
ceptions. There are certain words that take the ear back to the
vibration of spirit that cannot be corrupted. The Brotherhood calls

these *eternal words.* Can you tell me the difference between eternal words and regular words?"

"I always thought that words were just words," I said. "But apparently you are saying that there are certain words or combination of words that are so clear, they cannot be corrupted. I'm not sure what they would be, though."

"Let me give you two statements," he said. "First statement, *The truth shall make you free.* The second one is *The temperature right now is ninety degrees.* Now what is the difference between the two? What do you think Elizabeth?"

Elizabeth paused a few seconds in thought and replied, "The first is a very profound truth and the second is just a passing statement of fact."

"Now let us suppose you register both of these statements to the best of your ability, and then let a year pass. Are you likely to remember the first statement?"

"I think so," she replied. "It is so profound, yet so simple, it registers in a way that you just don't forget it. I do not remember the first time I heard this, but I know that I've never forgotten it."

"And how about the second statement? Are you likely to recall it after a year?"

"I doubt it," she said. "I can't remember what the temperature was yesterday, let alone a year ago."

"And why will you always be able to recall the first statement but not the second?"

"I'm not sure exactly. Like I said, the first was just much more profound."

"But, what makes it so profound – what makes it so different from the second statement?"

"One gives us a great truth, but the other is a piece of trivia."

"But they are both statements of truth," he said. "What makes one truth different from another?"

Elizabeth seemed to be at a dead end so I jumped in, "Most people merely think that one truth is like another, but there's obviously a great difference here. It's got to have something to do with the fact that we can easily remember the first, but not the second."

"And why is the first easily remembered?" he asked.

"I'm not sure. It's just a much more important truth than the temperature."

"Let me give you some more eternal words of the Master. *By their fruits you shall know them.* Tell me, have you ever forgotten this statement?"

"No," I said. "That's another profound truth that few will ever forget after they hear it."

"And why will they not forget it?"

"I'm not sure, but it seems to touch the soul."

"And why does it touch the soul?"

"It must have something to do with application," I said. "The truths of Jesus could be applied to a lot of things, but the temperature of the day is just one thing. It's true today, but not tomorrow. But something like, *By their fruits you shall know them* is always true."

John's eyes showed that he thought we had made a little progress. "So, the temperature is a truth that only applies to a moment in time and space, is it not?"

"Yes, I suppose one could word it that way."

"And how about the second truth?"

"I guess you could say it applies to all moments in time and space. It is as true now as when Jesus spoke it, but the temperature has changed millions of times."

"So, let me ask again. What is the difference between the two truths? Why is one only fleetingly true and the other always true?"

I thought for a moment and replied, "The words of Jesus seemed to enunciate principles or formulas that applied to many things, whereas a piece of data like the temperature only applies to one thing."

John's eyes brightened, "Now we're getting somewhere. Yes, there are words that do not pass away, eternal words, which give us more than pieces of information. Instead, they speak the language of the soul, which is the language of principles that leads to many truths. It can take a thousand facts to paint the picture of one principle, but one principle can lead to thousands of facts."

"Wow," I said. "I think you just spoke some more eternal words."

John smiled and said, "I think you are seeing some light here, but let me add something. Humankind has taken the greatest words of sages past and compiled them into books and called them scriptures. Not only have the Christians and Jews done this, but all peoples have done this from the beginning. What was there about these words that caused people to set them apart?"

"It was because they thought the writings contained the Word of God," I said.

"And why did they think they contained the Word of God?"

"I guess some teacher told them so."

"But that's not enough to cause the words to endure. What else?"

I reflected a moment and responded. "My mind goes back to the Book of Hebrews. I remember reading that when they were compiling the Bible and trying to decide which books should be included, they hit a snag with this book. The trouble was that no one knew who wrote it. Some thought Paul wrote it, but no one knew for sure. It could have been written by anyone, maybe someone with no authority. Finally, they decided to include it because of the content itself. The reasoning was that the words were so great they had to be the Word of God. So I guess my answer to you is that the scriptures of the world are basically selected for this same reason. The words within them are so inspiring that it is felt they had to come from God."

"Very good," he said. "In other words, for a work to be saved as scripture, the words have to touch the soul and spirit of the people. Something in them has to touch on principles that lead the reader to discover even more truth than the mere facts presented. Scripture then, is more than a holy book sitting on a table. True scripture are the words that enunciate true principles, which are the language of the soul. Now tell me this, are all the words of the Bible or other holy books scripture?"

"By this definition, I would say no," I said. "A lot of the Bible is just history and probably is no more scripture than any other accurate history. But the teachings in the Bible which touch the soul would fit in your definition."

Yes," he replied, "the canon may preserve important history, but history is only true scripture when an important principle is learned from it. True scripture are the teachings that cause the reader to reflect upon more than the data involved. It must lead to reflection upon true principles. Now I have another question for you. Where are the scriptures of today's world that are not in books that are called scripture?"

"Scriptures that are not called scripture?" I asked puzzled. "Sounds like a riddle."

"Not a riddle. Just a question," he offered.

"You got me. I have a lot of books on philosophy and meta-physics. Could some of them be scripture?"

"Some contain scripture, but these are only accepted by a few. Where are the scriptures recognized by the many?"

"Scriptures that are not called scripture recognized by the many," I mumbled. "I don't know, but I am very curious about the answer."

"The answer is in your bookcase."

"Really!" I said. "Where in my bookcase?"

"Let us take a look," he said, rising. We went to my main bookcase and John stared at one of the shelves. "It's on this shelf," he said, pointing. "Can you tell me which book it is?"

I looked back and forth on the shelf and couldn't spot any particularly profound book. In fact, this shelf contained what I thought were my more ordinary books. I was about to give up when Elizabeth pulled out a volume. "I'll bet this is it," she said.

I looked at the book, a book of famous quotations.

"Good feminine intuition," said John, taking the book from her hand and opening it. "Now I will read you a scripture." He ran his finger down a page, settled on a paragraph and said, "Here's a good one by Mark Twain, *Courage is resistance to fear, mastery of fear — not absence of fear.* Now tell me. Is this not as profound and thought-provoking as many verses of accepted scripture?"

"I suppose so," I agreed, nodding my head.

He then flipped though the pages and settled on another one, "Here's a good one by Elbert Hubbard, *Genius may have its limitations, but stupidity is not this handicapped.*"

Elizabeth and I laughed and she said, "That doesn't seem to have the reverence associated with scripture."

"Maybe not," he said, "but does it or does it not conjure up truth in your mind?"

"It really does," I admitted. "I have several images now dancing around in my mind of both genius and stupidity I have witnessed that verifies the truth of the statement."

"Yes, he said, "a good quotation that causes one to see more than the black and white words is more valid scripture than much of the Bible, even though it has not been approved by authorized conclaves."

"Ministers may not like that idea, but I can see that it is true," I said.

"Now the good thing about quotations is that humanity has recognized their value and, even though they do not call them scripture, the current civilization has done an excellent job in compiling them and making them available to the public. In fact, with the advent of the internet, the use of such quotations will only increase. This will be a positive development.

"In addition to quotations, a second common source of true principles is the many parables and fables that have been written through the ages. Aesop's Fables is a noted work that incorporates many true principles in simple stories, easy to remember. These were not written by one person, but were compiled from many stories that were popular in ancient Greece.

"Now let us go back to the table and continue."

We all went back to the table and sat down. John then continued, "There are other scriptures which have been used by thinking humans, some for many thousands of years, and these have never been compiled in a concise form. These scriptures are much better known than the famous quotations, for they are in the air and almost all people have heard of them. In fact, they have been in circulation so much that they are often called clichés. Can you name one that would be scripture?"

"My mother used to use a lot of clichés," said Elizabeth, "like *busy as a bee*. Would that be one?"

"That is indeed a cliché that has stuck in the public consciousness, but that is not what I am looking for. There are two types that are in popular use. The first is a descriptive one. This describes a situation or action in a clever way that helps to build a picture in the mind of the receiver of the thought of the speaker. These clichés fill an excellent purpose, but are not meant to provoke thought as do the ones in the second category.

"The second category of clichés is meant to deliver a principle of truth in a concise form that is easily registered and remembered. We could call these *truisms*. Can you think of one?"

"I think I know what you mean and I use them regularly myself," I said. "How about, *A bird in the hand is worth two in the bush?*"

"That is an example of what I am looking for," he said. "Instead of just describing a situation, a truth is enunciated, and that enunciation applies just as much today as it did centuries ago. The truth is reduced to such simplicity that no elaboration is needed."

"That's a good point," I said, "but what do these quotations and clichés have to do with the Third Key?"

"They have a lot to do with it. Data can be corrupted through transmission or translation, but a profound quote, or a good cliché, is rarely corrupted. When one sees the truth behind the cliché you just quoted, it becomes almost impossible to transmit it incorrectly. You can even change the words and the truth behind it will not change. For instance, you could say, *a fish in the hand is worth two in the lake.* The words are changed but the thought remains the same. This does not apply to a mere fact like the temperature. A true scripture conveys a thought that transcends the actual words, and when a thought of a true principle is transmitted and understood then it is almost impossible to corrupt."

"Interesting," I replied, nodding. "I must admit that I never thought of *a bird in the hand* as scripture, but I can see the truth of it. And I can see how clichés encapsulate a truth in such a way that it is never lost."

"And now I have a new assignment for you," he said. "You are to compile all clichés, or truisms, which convey truth and have registered in public consciousness, then place them in a future chapter of your books."

"I'd be happy to give it a try," I said, "but if I remember correctly, I have seen books of clichés before. Wouldn't I be reinventing the wheel?"

Elizabeth laughed and said, "You just did it. You used a cliché and probably didn't even realize it."

"You're right. I just used one to convey a truth and didn't even know it."

"People use these truisms much more than they realize," said John. "Now to answer your question, no, you wouldn't be reinventing the wheel. It is true there are a number of compilations of clichés, but these are different from that which you shall accumulate for two reasons. First, many compilations are of obscure phrases, not in the general consciousness; and, secondly, many of them are merely descriptive ones not related to encapsulating a biting truth. The Brotherhood would like to see you compile popular clichés that really portray a truth of some kind. We're more concerned with quality than quantity."

"Can't they just use their superhuman powers and materialize the selection they want?" said Elizabeth.

"Let me cover this point one more time," said John with a twinge of impatience. "The Brotherhood has their own work to do and it does not include doing for humanity what humanity can do for itself. It is the only safe way to handle the Law of Karma. Now, let us make sure you are on the right track with these clichés. Give me several that come to your mind and we'll see if they fit in with what we are looking for.

"Okay," I said, thinking. "You know there must be hundreds of good clichés, but it's difficult to think of them off the cuff."

"I have one," said Elizabeth. "How about, *Birds of a feather flock together.*"

"Yes, that is a good one," he said. "What truth does it teach us?"

"It tells us that people who have similar interest or thoughts will become friends and associate together," she said.

"And isn't it interesting," said John, "that when people hear these clichés they internally realize they are true, even if the truth lies beyond their normal thought process?"

"I can see that," I said. "Few people think about a principle like this – that like gathers with like, but will still use the cliché, feeling it is true. I just had another one come to my mind. How about *Rome was not built in a day?*"

"Good," said John, "and what truth does that carry?"

I reflected a couple seconds and replied, "Many people want to achieve greatness or do a great work and think it can be done quickly, but just as Rome was not built in a day, even so do other great works take time."

"That is an important lesson many seekers, and even disciples, need to register. Now give me another one."

"I'm not sure if this fits," said Elizabeth, "but when you showed up tonight I thought *what a sight for sore eyes.*"

"That's a cliché all right." he said, "And it's a good one, but it is a descriptive one and not a truism. This is why I am having you give me clichés so you will get a sense of what we are looking for. Don't worry about being wrong, just give me any that come to mind."

"How about *six and two threes*?" I asked.

"That's somewhat descriptive but it is also a truism," he said. "Can you see why?"

"I think so," I said. "It is true that there are many times in life where we are faced with a decision between two alternatives and it seems that one is just as good as another – or six and two threes."

"Your turn Elizabeth," he said.

"We must *take the time to smell the roses along the way*," she said.

"And what true teaching does this convey?" he asked.

"That we can't work or be serious all the time, but we must all take a break now and then to savor life."

"I think you're getting a sense of what a truism is. Now it's important that you understand what is not to be included. Give me three clichés that are not truisms."

"You know these are difficult to just come up with out of the blue, but I think I have one. *It's so quiet you can hear a pin drop*," I said.

"And why is this not a truism?"

"I suppose this would be a descriptive cliché," I said. It gives a beautiful description, but does not reveal a truth."

"How about this," said Elizabeth. "*Crazy like a fox.*"

"That's another good description. One could extrapolate truth from it, but it is not as obvious as some. This one is a borderline cliché. I'll leave it up to you whether you wish to include it; in other words, it's six and two threes. Now give me one more descriptive cliché."

"How about *run like the wind*?" I injected.

"That is definitely a descriptive cliché. It is an interesting description, but does not contain any imbedded truth. You've got the basic idea now of what we are looking for and that which we are not looking for. Now you must earn the right for the additional hints I have given you by compiling the best of the clichés which are also truisms. You can start tonight by writing down all that come to your mind."

"I'll do that," I said. "It'll be kind of a fun project."

"But don't forget that I have given you a lot tonight to think over as you search for the Third Key. You have gained an important revealing word, which is *corruption*. You have received hints as to how to avoid it. You have learned that each form has an originating word that remains incorruptible on higher spheres. Finally, you learned that certain words and phrases are protected from corruption. These are called eternal words and they do not pass away. You have much to contemplate as you seek to solve the Third Key."

"Thanks for the extra hints," I said. "I hope I can make proper use of them."

"I'm sure you will," he said, getting up to leave.

Elizabeth got up and stepped toward John and embraced him with a big hug. "I want to soak up all the strength I can from you before you leave," she said.

I joined in hugging them both for a few silent seconds.

Then we all said the Song of the 144,000 together. Afterwards John looked at Elizabeth and said. "You will have strength until tomorrow morning. Then you will have to deal with Philo and your returning illness. Do not despair. You will be stronger when this is all over. Reflect on the power of the Word. This can help"

We said our good-byes again and John exited, disappearing into the night, walking toward the city.

After taking a couple minutes to soak in the events of the night we sat back down at the table. We both noticed that the manuscript and the silver were gone. After shrugging our shoulders, Elizabeth said, "We need to get to work."

"Work?"

"Yes, remember John said to start the list right away. Here's a legal pad and a pen. Let's get started."

"I suppose you're right. We can't let any *grass grow under our feet* can we?"

"No we can't," she said, "and for truism number one you can list the one you just said about grass growing."

"Okay," I smiled."

I wrote "1. *Don't let the grass grow under your feet.*" We then listed others we had discussed so far and attempted to think of additional ones.

"It's funny," I said. "In normal conversations truisms just seem to come up naturally and effortlessly, but they are difficult to produce when you try and think of them."

"I have another," she said. *"There is a silver lining in every cloud."*

"That's an appropriate one," I said. "Now I just thought of one, *The grass is always greener on the other side of the fence."*

We continued brainstorming until we had a list of about twenty truisms. "That's a start," I said. "I'm sure there are several hundred good ones, but it's hard to just pick them out of the air. I think we need to write them down as they come to us."

"Probably," she said. "Maybe you can find some kind of book on clichés in the library that will contain some truisms we can use."

"Maybe," I replied, realizing that we could not delay bedtime much longer. Shortly afterwards we retired and had difficulty going to sleep. A certain dread filled us both as we waited for the morning when Elizabeth's problems would return.

CHAPTER EIGHT
Word Pictures

The next morning Elizabeth was ill, just as she was before her healing. I had to hire a temporary helper to keep the business going. Between caring for Elizabeth and the business I was extremely busy.

We mutually decided to not see the doctor again just yet. It seemed ordinary medical assistance would be powerless to help her. We believed that the only helpful course of action was to solve the Third Key whereby John would be obliged to fulfill his commitment to heal Elizabeth.

After running some errands I managed to find a few moments to drop by the library. At eight o'clock I finally made it home for the evening.

Elizabeth sat in her wheelchair, her shoulders slumped with her forehead propped up by a hand.. "How's my sweetie?" I asked kissing her on the cheek.

"Not so good," she said. "Not only has the disease come back, but I can feel Philo's presence. He's worse than the disease and is about to drive me crazy."

"What's it feel like?" I asked, kneeling down.

"It's difficult to describe. It's just a very disturbing vibration that seems to get some perverse pleasure in bringing me discomfort."

"He almost sounds like your personal Dweller on the Threshold," I said. "Have you tried the principle of attrition and not let him affect your consciousness?"

"I've tried to ignore him and it doesn't work. In fact it seems to just encourage him."

"I found in my experience with negative forces that to ignore them is really the wrong approach," I said. "You have to go beyond ignoring to using the principle of attrition."

"And how do you go beyond ignoring?" she asked.

"I found that ignoring negative forces is not enough. Ignoring can be a type of suppression that causes the negativity to fester in the background and come back later with greater force. What I finally discovered was to tune it out by an act of the will. That is, I had to place my consciousness in a state of mind that did not even recognize the existence of the negativity. This prevented the negative force from feeding on my energy and caused it to die through attrition."

"Sounds like you ignored it to me."

"Until you do it, it may sound that way. Actually, I did not ignore it in the normal sense. I never ceased realizing that it existed, but I did not allow my consciousness to recognize any effect upon me. It's hard to explain until you go through it," I added.

"So far you aren't helping me much."

I got up and paced the floor, thinking of a better way to explain my own experience. "Think of it like this," I said. "Suppose the neighbor's dog is barking while you are trying to sleep. You find it annoying and try to ignore the irritating sound. The trouble is the more you try to ignore the sound the more it can wind up bothering you. Have you had this happen before?"

"Now you're speaking a language I can understand," she said. "It's happened a number of times. The more I try to ignore the bark the more annoyed I get. Are you saying then that there's another solution?"

"Yes," I replied. "Instead of trying to ignore the bark, which just gives it more power to annoy you, let us suppose that you do the opposite and pay supreme attention, not only to the bark, but to yourself as the observer. First, examine the vibration of the bark and ask yourself what there is about it that you do not like. Then look within yourself and find that part of yourself that is disturbed by the bark. Next harmonize this part of yourself and the bark so they cancel each other out as if neither exists. This takes an act of the will to do, but once it is done the dog can bark all it wants and you are completely unaffected."

I looked at her face and saw she was following with interest, "Now imagine that the energy for barking comes from your own self. Because you are no longer giving energy to the source of irritation it will not be long before the barking ceases altogether, as if its batteries have run down. The amazing thing is when it does cease you will hardly notice because you have already cancelled out its negative effects."

"That helps a little," she said "I don't know if I can do it, but I'll try."

"It took me a while to figure it out. There's just no handbook for a situation like this. You'll just have to experiment until the right consciousness comes to you." I sat down next to her and said, "I wish I could do it for you."

She took my hand and said, "That's sweet. Your being here for me is the only thing that helps right now. But I'll think about your advice and try to make it work." She stared a moment at the empty space in front of her and broke the silence by asking, "So, did you find anything useful at the library?"

"Not much," I said. "There were two large volumes containing what was supposed to be clichés, but they were not much help."

"Why not?"

"Well, I read through the first hundred or so and didn't see a cliché or truism that I recognized. I don't know how they can call them clichés when no one has heard of them."

"A lot of compilations do not want to leave anything out so they'll include everything, even if they are very obscure," she said.

"Oh, well, *nothing ventured, nothing gained*," I said. "Say, that's one right there. I'll add it to the list."

"Way to *take the bull by the horns*," she smiled.

"Cute," I said. "I think the way to find these is through listening to regular conversation."

"Maybe," she said. "You know Wayne is really good with words. I'll bet he can help you think of quite a few of them."

"I think you're right," I replied. "You'd never know it by looking at him, but he does put some very clever spin on words at times. I'll call him up and see if he can do lunch tomorrow."

The next day we met at McGrath's Fish house. They have a combo special we both like a lot. After I was there a few moments

Wayne walked in, this time wearing one of his regular hats.

"Where's your Stetson?" I asked as he sat down.

Wayne said nothing for a moment, but I saw a certain look of disgust on his face that told me he had bad news to relate. "You had to ask me about my hat, didn't you?" He then let out a sigh and continued, "I hired a new guy a couple weeks ago – Jake, I may have told you about him."

"I think you mentioned him."

"Well, he seemed like a nice friendly guy and came on to me like he was my best friend. Then one day he asked me if he could borrow my hat – said he wanted to impress his girlfriend. He promised he would return it the next day."

"And I take it that he didn't return it the next day," I said.

"Not only that," he said, "but he left town with about a couple thousand dollars worth of tools along with my hat."

"Left town? Where'd he go?"

"Probably somewhere in Texas. One of the guys said he mentioned going back to the Panhandle somewhere. I filled out a police report but they didn't hold out much hope of finding him unless he returns to the area." Wayne then stared like Clint Eastwood, as if his eyes were burning right through me. "Damn!" he exclaimed, pounding on the table. "I miss that hat!"

"I keep telling you that you need to be more careful about the guys you hire," I said. "Your trouble is that you are just too trusting and good-hearted. If someone comes off the street with a sad story you'll hire him and give him your trust. There are some people who are just not trustworthy."

"You're right, of course, but sometimes I think I must have come from another planet where everyone could be trusted. It just seems wrong to me to live life distrusting people."

"But it's not a perfect world," I said. "Some people you can trust and others you cannot. Unless you have some type of intuitive knowledge, you must make people earn your trust."

"I suppose so," he agreed. "I just don't like living my life that way."

"It's better than the alternative," I said. "You get your profits and valuables stolen from you regularly because you are too trusting. Imagine how much better the quality of your life would be if you had nothing stolen the past couple years."

"You make a good case," he said, having no intention to follow my advice.

As Wayne brooded the waitress appeared and took our order. We each ordered a seafood combo with extra clam chowder.

"I hear Elizabeth is sick again," he said. "What's that about?"

"It's a long story," I replied.

"I've got a few minutes."

"Maybe another time," I said.

"So what does the doctor say?' he pried.

"We haven't taken her back to the doctor," I said sheepishly.

"Listen," he said, "I distrust doctors just as much as the next guy, but her life may be at stake here. You've got to take her in."

"Maybe this is where trust comes in," I said. "Neither one of us thinks the doctor will be able to do her any good. Instead, we have something else we're trying."

"What is it? Some quack or faith healer?"

"Nothing like that," I said. "But is does have something to do with faith. I'll explain more later."

"But it's one thing to trust someone with money that can be replaced, but if anything happens to Elizabeth you will lose her forever," he said with a little nervousness.

"I know the risks and I know what I am doing," I said. "I think this is one time that you really need to trust me."

"Like you say, I am a trusting guy, but you are pushing me to the limit here."

"All I can tell you is that we know the cause of her relapse and we know the solution and it has nothing to do with doctors. If you knew the whole story, you wouldn't send her to a doctor either."

"Okay," he said, "I'll trust you for now. It doesn't make sense, but I'll do it."

After eating our soup in silence, Wayne finally said, "So, are you still on your quest for knowledge or has the situation with Elizabeth completely distracted you?"

"The situation is a distraction, not only from any study, but with my writing, the business and everything important. I'll let you in on one thing. This quest for knowledge I am on has something to do with healing Elizabeth."

"And how is that possible?"

"I can't tell you. Like I said, you'll just have to trust me."

"It's not easy," he said. "You are just not being your logical self here, but I'll play along. What knowledge are you looking for today?"

"Well, it may seem kind of silly, but I'm looking for clichés."

"Clichés?"

"Not ordinary clichés, but clichés with truisms in them like *A bird in the hand is worth two in the bush.* A cliché like this teaches a true principle."

"So something like *the cow jumped over the moon* wouldn't fit?"

"Correct," I said. "That may be a cliché but there is no wisdom inherent in it."

"I think I get the idea," he said. "You mean something like *haste makes waste?*"

"That's it exactly. There are a lot of truisms like that containing inherent truth, familiar to us all, but difficult to recall off the cuff. Darn, I forgot to bring something to write on."

"Here's a napkin," said Wayne, handing it to me.

"I guess this will have to do," I said. "I wonder how many times great works have been started with a napkin."

"You never know," he said as I wrote down *Haste makes waste.*

"Can you think of any more?"

"Let me think," he said, putting his hand to his chin. "Here's a good one; *Hell hath no fury like a woman scorned.*"

"You got that right," I said. "That one is about as true as true can be."

"Now, now," he said, "you're letting your sexism show."

"Maybe so," I replied. "But it's still true."

"I know what you mean," he said, looking amused. "I'd rather fight a guy twice my size than deal with an angry female." He paused a moment and added, "So how many of these truisms do you have?"

"Not that many," I said. "Probably about thirty. I know there are at least a couple hundred good ones. Hey, I just thought of another one, *Finish what you start.*"

"Would that be a truism?" asked Wayne. "It's not really a statement of truth."

"But it contains wisdom which is just as good. It is usually very good advice to finish what we start."

"Something in the same category then would be something like, *Give him enough rope to hang himself.*"

"Yes, that would be a good one," I said, writing it down. "That can be used with wisdom and it also has a built in truth. Sometimes you just have to let a person continue in his error so he will learn his lesson. Anything else come to mind?"

"I'm sure I can come up with several. How about, *Extraordinary times require extraordinary methods?*"

"That's a great one," I said. "In fact, it exactly applies to Elizabeth's situation. This is an extraordinary time that requires extraordinary methods."

"It is quite extraordinary to attempt to heal her with truisms," he observed.

"You don't understand," I said. "It's not the way you think."

"I hope not."

"Anything else come to mind?" I asked.

"Just listening to you makes a number of truisms come to mind," he said. "Like *calling a spade a spade*. You're not making sense, but I will humor you."

I wrote that down and said, "Humor me some more. What else you got?"

"How about *Catch 22*? Sounds like the situation you may be in, whatever it is."

"Good," I said. "Keep going."

"Okay. *Don't throw out the baby with the bath water.*"

"Great," I said. "Now another one?"

"Hey, it's not that easy to just rattle them off. You think of one."

"Here's one that applies to you. *Don't cry over spilled milk.*"

"And how does that apply to me?" he asked.

"You lost your hat and it is like spilled milk that you can do nothing about. I don't blame you though. I'd be upset too."

"I'm just upset being reminded of it again – that damned Jake!"

"*That's the way the cookie crumbles,*" I added.

"And it's also *the way the ball bounces*, but I want my hat back. Damn it!"

"You're doing great," I said, attempting to get him back on

subject. "Keep them coming."

"How's this," he said, "*Every dog has his day*. Thinking of Jake stealing my hat brings that to mind."

"I guess you could also say *easy come, easy go*."

"You could," he said, "but that doesn't make me feel any better."

"How about this one?" I said. *"Cream always rises to the top."*

"That's what they say, but the way my life is going I think I'd rather go with *Good guys finish last*."

"Actually both clichés have truth in them," I said.

"How so?"

"The cream of the human crop isn't the traditional good guy. The stereotyped good guy is seen as boring and predictable, with no flare, anger or spirit of adventure. Remember back in high school that we couldn't get dates to save our lives?"

"That was a long time ago," he said.

"Well, I found out the reason."

"What was that?"

"We were good guys, boring, predictable and not interesting."

"You're probably right," he said. "Why do I get the feeling you're going to enlighten me on something?"

"Probably because I am. Anyway, I was quite frustrated in my quest for girlfriends when I discovered something. I looked for a common denominator in the guys who were popular with the girls and guess what I found?"

"They were bad guys," he smiled.

"Kind of," I said. "They weren't *evil* bad, but they were unconcerned about presenting the appearance of being good. They weren't afraid to treat the girls a little rough and even be obnoxious."

"I've always been kind of obnoxious," Wayne replied.

"But in high school you were obnoxious to the teachers. That doesn't count. You've got to be obnoxious to the girls."

"So I was channeling my energy the wrong direction to get the girl?"

"We both were," I said, moving my napkin out of the way as the waitress delivered our meal. "Let me give you an example.

When you're at a swimming pool with mixed sexes who do you suppose the girls find most interesting? The nice guy who wants to talk about his feelings or the obnoxious one who throws them in the pool?"

"The nice guy," injected the waitress as she was leaving.

"I don't think so," I replied.

"Come to think of it," said Wayne, "it does seem as if the obnoxious guy was the one who wound up with the dates."

"Exactly," I said. "But here is what I noticed. Girls I knew often told me what a nice guy I was, but when it came to dating, they wanted to go with the guy who threw them in the pool or treated them roughly in some way."

"I never thought about it that way," said Wayne. "But I can see you're right. Maybe the guy who wrote the cliché about good guys finishing last realized all this." He paused thoughtfully a moment and asked, "So, did you start being a bad guy when you realized what was going on?"

"I started experimenting with this bad guy principle," I replied. "I discovered it has to be done right. In other words, there must be good timing. You can't just go throw the girl in the pool out of the blue; it has to be done at just the right moment. If the timing is right, then being the bad guy thing is a big turn on for them. If the timing is wrong, then they'll think you are a creep. Anyway, after a lot of trial and error I finally figured out the right balance."

"You know, subconsciously I think I learned the same thing," he said. "When I started getting dates I quit trying so hard to be nice and was just myself. I think the missing ingredient is playfulness. You play like you're the bad guy while letting them know in subtle ways you're really a good guy."

"I think you hit the nail on the head," I said. "Girls don't want a real bad guy; they want a guy who pretends to be a bad guy. It's too *bad* we didn't know all this back in high school."

"Probably a good thing we didn't," he said. "We probably would have gotten ourselves in more trouble than we did."

"I did find something else," I said. "When I got older I lost interest in playing games and just let relationships happen naturally. I think females on the average did the same thing."

"I think both sides play a lot of games in their youth," he

said, "but seek to be more real in older age. Look at me. I don't try to play games at all any more. In fact I don't even try anymore. If someone comes along, fine; and if not, fine. They'll just have to accept me the way I am."

"Then you might be a bachelor for a while yet," I mused. "Believe me, when you meet the right person there's a certain amount of change and compromise that has to take place."

"I think I'm too set in my ways to attempt a serious relationship again," he said. "I tried it once and that was enough for one life."

"Yeah, but you were not completely in love. Like I've said before, just once, I'd like to see you *head-over-heels in love*. That would be a sight to behold."

"Maybe so," he said, "but a sight that is not likely. *Head-over-heels* - say isn't that a cliché?"

"Yes, but that's kind of a borderline one. That's definitely a descriptive one. *Head-over heels* kind of reveals a truth about love, but perhaps a frivolous one."

"How about, *It is better to have loved and lost than to never have loved at all?*"

"That's a good one," I said writing it down. "That contains a self-revealing truth."

"But do you think it is true?" he asked.

"Actually, I've never come across a popular cliché which doesn't contain elements of truth and the interesting thing is that almost all people will see it. The same is true of this one. I think everyone who has loved and lost still would not trade the experience for a vacuum. I know I have loved and lost before, but the experience is an ingredient of my makeup that I wouldn't want to be lost."

"Well, I've never really been in love so I haven't really lost or gained."

"One thing about believing in reincarnation is that if it doesn't happen in this life, it will happen in the next," I said.

"So are you saying *It's not over till it's over?*" he grinned.

"That's a good one," I said, "and you just reminded me of another one; *it's not over till the fat lady sings.*"

"I wonder what the fat lady singing has to do with anything?" he asked.

"I'm not sure. Probably something to do with the end of an opera. In either case they both convey the same idea; in other words, *six of one and half dozen of the other.*"

"Funny how these truisms, as you call them, just keep showing up when you *keep the ball rolling* with conversation.

"You're doing great coming up with new ones," I said. "Anything else come to mind?"

"Well, it's a lot harder when we're not in the middle of a thought. Let me see, how's this, *Ideas are a dime a dozen.*"

"That one certainly is a true principle," I said. "It's so much easier to think up an idea than to do the idea."

"You got that right. *He who hesitates is lost.*"

"But *hope springs eternal,*" I replied.

"I don't know if my brain can take any more of this," he said.

"You've been a big help," I said, writing more notes on the napkin. "I can see that to get a complete list, I'm going to have to pay attention to conversation for quite a period of time."

Wayne took a deep drink from his glass of water and changed the subject, "Do these truisms have anything to do with that Third Key you were searching for? I think you said it had something to do with communion."

"It does have something to do with it in a round-about way. These truisms are a means that humanity uses to encapsulate mini-truths in a way that they will not become corrupted. Remember last time we talked about the game of Chinese Whispers that we used to play, and how the original phrase gets distorted? The advantage of a good truism is that it is difficult to distort."

"How so?"

"Take a typical truism like *evil prevails when good men do nothing.* Anyway when one hears such a truism he remembers the idea rather than the exact words. As long as he remembers the idea and communicates the idea, then the communication will remain pure even if a couple words are changed."

"You're right as long as the person receiving it is paying attention."

"Yes, I suppose that is the one criteria, but the advantage is that a truism is very easy to pick up and register as far as the basic idea is concerned and once it is in the mind, it is rarely forgotten."

"Come to think of it, I can hear my mom now telling me as a

kid; *don't cut off your nose to spite your face*."

"And my mom," I added, "*Don't bite the hand that feeds you*."

"I told you I can't take much more of this," he smiled.

"Okay, I'll take it easy on you for a while." I took a sip of coffee and continued, "As I said, the Third Key I will be writing about will be called Communion. Here is basically what I have concluded since we last met. Spoken words are merely vibrations, which are symbols of some meaning or truth. Written words are symbols also, but composed of strokes which are like big vibrations. In other words, words are symbols that we use to communicate, but as the words are passed along, the communication gets corrupted just as the phrase does in Chinese Whispers.

"There are two ways to overcome this corruption. The first is to go back to the original phrase and restore its meaning. This happens in the game when the originator of the phrase reveals to the group that which he first passed along. This instantly corrects all that was corrupted. The second way is to make the communication so clear that corruption becomes close to impossible. This is accomplished by concentrating on communicating a principle or idea rather than the actual words. This is the genius behind the truisms. They take a common sense idea and clothe it with a catchy phrase that makes it easy to pass on without distortion. These phrases, which contain unforgettable ideas, are called eternal words – words that do not pass away"

"Eternal words," Wayne said in contemplation. "That's a catchy phrase by itself. *Words that do not pass away*... Isn't that phrase from the Bible?"

"Yes, Jesus said that about his words, that they will not pass away."

"You've got to give credit to him there," he said. "Even though there is not enough evidence to prove to scholars that he even existed, one cannot argue that the words attributed to him have endured."

"And will continue to endure. Can you think of a time that the golden rule will not be in use?"

"Good point," he said. "So, have you got this Third Key all figured out to your satisfaction? Or are you still looking for something?"

"I'm still looking," I said. "I think I have most of the questions. Now I must find the answers, but even more important, I want to comprehend the whole principle behind effective communion."

"There are quite a few books already written on the subject," he said. "Any idea as to what you are looking for that hasn't already been covered?"

"This basic idea of eternal words has not been elaborated on as far as I know. This communion principle goes far beyond human to human. I think the real key lies in communion between Spirit and human instead. Truisms from the Bible and the general consciousness of humanity represent the closest general humanity can approach divine communication. Human communication can be corrupted, but divine communication cannot be."

"So, you're saying that something like *a picture is worth a thousand words* is a divine communication?"

"Well, let us take one of the most divine phrases we know like *Love your neighbor as yourself.* The truism you just quoted presents a true principle in catchy language just as Jesus did. In fact you could even put the two truisms together like this: *Seeing a demonstration of helping and loving your neighbor is better than speaking a thousand words about it.*"

"So, instead of having modern prophets and Messiahs writing scripture, all we need do to find the modern holy writ is to look for truisms in common speech," Wayne said, only half-joking..

"When you think of it, that's basically what Solomon did when he wrote the book of Proverbs, and today those truisms are considered scripture."

"So, is there anything else in the modern vernacular you would equate with scripture – like the words of Einstein, philosophical or spiritual writers?"

"Anything that paints a picture of a true principle would be eternal words or scripture. Sometimes this can be accomplished with a truism of a few words like *still waters run deep.* Other times it may take a whole book to paint an accurate picture of an idea or principle."

"It sounds like you have some good ideas to write about," he said. "What is it that you do not have figured out yet?"

I sat back, took a sip of coffee and replied, "While it is true that we do communicate some ideas that convey the concept, there

is still a lot of bad communication and corruption as illustrated in
the Chinese Whispers game. Have you ever woke up in the morning with an idea or an inspiration and then it's gone a few minutes
after you get up?"

"Yeah, I have that happen now and then. You have to really
put a lot of attention on the idea or write it down if you want to
keep it."

"And then there are times that you only seem to retain part of
it," I said. "A modern-day prophet or teacher has several problems in communion. First, even though he may receive the truest
of impressions, he has the problem of interpreting it with his mind.
Then his mind has to put the ideas into words that paint the correct
picture. Finally, the picture may seem clear to him but may be
misinterpreted by the reader. Then the reader may explain the
writing to a friend which corrupts it all the more."

Wayne seemed to absorb what I said and replied, "But if the
teacher can clothe the ideas in what you call, *eternal words*, corruption is then minimized."

"When you think of it," I replied, "perhaps the most corrupted
writings we have concern our history. They say the victor is the
one who writes history. Since a lot of our history only presents
one side of the story, there is probably a lot of distortion, even if
written by the most objective historians."

"But you even have your eternal words related to history,"
Wayne said with a look in his eye that told me he had something
clever to reveal.

"Really. What's that?"

"Nursery rhymes."

"Nursery rhymes?" I asked, somewhat puzzled.

"Most people don't know this," he said, "but many of the
nursery rhymes spring from true historical events. During much
of our history the people were not free to speak their minds about
the leaders or events of the day. If they did they were either tortured or executed. What they did instead was to translate the events
into symbols in the form of nursery rhymes that were passed among
the common people, but ignored by the authorities. The interesting thing is that people are now much more familiar with the nursery rhymes than they are of the history they represent. This goes
along with your idea that a principle, or eternal words, live on

while the data is forgotten."

"That's fascinating," I said. "You mean something like *ring around the rosy* has historical meaning behind it?"

"Exactly," he said, "and that's an interesting one. This rhyme was about the bubonic plague in London and the ring around the rosy was a red ring around a rosy rash that was the symptom of the plague. *We all fall down* refers to those who died."

"Amazing," I said. "Where in the world did you learn something like that?"

"In a box of books I got at the auction a while back. Several contained some odd facts of history and quite a few were on nursery rhymes. Some were quite fascinating. You remember reading about Humpty Dumpty?"

"Sure."

"During the English civil war Humpty Dumpty referred to a cannon strategically placed on the protective wall of St Mary's Wall Church. A cannonball from the opposition caused the wall to crumble and all the king's horses and all the king's men could not place the crucial cannon back on the wall again. The people were able to make fun of their king's army with this rhyme without losing their head."

Wayne took another sip of water and continued, "Nursery rhymes have been a tradition in our history for quite some time, but there were quite a few written during the reign of King Henry the 8th."

"Can you remember a couple?"

"Old Mother Hubbard was a famous one. She went to the cupboard to get her doggie a bone. Mother Hubbard was a cardinal who refused to give the king, who was the doggie, a divorce. The divorce was the bone."

"That's pretty fascinating. So when we recite these rhymes to our kids we really have no idea what we are really saying."

"The details are lost," he said, "but the basic idea that once made it so popular remains. Jack Horner was another interesting one from that period. Jack was to deliver twelve deeds to King Henry the Eighth as a Christmas gift, but stole one of them for himself, which made him rich. This was the plum that he pulled out of the pie.

"The story of Jack and Jill refers to another famous king and queen. King Louis XVI was Jack - who was beheaded (lost his crown) followed by his Queen, Marie Antoinette."

"It's funny that most people have no idea of the real stories they are reading their kids through nursery rhymes," I said. "But you are right, nursery rhymes goes right along with the eternal words idea. They have encapsulated interesting points of history with word pictures that will never be forgotten. Unlike truisms, instead of giving us simplified truths the rhymes give us human blunders. Perhaps they too are part of the divine plan."

"Divine plan?" inquired Wayne.

"Yes," I responded, "It's as if part of God's plan in communicating with us is to cause us to recognize and circulate certain truisms, quotations and rhymes that just stay in the public consciousness. By using rhymes to make fun of our folly we perhaps instill in our consciousness the wisdom to not repeat the mistakes of the past."

Sounds like a stretch, but anything is possible," he said. "So, have you got your ideas together on this Third Key?"

"This eternal words idea is an important ingredient," I said. "They help mankind to preserve certain important truths and concepts. But even with their help many truths get watered down and lost individually and collectively. What causes this is the principle of corruption. As teachings, data or history is passed on they lose their purity with each new interpretation, book or writing on the subject. What I need to finish the Third Key is the knowledge of how to prevent the corruption that always creeps in."

"I don't think there is anything you can do to stop it," he said. "Just look at how political candidates twist each other's words and you'll see what you are up against."

"True," I said. "But as individuals we do not have to make the same mistakes inherent in the general population. If a person were to understand the true principle of communion he would be able to receive and pass on truth without corruption. When many individuals learn to do this, eventually the distortion and corruption of true events and principles will not be tolerated. Imagine living in a society where there is no distortion of meaning."

"That's *pie in the sky* thinking," he said. "Like I said, we have a long way to go."

"Good cliché," I said, "but it's descriptive and not a truism.

A thousand mile journey must begin with a first step."

"So, what is the first step?"

"To receive and send truth without corruption," I said.

"We've talked about sending truth," he said. "Apparently, you see the idea of your eternal words, or painting pictures with words, as a means to assist in this. But keeping a message pure will do little good if it is already garbled when it is received."

"Good point," I replied. "If I receive a message that is already corrupted then it does little good to preserve it as is. One must have a reliable source, as well as not participate in corrupting the message."

"Good luck in finding a reliable source," he said. "Just take a look at the news tonight and ask yourself how much filtering has transpired before you get it."

"I agree," I replied. "The media is a good example of distortion. They corrupt by what they leave out, by selective quoting, selective emphasis and what they decide to cover. But if they give an actual quote or show a real video, you know you are taking in something that really happened."

"But because of editing or what they may leave out, the viewer may be completely deceived."

"True," I said, "but the video or quote is still real. That is the most important thing to take in. I have often heard a quote followed by an interpretation that didn't seem right. Then, when I discovered the full text, I found the truth was much different than the twist placed on the quote by the media."

"So it doesn't do much good to pass along messages from the media without corruption because they are already corrupted."

"You're right, but my point is that there are morsels of real truth even in the most corrupted communication. If we take those morsels and follow them back to their source, then we can discover truth."

"Even here, you've got your work cut out for you," he said. "It's quite possible that the original quote was a complete distortion of reality to begin with."

"But even if untrue, the original quote at least represents part of what the person actually said." I reflected a moment. "You've brought up a good point though. Arriving at that which can be relied upon as being one hundred percent true is a Herculean task."

Wayne leaned back in his chair, signaling that it was time for him to go. "I guess you could say you are fifty percent there if you can determine that your quote is what was actually said. The other fifty percent is the tricky part. Let me know what you come up with on our next visit."

"This discussion has helped," I said. "It has given me *food for thought*."

"Is that a truism or a descriptive cliché?" he asked, grabbing a toothpick and rising to his feet.

"I think that's another borderline one," I replied.

"I've got an appointment and have to be going," he said, "but it's been interesting. This new you is providing me with entertaining discussion. Sometimes I almost wonder if you are having ideas planted in you by some unseen being, but then I figure you must be merely doing a lot of reading to prepare for writing your books."

"Actually, I haven't had much time to read lately," I said.

He smiled, put his hand on my shoulder and replied, "That's probably a good thing. I think you've probably read too much already."

"Maybe," I replied, "but sometimes the most pure truths are not taught in books."

"Perhaps," he said as we departed.

CHAPTER NINE
Truisms

My list of truisms grew as I focused on finding them. Each truism was deemed to have some built-in truth expressed in a simple but unique way. Many popular clichés were omitted because they were merely descriptive, not expressing an inherent truth.

Also not included on the list were the many truisms contained in the Bible as they are already recognized by many as containing truths. Instead I sought to include truisms as true as scripture, but not ordinarily recognized as scripture.

TRUISMS
Popular Eternal Words of Our Day

A bird in the hand is worth two in the bush
A half a loaf is better than none
A miss is as good as a mile.
A new broom sweeps clean
A penny saved is a penny earned
A picture is worth a thousand words
A rose by any other name is still a rose
A silver lining in the cloud
A stitch in time saves nine.
A thousand mile journey begins with the first step
A watched pot never boils
A woman's touch
Absence makes the heart grow fonder

Actions speak louder than words
After the rain comes a rainbow
All good things come to an end
All is fair in love and war
All the world is a stage
All things come to him who waits.
Can't be all things to all men
All work and no play make Johnny a dull boy
All's well that ends well
Always look at the bright sight of life
An apple a day keeps the doctor away.
Another time - another place
Anything worth doing is worth doing well
As the twig is bent so is the tree inclined
Back to square one
Beauty is as beauty does
Beauty is in the eye of the beholder
Beauty is only skin deep
Beginners luck
Better feeling pain than feeling nothing at all
Better late than never
Better the second time around
Bide your time
Birds of a feather flock together
Blood is thicker than water
Borrow from Peter to pay Paul
Boys will be boys
Bringing the mountain to Mohammed
Burn the bridges behind you
Call a spade a spade
Can't get blood out of a turnip
Can't put the genie back in the bottle
Can't turn back the clock
Cast one's bread on the waters
Cast you fate to the wind
Catch 22
C'est la vie
Charity begins at home
Cheaper by the dozen

Cheer up, it's not the end of the world
Chickens come home to roost
Come hell or high water
Crazy like a fox
Cream rises to the top
Crime doesn't pay
Cry wolf
Cut the apron strings
Dark night of the soul
Desperate times require desperate measures.
Divide and conquer
Do as the Romans do
Do not look a gift horse in the mouth
Don't beat a dead horse
Don't bite off more than you can chew
Don't cut off your nose to spite your face
Don't put all your eggs in one basket
Don't throw the baby out with the bathwater
Don't bite the hand that feeds you
Don't count your chickens before they are hatched.
Don't cry over spilled milk
Don't kick a man when he is down.
Don't let grass grow under your feet
Don't put the cart before the horse
Don't worry, be happy!
Dot the Is and cross the Ts
Early to bed, early to rise makes a man healthy, wealthy and wise.
Easier said than done
Easy come easy go
Energy follows thought
Even God hates a coward
Every cloud has a silver lining
Every dog has its day
Every man has his price
Every rose has its thorn
Everyone loves a parade
Evil prevails when good men do nothing.
Extraordinary times require extraordinary methods
Eyes are the window of the soul

Fight Fire with Fire

Finish what you start

Fool me once, shame on you. Fool me twice shame on me.

Fools rush in where angels fear to tread.

For the want of a nail

Forewarned is forearmed

Give a man a fish and you feed him for a day. Teach a man to fish and you feed him for life.

Give him a dose of his own medicine

Give him enough rope to hang himself

Give the benefit of the doubt

Good guys finish last.

Haste makes waste

He who fights and runs away lives to fight another day

He who hesitates is lost

Hell hath no fury like a woman scorned.

Hear no evil see no evil

Here today, gone tomorrow

History repeats itself

Home is where the heart is.

Honesty is the best policy

Hope springs eternal

I used to think I had it bad because I had no shoes, until I met a man with no feet

I would rather wear out than rust out

Ideas are a dime a dozen

If it doesn't kill me, it makes me stronger

If it seems too good to be true it is

If nothing changes - Nothing changes

If the shoe fits, wear it

If they look weird they are weird.

If you can't beat them, join them

If you find a turtle on a fence post you know it didn't get there by accident

If you had time to do it twice, you had time to do it right the first time.

If you make your bed you sleep in it

I'm mad as hell and I'm not going ton take it any more.

I'm only human

It could be worse
It has to get worse, before it gets better
It is better to have loved and lost than to never have loved at all
It takes money to make money
It's better to be thought a fool than to speak and remove all doubt
It's always darkest before the dawn
It is better to love and have lost than to never have loved at all.
It's not over till it's over.
It's not over until the fat lady sings.
Keep both feet on the ground
Keep the ball rolling
Kill two birds with one stone
Kills the goose that lays the golden egg
Know which side one's bread is buttered
Laughter is the best medicine
Leave a sinking ship
Leave no stone unturned
Leopard doesn't change his spots
Let bygones be bygones
Let dead (or sleeping) dogs lie.
Let the chips fall where they may
Let us cross that bridge when we come to it
Life is a bitch
Life is like a roller coaster
Life is what happens while you're busy making other plans
Live & learn
Live and let live
Look before you leap
Love hurts
Love is a many splendored thing
Make hay while the sun shines
Making a bad decision is better then making no decision at all
Methinks the lady doth protest too much
Money doesn't grow on trees
Money makes the world go around
Money talks bull shit walks.
Monkey see, Monkey do
My own worst enemy
My time will come

Nature abhors a vacuum
Necessity is the mother of invention
Never say never
Never too late
Never trouble trouble till trouble troubles you.
Nip it in the bud
No free lunch
No good deed goes unpunished
No guts, no glory
No man is an island
No news is good news.
No pain no gain
No rest for the wicked
Nobody is perfect
Nothing ventured nothing gained
Nothing's sure except death and taxes.
Nothing succeeds like success
Old habits die hard
One bad apple spoils the whole barrel
One man's cure is another man's poison
One size fits all
One step at a time
One thing after another
Opposites attract
Out of sight, out of mind
Parting is such sweet sorrow
Pie in the sky
Play with fire
Plow with the horses we have
Practice makes perfect
Practice random acts of kindness and senseless acts of beauty.
Practice what you preach
Proof is in the pudding.
Put your money where your mouth is.
Puts on his pants one leg at a time
Que sera, sera
Read the handwriting on the wall
Reading between the lines
Reinventing the wheel

Rich get richer and the poor get poorer
Roll with the punches
Rome was not built in one day
Save for a rainy day
See how the wind blows
Shit Happens
Show must go on
Six to one and half a dozen of the other
Smell the roses along the way
Some day my ship will come in
Squeaky wheel gets the grease
Stand or walk in another's shoes
Still waters run deep
Success is 1 per cent inspiration and 99 per cent perspiration
Swallows return to Capistrano
Take the bitter with the sweet
Take the bull by the horns
That's the way the ball bounces
That's the way the cookie crumbles
The best laid plans of mice and men
The best things in life are free
The bigger they are the harder they fall
The calm before the storm
The captain goes down with the ship
The early bird gets the worm
The eyes are the mirror of the soul.
The grass is always greener on the other side.
The great unwashed
The harder I work the luckier I get
The mills of the gods grind slowly
The more things change, the more they stay the same.
The only thing that is sure is Death and Taxes...
The pen is mightier than the sword
The straw that broke camel's back.
The stuff that dreams are made of.
The truth is somewhere in the middle
The way to hell is paved with good intentions.
The weak link in a chain
The wind at your back

The world is your oyster
The worm turns
There are plenty more fish in the sea
There are two sides to every question
There is a light at the end of the tunnel
There is nothing to fear but fear itself
There's always something
There's more than one way to skin a cat.
This too shall pass.
Three is charm
Thoughts are things
Throw caution to the winds
Throw good money after bad
Time heals all wounds
Time waits for no man
Time will tell
To be or not to be
To thine own self be true
Today is the first day of the rest of your life
To die a thousand deaths
Tomorrow is another day
Too many cooks spoil the broth
Trust in the Lord, but keep your powder dry
Truth is stranger than fiction
Turn over a new leaf
Two heads are better than one.
Two wrongs don't make a right.
United we stand; divided we fall
Unable to see the forest for the trees
Wake up and smell the coffee
Walk a mile in another's shoes
Walk where angels fear to tread
War is hell
Water under the bridge.
What goes around comes around
What goes up must come down
What you see is what you get.
What's good for the goose is good for the gander
When at first you don't succeed, try, try again

When in Rome do as the Romans do
When it rains, it pours
When the going gets tough, the tough gets going
Where there's smoke there's fire.
Win Some - Loose some
You are as young as you feel
You can catch more flies with honey than with vinegar.
You can lead a horse to water but you cannot make him drink
You can win by not losing
You can't win for losing.
You can't have your cake and eat it too
You can't make a silk purse out of a sow's ear
You can't teach an old dog new tricks.
You can't win them all
You can't judge a book by its cover
You can't put a square peg in a round hole
You don't change horses in the middle of the stream
You get what you pay for.
You play the cards you are dealt.
Zero is sometimes better than something.

CHAPTER TEN
A Key Hint

Over the next couple of days, I became more concerned about Elizabeth. She attempted to use the principle of attrition to diminish Philo's hold on her and free herself from her disease, yets she seemed to be losing strength almost hourly.

One night she was so weak that her body was almost limp as I lifted her out of her wheelchair and placed her in bed. I snuggled up to her and whispered words of comfort into her ear. I shuttered, as I did not feel her normal warm response to my affection. Instead, there was a moment of uncomfortable silence.

Then she shouted out, "God must hate me! I'm still being punished for my sins!" She turned over, profusely weeping, her body shaking.

I put my arms around her and she threw them off, "Leave me alone. I just want to give up and die. I should have died the last time Philo attacked me. I deserve to die!"

I was alarmed, but comforted myself in the fact that this seemed to be a temporary emotional release for her. I continued without much effect to comfort her until she seemed to go to sleep. I lay beside her for some time just thinking about the situation, feeling helpless to be of assistance. Finally, I drifted off to a restless sleep.

After what seemed to be a couple hours of extreme restlessness, a feeling of alarm seemed to gather in my consciousness. I tried to ignore it and wander back to sleep. The feeling grew more intense until I heard the sound of bells ringing. I rose up saying, "John, is that you?"

To my surprise, instead of seeing John to the side of my bed I saw Elizabeth standing beside me. "Elizabeth, you're standing! What happened? Did John heal you? Is he here?"

She ran one of her hands softly through my hair, saying "Yes, my darling. John is here. We'll be having tea with him shortly. All is well."

A part of me felt like relaxing as she touched me, but another part of me was wary, as something did not feel quite right. "Close your eyes, my sweet, as I make you feel my pleasant touch." I tried to relax, but fortunately not completely, as I noticed a disturbing, ever-so-slight flash of light. In her other hand, Elizabeth had a kitchen knife that was quickly descending toward my heart. I reacted as quickly as I could, but only had time to deflect the blow, which landed with partial force upon my stomach, causing a good-sized cut about three inches long, with quite a bit of bleeding. Fortunately, the knife itself was not lodged within me.

I rose up and grabbed her, "Elizabeth! What are you doing?"

To my amazement she responded with great force and pushed me so hard that I rolled off the other end of the bed on to the floor. I sensed great danger and rose to my feet as quickly as possible. I looked toward the body of Elizabeth and said, "You're not my wife are you?"

"You could only wish," said a voice in a whisper that did not sound like Elizabeth.

"Philo!" I exclaimed.

"How do you like my new body?" he asked menacingly, walking toward me with the knife. As he approached he wiped a drop of my blood off the blade and put it on his (Elizabeth's) tongue. "Nice," he said in an ugly whisper. "I want more."

As he lunged at me I grabbed a pillow from the bed and placed it in the path of the knife and moved slightly to the side. Elizabeth's body fell on the floor. I realized I had to act fast and jumped on top of her and held her tight. I figured correctly that with Philo in possession her strength would be much above normal. Philo (in her body) then rose up and lifted me with him. I grabbed him in a headlock as he moved with great force and tried to shake off my hold, but I held on for dear life until Elizabeth's body finally collapsed on the floor.

She seemed to lay lifeless, but I held her pinned to the floor. "Elizabeth," I whispered. "You must fight this man. Come back to me."

After a few seconds, she replied in a normal voice, "I'm back, but my neck hurts. Please let go."

I noticed that her hand was still strongly gripping the knife and replied, "Let go of the knife."

"After you die!" he shouted as he attempted to stab me again. Fortunately, I was on guard and held him tight. He squirmed with great strength, much more than Elizabeth would normally have, but not quite superhuman. It was the strength of a fairly strong man which apparently was all he could muster out of Elizabeth's body at this time. I continued to hold tight to her body, but just tight enough to hold Philo down. I was in a Catch 22. I needed to protect myself, but didn't want to do any permanent damage to Elizabeth.

"Elizabeth," I whispered. "Do you hear me? Come back."

Philo continued to fight back, squirming to get free.

"I love you Elizabeth. I love you," I said over and over sensing this had a disturbing effect on Philo. He struggled for a few minutes and then went limp a second time. "Elizabeth, come back," I pleaded again.

She seemed to rouse herself and said, "I am here."

"Let go of the knife," I demanded.

This time she released it. I quickly grabbed it and threw it across the room, pinning her down again.

"Let me up, my head hurts."

"I must be sure it is you first."

"Of course, it is me. Now let me up."

"Do you love me?"

She gave me a strange stare that made me nervous and then said, "Of course I do. Now let go."

"Say it," I demanded. "Tell me you love me."

"I said I do, now let me up. My whole body hurts. This is not the time to be affectionate."

I became more suspicious because without Philo in her body she probably couldn't even get up.

"I won't let you up until you tell me you love me."

"Get off me now!"

"Tell me you love me."

She then gave me a cold silent stare and then tried to squirm free. When I held her tight she spit in my face.

"Thanks for letting me know you are Philo," I said.

Philo continued to struggle in her body, but seemed to grow weaker as it became easier to hold him down. Apparently, the strength of her body was wearing down. Then I had a horrifying thought. What if Philo has permanent possession of Elizabeth's body? What then? It was unthinkable.

I held her body tight for what seemed like an eternity praying all the time. Finally, her body went limp again. One more time I tried to bring her back, "Elizabeth. Please come back and let it be you." I then laid my head upon her breast and whispered softly, "I love you."

Immediately after I said this, her body began to stir. She put her hand to her head and said, "Where am I? What am I doing on the floor?"

This was an encouraging response, as it seemed like something she might say in returning to her body. Even so, I had to make sure and grabbed her tight.

"Why are you restraining me?" she asked. Then she noticed my wound and said, "You're bleeding. What has happened?"

"You must trust me for just a moment," I said. "Now look me in the eyes and tell me you love me."

"Of course, I love you, now let me up so I can help you."

"Sweetheart. Something very strange has happened while you were out of your body. Please trust me and tell me you love me the way we do when we make up from an argument."

She held still, looked me in the eyes, and said, "I love you. I'll always love you."

There was something about the way she spoke the words and the vibration about her that told me that this was indeed Elizabeth. I let go of her and she struggled to sit up. Realizing that she was weak again without Philo possessing her, I helped her into bed.

"I don't know what happened, but you are bleeding from your stomach. Call 911."

I had almost forgotten my wound and now realized that I had lost quite a bit of blood and noticed there was blood all over our bedroom carpet.

"I don't think I can call 911. Since this is a knife wound they'll ask questions and you may be accused of doing this to me. Where are the sewing needles?" I asked.

"What are you thinking?" she asked.

"I'm going to sew myself up," I said.

"You're not a doctor," she said. "Please, you need a professional to look at that wound."

"It's long, but not deep. I think I can just sew it up myself. If I remember right, the sewing materials are in the hall closet."

She said nothing so I went and found a needle and thread, went in the bathroom, cleaned and sewed the wound up myself and placed a bandage on it. It was a nerve-wracking experience, but something that I felt had to be done. After it was over I went to Elizabeth.

"You silly guy. You just can't sew yourself up like that. You might die of some type of infection, or at best it won't heal up properly."

"We'll play it by ear," I said. "Let's watch the wound and see how it heals."

"My head hurts," she said. "What happened?"

After I told her the story she replied, "Oh, no. Look what I've done to you. And to think what could have happened…"

"But it didn't. I'm going to be okay. This is not your fault. It's Philo."

"But I allowed it somehow. I could be a great danger to you. Maybe I need to go away somewhere," she said with tears running down her cheeks.

I grabbed her shoulders, "You're not gong anywhere. I'll tell you what caused this. You became too negative. You felt like you were cursed and God hated you. You have to shift your attention to the positive, to the love of God. If you do this Philo will have no power over you."

"How do you know this?"

"I just know," I said. "You must trust me on this. We'll see this through together no matter what." I gave her a hug and she squeezed back, signifying her silent agreement.

"Just don't let me hurt you," she said. "I don't know if I could live with myself if I did you any real harm." Suddenly her eyes widened and she withdrew.

"What's wrong?" I asked.

"Nothing, I think. Turn around."

I turned around and it was John. At least I thought it was. So many tricky things have been happening lately that I had to check, "John, is it you?"

"Sorry, I didn't knock," he said. "I didn't think you'd mind, considering the circumstances."

This set my mind at ease, for not only did it sound like John, but the vibration was also familiar. "Great to have you here," I said, giving him a quick handshake followed by an embrace.

"You're hurt," he said, looking at my wound.

"The silly guy," said Elizabeth. "He sewed himself up. Can you help him?"

"Let's take a look," he said, pulling the bandage off. "Actually the stitching isn't bad." He then pulled a small bag out of his knapsack and handed it to me. "Make a poultice out of these herbs and apply it to the wound. It will aid in healing and prevent infection."

"Can't you just touch him or something and make him better?" she asked.

"There is a law that must be adhered to before something like this can occur. All healing must occur from the bottom up. The tiny lives that compose these herbs have a right to fulfill their destiny just as we do. Now is their chance to serve a purpose greater than themselves. We do not want to deny them this. What the world calls miracles can occur only after we have done all we can on our own to accomplish the same purpose."

He then walked over to Elizabeth, extended his hand, and said, "You need some strength. Grab my hand."

She took his hand in hers. Then John said, "Universal energy flows into me, through me and to you. Do you feel the flow?"

"I think so," she said with reservation.

"Feel again," he said.

She closed her eyes as if concentrating and after a few seconds her eyes lit up, "Yes. Now I feel it for sure. It's like warm electricity flowing through my body."

"Just a few more seconds," he said, pausing. "There."

Elizabeth lifted herself up on the bed and said, "I feel like I may be able to get out of bed."

"Go ahead," he said.

She lifted herself carefully off the side of the bed and I held her hand as she stood. "I think I can walk," she said. Then she took a few steps and seemed to be okay on her own.

"Will this be temporary again?" I asked.

"I channeled some extra vital energy, or prana, to her. This will give her strength for most of the day," he said, looking at Elizabeth. "Do you feel well enough to make us a hot beverage?"

"I think so," she said. "How about some coffee?"

"Sounds good," he said. "That would be a nice change. Where I've been lately they do not drink coffee."

"So where have you been lately?" I asked curiously.

"Like I said, a place where they do not drink coffee. I think they call it hell," he replied with a deadpan look.

There were a few seconds of uncomfortable silence on my part as I was trying to absorb this statement. Then John chuckled and I was relieved to rediscover that even advanced entities like John have a sense of humor. However, he never did reveal where he had been.

I made a poultice of the herbs in the bathroom and applied it to my wound. It felt very soothing. We then went downstairs and settled round the table. The aroma of fresh ground coffee filled the air as we took our first sips.

"Those herbs feel great," I said. "I swear I can feel those little lives being thrilled to assist me."

"Your perception may not be that far off," he said.

"Interesting," I replied.

"So, how have you been doing on your collection of truisms?" he asked looking at me.

"I've got a good start. There are collections of clichés to research, but there does not seem to be any collection of popular truisms as you defined them. I just have to write them down as they come to me; and they are very illusive. When one comes to mind, if I do not write it down right away, it seems to flee from my memory."

John smiled and said, "Like *here today, gone tomorrow*."

"More like *here one minute gone the next*," I said adding a play upon the truism. "I've collected all I have so far on the computer. Let me get you a print-out."

I went to the work room, retrieved the print-out and handed it to John. "I think there are about a hundred of them there. I've rejected about three or four for each one I have kept," I said, sitting down.

"Good," said John. "I'm glad you remember that not every cliché is a truism. A truism must reveal or hint at some built-in thought which touches upon a true principle." He poured over the list for a moment and added, "This is a good start. You should be able to acquire several hundred more before you're done. Just remember to go after quality rather than quantity. If the statement isn't widespread in public speech or doesn't carry an inherent truth, it is best to not include it."

"Understood. I'll just attempt to keep the eternal words," I said.

"Yes," said John. "Now let us examine where we left off last time. Basically, the main principle, which interferes with communion, as it proceeds through the various layers, is *corruption*. As the normal clothing of a thought, which we call words, is passed from one interpretation, translation or opinion to another, corruption sets in. The interesting thing is that the person doing the corrupting usually thinks he is making an improvement when he is really taking away from the genius of an original thought. A reason that corruption of ideas in words is so universal is that each person wants to add his creativity to the whole. This is fine as long as it stands alone and is identified as his own creative work, but is not so good if he takes the thoughts of another, changes them and presents them as unchanged. What we are talking of here is closely allied to the principle of entropy. Do you understand how this works?"

"I think so," I replied. "It's the tendency of all organized form to break down and lose its organization unless some intelligent force prevents it or reorganizes."

"That's a reasonable definition for it gets at the principle. Give me an example."

I reflected and said, "Let's say I build a sandcastle. If I leave it alone and apply no intelligent force to maintain its existence, the random elements will come along and wear it down until any sign of intelligent creation is gone, and all we have is a smooth beach."

"So, how would you counter this entropy and maintain the sandcastle?" he asked.

"All form disintegrates, but a sandcastle does so very quickly, so I would have to stay at the beach day and night and keep rebuilding it."

John reflected a moment and answered, "The deteriorating sandcastle represents our normal communications in this world. The original form or meaning quickly deteriorates as it is passed from one person to another unless there is an intelligent correction. This is one reason why widespread gossip is so destructive. As the original communication goes through the layers of people, the meaning is corrupted. Because of this, sometimes even a positive statement about another can turn into a negative in the end. Even though it is the nature of entropy and corruption to cause all intelligent form and thought in this world to deteriorate, there is a solution which is found in the original idea. There was a time when the first playful human went to the beach and made a sandcastle. Others walked by, saw it and thought it was a cute idea. But then it wasn't long before the wind and the waves made it disappear. Tell me this. When the first sandcastle was destroyed, did this spell the end to them?"

"No," I said. "Others saw the sandcastle and thought it was a neat idea. Since then millions of them have been created."

"So, was the first sandcastle really destroyed then?"

"I suppose that only the form was destroyed, but the idea remains."

"But was the form destroyed? Do you not see the form of a sandcastle on most every beach you visit?"

"I think I see what you are getting at," I said. "The idea of a sandcastle, along with its form, continues to exist even if the elements that represent the form crumble."

"Yes," he said. "The sand is not the form of the castle, but represents the form. All form represents an idea and all ideas are founded upon some eternal principle. We have therefore the eternal triangle of form, idea and principle. An eternal word is a word that conveys the true idea so it will never be lost or destroyed. The first sandcastle is long gone, but the original idea is recreated every day, and can be seen on beaches as long as human thought continues on this planet."

"Interesting," I said. "So the first sandcastle still exists amidst all the beaches of the world as it is recreated by fun-loving people. I guess we must learn to differentiate between real form and that which makes up the form."

"Exactly," said John. "Even though the first sandcastle was not written with a pen or spoken with the mouth, it was nevertheless an Eternal Word that shall not pass away. There are many other ways to write or speak to the mind of another without the use of pen and ink."

"Like pictures," injected Elizabeth.

"Actually, all physical communication boils down to pictures," he replied. "Even the basic alphabet is composed of pictures of symbols, which, when pieced together, create a bigger picture. The first letter of the alphabet is a picture of a sound, whereas a sandcastle is a picture of many sounds."

"So you could say that the sandcastle is *a picture worth a thousand words*," she said.

"Good point," he said. "What we call pictures are many smaller pictures placed together to present a grander imagery. The picture, or form, of the sandcastle is temporarily manifested through the sand. The sand is not the form, but the manifestation or vehicle of the form."

"So we could extend this and say that our flesh and blood and bones are not the real form of our bodies, but the manifestation of that form," I said.

"Correct," he said.

"It's funny," I said. "I always thought of form as being temporary because this is taught in many different teachings from the East. You are adding a new insight in telling us that it is only the manifested form that is temporary, but the form itself is an idea which is eternal."

"Yes," he said. "This principle has either been misunderstood or left out of many teachings of the past. Every form is eternal because the idea behind each form has no beginning and no end. All ideas of form come into manifestation eventually, exist for a time and then go out of manifestation. Even so, the existence of the form remains on subtle planes."

"Fascinating," I said, mentally readjusting my belief system.

"Now, let us go back to the question from my last visit," he said. "If you are the originator of words conveying ideas, forms and principles, how do you prevent your words from being corrupted? If you are the first receiver, how do you make sure you hear and pass it on properly? We must recognize that the typical earthly teacher cannot always go back to the physical source, but there is much he can do. What is it?"

I reflected and replied, "If we go back to the game of Chinese Whispers, and I am the first person receiving the message, then I must make sure I receive the message correctly."

"And how do you do that?"

"I suppose I must listen carefully."

"Listening is not enough, but it enables you to do what?"

"To hear."

"And hearing enables you to do what?"

"I'm not sure."

"You need to be sure. This is the Key Word we are approaching."

"The Key Word!" I said excitedly. "I didn't expect to be close to it for another couple visits. Did you say the Key Word?"

"You listened. You heard, but did you apply the Key Word to what I just said?"

Elizabeth pushed me on the shoulder and said, "I think we may be missing something. Pay attention."

"Okay, Okay," I replied to her. I looked at John and replied, "I listened, I heard, but apparently have not applied the Key Word. Am I close enough to get it this visit?"

"Are you? If you applied the Key Word you would know."

"Something says yes," I said with some excitement.

"And what is that something?"

"Intuition, soul, the Spirit, the God Within, the Oneness Principle. It could be any of these."

"These are available to every person on the planet, yet very few receive communion from them. What is the difference between the one who receives communication and the one who does not?"

"I don't know. Maybe the one who receives just puts more attention on it."

"And placing more attention on it causes him to do what?"

"It causes him to understand."

"But before he understands he does what?"

"Hmmm." I reflected. "I think I am at a dead end."

"You're making it too complicated for yourself. Now I am going to slowly sip on this cup of coffee and finish it. If you do not have the Key Word by the time I am finished, I will be somewhat disappointed and your lesson will be delayed."

"I can't take that risk," I said. "I can't risk delaying Elizabeth's healing."

"Then you had better get busy thinking," he said. "And thinking of your problems will just get in the way. It is best if you empty your mind of all concerns as I finish this cup of coffee." He then took a big sip, leaving the cup about half full.

This took me back to the pressure I felt when he forced me to retrieve the first Key Word. I felt fortunate this time, for he said my failure would delay my lessons. The first time this happened he indicated that my whole mission may be aborted. Even so, a delay could wind up costing Elizabeth her life, so the pressure seemed just as great. Meanwhile, as I was worrying John took another sip of coffee.

Seeing him casually sipping the coffee jolted me to reality. I had to put all concerns out of my mind. I had to forget about Elizabeth, forget about my mission, John, my fate and concentrate only on the Key Word. I listen, I hear and then understand. What comes in between? What could it be?

John took another sip. "Stop drinking," I said. "I think I may have it."

"Okay," he said, putting his cup down.

"I listen, I hear and before I understand I receive. Is *receive* the Key Word?"

"Is it?" he asked.

"I'm not sure," I said sheepishly.

"You have one chance at this time to get it, so it had better be right. Is that your guess?"

I wanted to say yes, it seemed the logical answer, but then I studied John. There was something about the look in his eye that unnerved me. It made me unsure that *receive* was it. I tried to tune into his mind through the Oneness Principle, but sensed he had a barrier that blocked me. Still there seemed to be something in the ethers like a very faint echo. I studied his aura, the atmosphere around him, but to no avail. Now if this were Elizabeth, I could read her like a book; but as John got back to drinking his coffee, as if he had not a thought or care in the world, I found the decision very difficult.

John put his cup down and looked at me. "Is that your guess?"

"Let me think," I said. I sat back and closed my eyes and attempted to bypass thoughts about Elizabeth, John, coffee and go directly to the Oneness Principle. How did the word *receive* reverberate in the world of the soul? It may be the right Key Word for some questions, but was it right for this one? After a moment's concentration I opened my eyes, looked at John and replied, "No. That's not my guess."

"Then what is?" he said, placing his cup, less than a quarter full, back on the table.

"I'm not sure yet," I said, feeling like my head was throbbing.

"Just relax," he said. "You concluded that *receive* is not the Key Word, but you used the Key Word to come to this conclusion. What is the Key Word?"

"I have been using the Key Word?"

"Indeed," he said, taking another large sip, leaving only one more swallow in the cup. "Now what is the Key Word?"

"The Key Word?" I thought to myself as I threw myself limp back on my chair. I hated being under such pressure, but there was no time to feel sorry for myself. *Listen, hear, Key Word, Understand.* What could it be? Then my eyes lit up. The key was in the hint that John had just given me. I used the Key Word to determine that the word *receive* was not correct. What did I just do to reach this conclusion?

Yes. That was it. I had just done it

CHAPTER ELEVEN
Using the Third Key

I glanced at John. He was swirling the last swallow of coffee in his cup. There wasn't that much time. What did I just do? How did I use the Key Word to conclude *receive* was not it?

My mind raced for a few precious seconds as I reviewed. What was the main reason I rejected the word *receive*? I looked at John and studied his expression, the feel about him. He seemed to reveal less than a good poker player, but I did perceive something, however subtle, that gave me a clue.

John put the cup to his mouth to take his last drink. "I think I have it," I said.

John finished off his cup and replied, "Why just think? Why do you not know?"

"Because this word seems to go against the grain of communion or higher contact as presented in any teaching I have studied. I wonder why great teachers of the past have not taught it."

"Do you recall past teachers using the Key Word of Decision in relation to who or what you are?" he asked.

"No."

"Do you recall Buddhists or any other religion teaching that the Second Key of Judgment is a positive thing?"

"I suppose not," I replied.

"Then why would you doubt yourself because the word in your mind is unorthodox?"

"You're right," I replied. "My only considerations should be whether or not I have the right word, that it fits into all the clues, and that it registers with the soul."

John smiled approvingly. Suddenly Elizabeth spoke up, "Can we talk in private a moment before he gives the answer? I've got a big investment in this and I want to see if it makes sense."

John nodded in approval.

Elizabeth took me aside and asked me what I thought the word was. After I told her she said, "What makes you think that's the word?"

I quietly and logically explained my reasoning.

"Are you sure you are right?"

"Pretty sure," I said, "but I'm under such pressure it's difficult to tell if I am getting it from my soul or if I am just guessing. What do you think?"

"I don't know. You could be right. It's difficult to tell." She then put her arms around me, kissed me and said, "I'll love you either way, but please be right."

As we returned and sat down at the table John said, "It's time to give me the word."

"I think the Key Word is either *perceive* or something to do with *perception*; maybe even something like *right perception* or *correct perception*."

"And what makes you think this?" he asked.

"You said that I used the key to eliminate *receive* as the word. I reflected on what I did and the key thing I did was to study you. Even though you seemed to have a wall up that was impenetrable, I caught a glimpse of your eye and perceived something, something that told me that *receive* was not the word."

"You're looking me in the eye again," he said. "What do you perceive now?"

"I perceive a sense of approval, that I must be on the right track," I replied, mentally crossing my fingers.

"I think I see it too," said Elizabeth. "Tell us that we are not imagining things."

John smiled and replied, "Maybe I need to play more poker. I'm supposed to have the ability to veil my thoughts."

"There's nothing physical that I can put my finger on just a sense I got from your eyes. They say that the eyes are the window to the soul."

"Good truism," he said. "Fortunately, the Dark Brothers cannot see into the soul. Their perception is rarely correct when trying to read a disciple."

"So perception is correct then?" said Elizabeth with excitement in her voice.

"Close enough," he said.

"We got it!" Elizabeth exclaimed, throwing her arms around me. "Now I can be healed for good."

"Not so fast," said John. "If you reflect on my teachings you will recall that finding the Key Word and the Key are two separate things. Tell her Joseph."

We sat back down and I tried to put it to her as palatably as possible. "He's right, but the good news is that finding the Key Word brings us very close to understanding the principle behind it, which is the Key itself."

"And how close do you think we are?" she asked, looking very concerned.

"Now that I know we are headed in the right direction, all kinds of thoughts and ideas are flashing through my mind. If I understand correctly we will now have some more dialogue with John and then we'll know where we are. Am I right John?"

"You are," he said. "You will remember that the first Key Word was Decision, but the real key lies in understanding that the essence of your individuality comes from the power within you which makes that decision. This is the principle of life itself, or what you are. The second Key Word was Judgment, but the key is the point of truth that judgment discovers. Now you have discovered the Third Key Word, which is Perception. More precisely we could call it the Ninth Noble truth of Right Perception. The next step is to discover the principle behind it and come to an understanding of it. Then the final step will be to demonstrate your knowledge by applying this key and all you have learned to commune with the divine."

"This is new," I said. "You've never asked me to demonstrate understanding before. What is expected here?"

"Even I do not know that yet," he said.

"And when will you know?"

"I will be reporting to the Brotherhood shortly," he said. "They will assess your progress as well as the book and determine an assignment for you to demonstrate mastery of the first three keys. If you can fulfill the assignment then I can permanently heal Elizabeth as I promised."

"It sounds like this assignment could be a hurdle I never anticipated. I was under the impression that I was to get the first three key words and a basic understanding and that would be it."

"It is," he said. "But, if you cannot demonstrate a basic understanding, then perhaps that understanding has not really been achieved."

"I see your point," I said. "I hope you make it clear to the Brotherhood that I am not Superman and they give me something within my ability."

"I will speak on your behalf when the time comes," he said. "Now we cannot waste any more time. Let us proceed with our discussion. Why is *right perception* so important in the discovery of truth?"

"Well, I suppose we could go back to the Chinese Whispers game as an example," I said. "If each person perceived the phrase accurately as it was passed around, then there would be no corruption."

"Unless someone was to make a garbled transmission," added Elizabeth.

"But he'd just about have to do that on purpose if he perceived the correct phrase to begin with," I said.

"Correct," said John. "The moment perception of reality is altered; we have the beginning of corruption. That which *is* must be correctly perceived as it is to negate corruption and sustain the truth, whatever that truth is."

"But like we said earlier, as a phrase is passed through a number of people, then human error creeps in and corruption becomes unavoidable," injected Elizabeth.

"Yes," said John, "Corruption is unavoidable when you are passing black and white data between numerous fallible humans, but each of us is only one, not many. The individual can learn to perceive correctly and thus not add to corruption. Eventually, when many learn this then the many can play the game with no corruption. Incorrect perception is accepted in this world by most people and thus most teachings become corrupted over a period of time."

"I notice you said most. Are there some teachings that are not corrupted?" I asked.

"Those teachings that relate an idea or principle such as the truisms or encapsulated principles are not easily corrupted," he said. "The communication and perception of Eternal Words is not dependent on the exact wording; it is more like painting a picture of a truth or principle. When the idea is correctly perceived then it is not forgotten and is passed on with no corruption."

"So you are saying that the principle of communion is sustained through right perception of not only exact words, but also intangible ideas?"

"That and more," he replied. "But the principle of right perception is much vaster than you presently realize. Look at Elizabeth and tell me what you perceive."

"Lots of things I suppose. I see a good-looking female, my wife, who has brown hair, blue-green eyes, and approximately five foot three. I guess I could go into a lot of detail and continue for some time."

"You have basically related two things you perceive about her. First are details of her physical description. This could be extrapolated to many boring details, such as the number of gray hairs on her head. But such data communicates very little about the person."

"I don't think you'll see any gray hair on me," she added righteously. "Not unless I don't color it for a few months."

"Or unless you are seen as you really are," he said, "but then Joseph used a word that communicated more than mere data. What was that?"

"I said she was my wife," I responded, apologetically smiling at Elizabeth for jumping in.

"Correct," he said. "Now note that the word *wife* communicates a range of ideas involving marriage, sex, relationship, children and so on. When this word is perceived concepts appear in the mind with much richer meaning than mere hair color. Now, looking beyond physical attributes, what else do you perceive about her?"

"She's my friend, my companion, my partner."

"Yes, these are words that again convey much more than perceived with regular physical sight. These are correct concepts about Elizabeth that you have perceived. What else do you perceive?"

"I'm not sure."

"But you perceive more than you just told me. How can you perceive and not know that you are doing so?"

"I'm not sure," I replied, smiling. "Maybe I do not correctly perceive all that I perceive."

"Perhaps," he said. "Surely you perceive some of her qualities. For instance, is she a loving person?"

"Yes, of course," I responded quickly.

"So you perceive more than you thought you perceived. Now concentrate on your perception and tell me more about her."

"She's friendly, has a nice personality, a loving heart I suppose I could go on."

"So how do you know these things about her? Is it the same way you perceived she had brown hair?"

"Not exactly," I said. "I discovered her hair color the instant I first laid eyes on her, but her personal qualities took a little longer to recognize. Although, I must admit that I had a good impression of her from the beginning."

"So how did you happen to perceive that she has a nice personality?"

"As I got to know her I observed how she responds in different circumstances and to different people as well as how people respond to her. It's difficult to put in words exactly how I perceived or concluded this."

"Let me help you then" he added. "Perhaps we could say that you perceived in a point in time and space that her hair was brown, but that you perceived through numerous points and various spaces these deeper qualities about her."

"That's an interesting way of putting it," I said. "You have to select a point in time and space for a woman's hair color because at another point in time it could be different."

"Hey," said Elizabeth. "That's our nature." We're just trying to look our best for you."

I wisely didn't argue and continued, "You've made an interesting point. The deeper qualities are not perceivable at a glance but must be seen over a period of time and in various locations or circumstances to be rightly understood."

"And consider this," he added. "Everyone with normal vision can see the color of a person's hair or eyes, or whether they are tall or short, but these deeper qualities are not perceptible to all." He then looked at Elizabeth and continued, "Joseph says you are friendly. Have you met people who think otherwise?"

She rolled her eyes toward the ceiling as if accessing her memory and replied, "Most people think I am friendly, but there are a few who do not. I was calling our past due accounts a while back and several became quite belligerent. I think one guy thought I was the devil himself."

"She can be quite aggressive when it comes to collecting money," I added.

"I'm sure she can," John smiled. "And how about friends and acquaintances? Have some of them not seen you as friendly?"

"Well, to be honest I had an old boyfriend who thought I was the meanest person in the world after we broke up, and then there was a woman I worked with who just turned on me for some reason and seems to have hated me ever since. She has been very rude and I must admit that I haven't been that nice in return. I don't think she sees a friendly bone in my body."

"That doesn't alter the fact that you are a friendly person overall. Why do these two people not perceive this?"

"They were both offended so they seem to be looking for the negative instead of the positive."

"Would you say they are viewing an incomplete or corrupted version of you, like the final communication in Chinese Whispers?"

"That sounds right," she said.

"And would you say that the friendly version of you is the true reality like the original phrase in the game?"

"I would hope so."

"And what do these two people have to do to see you correctly?"

"I think I see where you are going," I said. "They perceive a corrupted version of Elizabeth, but unlike Chinese Whispers, they are responsible for the corruption. If they look upon Elizabeth as she truly is, they will perceive a friendly person."

"Yes," said John. "Now if Elizabeth were to appear before one hundred people with normal vision wearing a bright red dress how many do you suppose would perceive the red in the dress?"

"I would think it would be all one hundred," I said.

"It is equally as easy to perceive that she has a friendly personality so why would a couple out of that hundred not perceive her friendliness?"

"I would say their wrong focus has altered their perception," I said.

"Would you?" he asked in a challenging tone. "Which perception would have been altered? Could they not have seen her smile?"

"Well, I suppose if she smiled in their presence they could not have missed seeing it."

"How about her pleasant laugh? Was this beyond the hearing of these negative ones?"

"No. If she were to laugh, anyone with normal hearing could hear it."

"And she often offers help to those in need, including the woman offended at work. Could she not see, hear and feel the offer?"

"I did offer to help her several times," said Elizabeth. "Why am I surprised you know this?" She paused for a few seconds and added, "Yes, she had to be able to perceive that I was offering to help her despite her personal negativity."

"Then why did she not seem to perceive sincerity when most other people can?"

"I would also say the key is wrong focus, but I perceive by your reaction that is not correct," she said.

"You perceive correctly," he said. "Think on this. She sees your friendliness, your smile and your offers to help, but she refuses to accept that which she perceives. What would you call one who denies that which is clearly perceived by the senses?"

"I'd probably call them dishonest," I said guessing.

"Now we're getting somewhere," he said.

"So the key to right perception as far as physical and personality perception goes is what?"

"I suppose it is as simple as just being honest with ourselves," I said.

"Exactly," he said. "If we are honest with ourselves we will admit we perceive that a red dress is red and we will see when a person is being friendly, even if preconceived notions dictate otherwise. Make a note that *honesty* is the first key to right perception." He then paused a moment in thought and continued, "You will be amazed to discover how much illusion is in circulation in the world because of simple dishonesty about that which is perceived. More often than not, two people are in an argument because one or both of them are not honestly accepting that which was perceived somewhere in their past, or even the present. On the other hand, there is more to right perception than honesty. Can you tell me what it is?"

"I still think focus is part of it."

"It is," he said, "but only a small part of what we have covered so far. How much do you have to focus to perceive that a red dress is red or that someone is giving you a friendly smile?"

"I see your point," I said. "I can see that such things take more honesty than focus to perceive correctly."

"In addition to honesty on a physical level, what else would be involved?" he asked.

"Would it be honesty on an emotional level?" I ventured.

"Correct," he said. "There are numerous senses beyond the physical and an important one for the perception of personality communication is emotional feeling. If someone smiles at you, how can you know if it is sincere?"

"If it is sincere you get a feeling about the communication that goes beyond the physical senses," I said.

"Yes," said John, "but honesty is not left behind. If you are honest about what you perceive through both the physical and emotional senses, then your perception of a smile, a laugh or a helping hand will be accurate. Grievances are the result of self-deception and cloud all perception. Honest emotional communion is the second key to right perception."

"Interesting," I said.

"So let us move to higher levels of perception and see where it takes us," John continued. "Look at Elizabeth again and tell me something else you perceive not related to her physical looks or personality."

"Hmm," I mumbled, trying to assess what John was getting to. "I would say that she is pretty intelligent."

"And how did you perceive this?"

"Well, it's not really something I can tell by just a glance, even though many intelligent people seem to have an intelligent look about them. Others who don't look so bright sometimes turn out to fool you. I guess I would have to say it took a little time to perceive her intelligence."

"You know, it's the dream of every woman to be loved for her mind," said Elizabeth. "Now I want you to remember what you are saying here the next time I'm all thumbs on the computer."

"No problem," I said. "After all, I haven't figured out how to set your alarm clock yet. None of us knows everything except maybe John."

"Don't look at me," he said. "I don't know how to set her alarm clock either."

Elizabeth and I laughed appreciatively at his humor, "I suppose we have to look at the thinking and actions of the whole person to correctly perceive their intelligence," I said.

"Ascertaining intelligence is more than that," he said. "Tell me, can one who does not speak Spanish tell if another is correctly speaking the language?"

"I don't suppose so."

"Why not?"

"One cannot judge that which he cannot do himself or understand."

"And can one with little wisdom, understanding and intelligence correctly perceive one with great wisdom, understanding and intelligence?"

"Probably not," I said.

"Intelligence perceives intelligence, wisdom perceives wisdom and love perceives love," he replied. "One can only fully perceive in another that which he has already achieved. If you are more intelligent than Elizabeth then you can accurately perceive her intelligence level. If you are less intelligent, you can only perceive her intelligence up to your own level. In this latter case, you may recognize her as a higher intelligence, but not fully comprehend it."

Elizabeth smiled, "This explains a lot. No wonder you have difficulty understanding me."

"Hey! He didn't say who was the most intelligent," I retorted, smiling mischievously.

"The point is that these subtle qualities are achieved in a different way than physical or even character qualities," he said. "Intelligence, for instance, is partially perceived through the physical senses. You can detect a person's memory, their coordination, some artistic ability and so on. Then additional intelligence is perceived emotionally. There is truth to the recently coined phrase *emotional intelligence*. But the subtle things must be perceived by the intelligence itself, painting the full picture to the consciousness using discernment."

"So is the third key to Right Perception discernment?"

"Close," he said. "The third key to understanding the greater Third Key of Communion is *discernment through intelligence.*" He paused a moment and looked again in Elizabeth's direction. "Look again at your wife and tell me what else you perceive."

"Do you still see my glowing intelligence?" she quipped.

"How could I not?" I replied, humoring her. "I suppose there are a number of other things I could perceive such as her creative side, her determination or other characteristics. Why do I get the feeling this is not what you are looking for?"

"Because you are beginning to perceive on the next level. Go beyond that which is normal perception and tell me more about Elizabeth?"

"I'm not sure what you mean by the next level."

"How did you just know that regular perception was not what I was looking for?"

"I'm not sure. I just sensed it."

"You just perceived it, but how?"

"I'm not sure," I said. "I guess it has something to so with what they call the sixth sense. I get a sense of other people's thoughts and feelings now and then."

"It is true you are beginning to sense on a higher level, but what is the vehicle, or means, through which you perceive?"

"Such communication is not through regular physical hearing or sight. It seems to come though either the emotional, mental or maybe spiritual part of myself."

"You are perceiving in the right direction," he said. "Now, look again at Elizabeth, use your higher perception and tell me what you perceive."

I looked at Elizabeth for a moment and attempted to sense her feelings and thoughts. "She's been a real trooper tonight and in good humor, like her regular self, but she is very concerned about her illness and whether or not she will really be healed. She doesn't want me to be overly worried about her."

"Indeed," said John. "You've both been troopers. I will not promise you what will transpire in the future, but I will say there is great reason for hope. Hope is an aspect of faith; and hope, motivated by purity of heart, is a source of great power to cause the materialization of that which is the object of desire."

"Thanks for telling us this," I said.

Then John arose and walked over beside me, "Keep looking at her," he said. He then touched the top of my head with all his fingertips followed by placing his right hand on my forehead for a couple seconds. Then he withdrew and sat back down and said, "What do you see?"

"The same as I did before," I said.

"Look again."

"I'm looking and still see... Wait, I am seeing something different. Her body appears to be glowing with light, except for several darker patches around the head and throat."

"You are seeing the light of her etheric body or the physical double. Now look slightly away from her body."

"Wow! I see brilliant neon colored lights radiating up to a foot away from her body. This must be her aura. I've caught glimpses of auras before, but never this clear."

"What colors do you see?" asked Elizabeth.

"Yellow is dominant," I said, "but I'm also seeing some violet, gold, green and blue. I also see a couple dark patches again. I get the feeling this has something to do with her illness."

"It does," said John, "Now look again."

"I see a light blue cloud rotating clockwise around her body. It seems to stretch out about an arm's length from her body and be somewhat egg shaped."

"The human being has many correspondences to an atom," he said. "The physical body is like the positive nucleus, and this fine rotating matter corresponds to the rotating negative electrons. Now, look again, slightly further out."

I seemed to have the power to readjust my vision and, after having done so, I saw the most fascinating vision of all. It was an egg-shaped outer film which had geometric forms dancing upon its surface. I watched them in fascination. They moved, they vibrated, they morphed and they changed. "This is amazing," I said.

"What do you see?" asked Elizabeth, raising her eyebrows slightly.

Even as she spoke I saw several of the symbols change as if there was a slight movement of a kaleidoscope.

"There's a film encircling your body like a great television screen. All kinds of geometric forms are dancing on it, some of them changing. What does it mean?" I asked, turning my head laterally and leaning closer.

"Yes. What does it mean?" John said. "Look deeper."

I attempted to adjust my vision once more, and this time I saw geometric forms floating in front of me. "Now I see what I think are my own geometric forms. Some of them seem to be effected by the movement of similar forms from Elizabeth."

"You are in communion on subtle levels beyond the apprehension of your regular consciousness," he said. "Again, I ask, what is the meaning?"

I looked closely at the forms near Elizabeth and sought once more to readjust my vision. After making several attempts I found that it was not so much a readjustment as a moving to a higher level of understanding. As I finally found the right focus I discovered a new perception. "I can understand the meaning of the symbols as I concentrate on them." I exclaimed. "The ones with the greatest motion are her current thoughts. Others represent her past. I can see that old boyfriend she mentioned. You really liked him at first, didn't you?"

"If you want to know; then read my thoughts."

"All right," I said, accepting the challenge. I refocused and replied, "You're thinking it is none of my business and, besides, you want to forget all about the guy."

"Wow," she exclaimed. "John, tell him to stop looking. There are a few things I'd rather keep to myself."

"If it is important for your privacy, he will not be able to see it," he said. "Now notice that there are layers of symbols. Adjust your perception once more."

After several attempts I discovered how to make the adjustment and I saw there were numerous layers. I focused on one of them, "She was here during the American Revolution," I said, "and was married to a warrior."

"Look again," he said.

"Now I see the life where she linked up with Philo and persecuted the Templars, including me. This was a tough life for both of us."

After I examined a couple others of her past lives, it deepened my appreciation of Elizabeth and who she is now.

"Now look outward, beyond the symbols of the present."

To my amazement I saw Elizabeth and one who I assumed was me living several hundred years in the future. It seemed to be an era of peace and prosperity. We were both students of something called the *Higher Way* as well as teachers of a philosophy we merely called *The Path*.

"How could I possibly see a future life?" I asked. "I thought you told me the future is not set. You said that there is a chance that the era of peace could be frustrated if disciples do not do their job."

"This is true," said John, "but your soul looks upon the most probable future and projects this to your inner vision in the most helpful and positive way possible. If two future life paths have equal probability, it will create a projection of the one that will be most helpful to catch your attention. This is one of the reasons that, despite their temporary failures, humanity always redirects toward the good, the beautiful and the true. In the end, that which is considered the good always wins out."

"So are you saying that, unknown to us, we all have a positive future projected on our inner view screen and this gives us an inner hope and optimism? In a strange way this makes sense."

"You understand correctly," said John. "If we listen to the inner core of our being we will always follow the right path and have an inspired hope. There are a lot of outward temptations that can distract us. Now, refocus once more and concentrate on the core or heart of Elizabeth's being."

I attempted to see that which I had not seen before and focused on what I felt to be her center. This time the experience went beyond seeing. It felt as if I entered into her and went through some kind of portal. I found myself amidst beautiful flowers and gardens. As I was surveying the scenery I heard a very feminine voice behind me, "Joseph."

I turned and viewed the most beautiful woman I had ever

seen, dressed in a glowing white robe. As I looked upon her almost translucent face she looked very familiar. She looked like Elizabeth, but a perfected Elizabeth. I always thought my wife was attractive, but this version of her was amazing in its beauty and symmetry. "Elizabeth, is that you?" I asked.

"Yes and no," she replied with the most melodious and soothing voice.

"You must be related to John," I said. "What do you mean by yes and no?"

She smiled and said, "Elizabeth is an extension of me. I am her spiritual mother, her solar angel. I will be her inner guidance until she matures and graduates from the human school. That is all you need to know for now. I love you."

Suddenly this angel and the scenery disappeared and I found myself sitting back in my chair. I looked at Elizabeth and then John. "I just saw her solar angel, but you knew that, didn't you? You made this extra vision possible."

"I assisted, but you made it possible. The question is how was this new perception possible? Why were you able to see beyond what you have seen before?"

"It was probably something you did when you touched me," I ventured.

"Yes, I did give you some stimulation, but nothing would have happened if you had not looked. What made you decide to look at that which before was invisible?"

"You told me to," I said, figuring the answer couldn't be that simple.

"And why did you do what I told you to?"

"I suppose it is because I have learned to trust and believe in you."

"And why had you never looked for Elizabeth's solar angel before?" he asked.

"Such a thing never occurred to me."

"And did your belief on my word make it occur to you?"

"It seems so," I replied.

"Did it ever occur to you that we are coexisting with numerous other worlds at this moment, and if you truly looked you could see them?"

"I have considered that we are coexisting with other worlds, but it never occurred to me that I could see them."

"Why not?"

"I'm not sure," I said. "There are probably a lot of things that are in front of my nose that does not occur to me."

"You can say that again," chuckled Elizabeth.

"So how do you get them before your consciousness so it occurs to you to look and to perceive?" asked John.

"I'm sure it helps to have a teacher such as you plant the ideas in my mind."

"And if there is no teacher like me what do you do?"

"I suppose I have to stimulate myself and come up with new ideas."

John leaned back in his chair and continued, "Something can be right in front of you and if you do not look you will not see it, even if the thing is easily visible. In the not too distant future many humans will see beings from coexisting worlds just because they are willing to look and believe that they can perceive. The key to higher perception is a belief that you can see more. No matter how much you have perceived in the past, there is always more to see, but you must train yourself to see the real, or have right perception; without this key you will be deceived.

"One thing I want to see is us arriving at the end of the Third Key," I said. "What else am I expected to know or to do?"

"Until we meet again you must practice seeing," John answered, looking intently at me. "There are many more things to perceive than you have seen tonight. You must learn to find new vision on your own without help from me. Each day you must ask, what is it you are not seeing, hearing, feeling, smelling, tasting or perceiving? Can you hear, feel and smell on a higher level? Think on these things, for you will soon be tested as to your understanding and ability to apply the Third Key of Right Perception."

"What can I do to prepare?"

"Look, hear, feel, taste, smell and understand. During this next week you will retain some of the charge I have given you and will be more sensitive than normal. Apply yourself and reflect on how all three keys interplay as well as applying the third Key of Perception. Always be aware of what is available to perceive. After this period of gestation, I will return with your assignment and the Brotherhood's decision on the book."

"Does it have to be a week?" I asked, hoping to speed things up so Elizabeth could be healed.

"It has to be a week. You need to prepare your heart and mind for that which is to come. It is now time for me to go," he said, reaching out his hands to us. "Let us say the Song for I must be on my way."

We said the Song of the 144,000 together and John again went out the front door, walking down the street until he seemed to disappear.

At that moment, a week seemed to be a very long time.

CHAPTER TWELVE
Using Higher Perception

The next morning as I was preparing to go to the office Elizabeth grabbed my hand and said, "Remember that young man I said who had previously called wanting to help you?"

"Not another one," I said.

"I know you didn't have much luck with the first two, but this one sounded different. This is the fourth time he's called and he doesn't sound like he's going to give up. Besides, he sounds nice so I made an appointment with you for lunch at Denny's again. It seems that everyone wants to meet you at Denny's."

"I wish you hadn't done that. Who knows what we are in for this time?"

"Maybe you can use your extra sensitivity that John gave you to see if he is another plant from Philo."

"Maybe," I said showing some irritation. "What's his name?"

"Chris."

"With a name like that I just hope this one doesn't think he is Christ come again," I replied.

"He didn't sound that type," she replied. "But you never know."

"How will I recognize him?"

"He says he will be wearing a bow tie. That's his trademark," she said.

"Okay," I said, rolling my eyes

Chris was easy to find. He was the only person in Denny's wearing a bow tie. As I approached him, he stood up. I assume you are Chris," I said, extending my hand.

He nodded, smiling, saying "Chris it is."

We both sat down in the booth facing each other. I looked him over and was sure he was also examining me. He was a young man in his early twenties, very well groomed, wearing a sporty jacket that went well with his bow tie. He was a good-looking guy with slicked-back dark, almost black, hair. He looked like he could have just come out of a young people's Christian choir practice.

Chris looked at me with an admiration that made me a little uncomfortable, "I presume you are J J Dewey, the famous author of The Immortal."

"Far from famous at the moment," I said, feeling he was trying to impress me.

"Ahh, but you underestimate yourself. With such a fantastic story under your belt, it is only a matter of time before your name is known far and wide."

"Then I guess I need to enjoy my anonymity while I can," I replied.

"You mean you're not looking forward to becoming famous?"

"If I have to become well-known to accomplish my mission I'll go along with it, but there is much to be said for the peace and quiet of a normal life."

"Perhaps," he said. "When I was younger I was attracted to the idea of being a movie star and all the glamour that went along with it. But then I had a personal experience that redirected my focus."

"What kind of experience?" I asked.

He reflected a moment and replied on a serious note, "I had an intimate experience with God. That's all I can say, but I will add that He gave me a mission of my own."

"And what is that?"

"God has given me the ability to recognize his servants and the mission to help them. I have recognized you as a servant, Mister Dewey, and now that I have found you I need to give you assistance."

"And what type of assistance do you want to give?" I asked with growing curiosity.

"To fulfill your destiny, the mission that John gave to you. The trouble with your present situation is that you only see the tip of the iceberg. You know you have a mission, but only have a vague idea of what it entails. For some reason God has shown me your future and has commissioned me to assist you to make sure you fulfill your assignment. You may not desire fame, but you will have fame. You shall also eventually have large sums of money to assist you in the work and become known as a man possessed of great power."

"Sounds interesting, especially the large sums of money. Got any bags of it lying around you don't need?" I joked.

Chris leaned forward, "This is serious. You will have wealth, power and fame. There is always a danger of such things going to a person's head, so part of my mission is to make sure you stay humble."

Just what I need, I thought to myself, *an acolyte trailing me around with a mission to keep me humble.* "So if you see me not being humble, what will you do to make me humble?"

Chris stared at me for a second and replied, "Mostly just be your conscience. If God tells me you are going astray, I'll let you know about it."

"And if I do not listen, then what?"

"I'm not sure," he replied. "What do you think God would do if you did not listen to Him?"

"Probably just let me stumble along, but that's a moot question because you're not God," I said, a little challenging.

"But if I hear the voice of God and relate it to you, it is the same as God himself speaking to you."

"Not quite," I replied. "It is only the voice of God to me if that voice is verified to me within by what John calls the Oneness Principle. If I receive no such verification I will use the highest discernment available to make a judgment."

"Understood," he said. "But that does not relieve me of my responsibility to follow what I receive."

"Perhaps not," I said, "but in attempting to follow the highest you know, just make sure you do not attempt to interfere with my free will in following the highest I know."

"I suppose only God would have the right to do that," he said.

His statement made me a little nervous since he saw himself as the voice of God. It made me wonder if Chris was another plant from Philo. *I wish I knew for sure,* I thought to myself. Then I remembered that John had given me an increase in sensitivity. Perhaps I could use it now to find out. I looked at Chris with the intent of seeing a link with Philo. As I concentrated I saw a vision of Philo still in his hospital bed. From his body I saw six energy streams of smoky light that linked him with the consciousness of six individuals from six locations. To my relief there was no link to Chris. This led me to conclude that Chris was at least his own man. This did not mean that he was harmless, but it was nice to know I wasn't talking to a Philo clone.

"You okay?" asked Chris.

"Yeah, sure," I said coming out of my short trance. "So, tell me. Why did you want to meet me today?"

"Part of the reason was to explain my mission to you and the other part is to implement it by helping you to get the work in motion."

"And how do you suggest we do that?"

"You need to present your message before the people. We need to have meetings, hold seminars, book speaking engagements."

"The only problem with that is with operating a business and current personal obligations, I haven't even had the time to start Book II let alone organize seminars or handle speaking engagements."

"That's why I am here," said Chris. "I will organize everything for you and all you have to do is show up and speak. I'm sure you could manage some time for this, couldn't you?"

"It's possible," I said. "I couldn't manage much else though. What do you suggest I speak on?"

"What do you think?" he exclaimed. "You'd speak about John and his teachings. The public would eat it up."

"There's only one problem," I said. "I cannot speak directly for John to the public. The book is presented as a combination of fiction and fact as far as the story line is concerned. John may be real or fiction or the real teacher may be someone other than John. This situation must continue until I finish the books."

"It makes a lot more sense to me for you to speak in John's name. That way you'll attract a lot of attention."

"But from who?" I asked. "I've been around the block as far

as channeling and New Age gurus are concerned. Most of them set up an authority figure that is some other worldly person who is seen as infallible and not to be questioned. If I were to speak in the name of John, a Master, or some other larger-than-life figure, then believers would not question nor look to their souls on the inside. Instead, they would be looking outside themselves for the truth. They would be asking me what John says about a thing and if I told them they would accept it without question. On the other hand, if I merely give them the answer from myself in my own words then they are forced to fall back on their own selves for the answer."

"That's all well and good," he said, "but without John you don't have much going for you."

"But we have the book and soon we'll have a number of books to promote the teachings."

"The book is a powerful tool," he said, "but we need you to acknowledge John's existence and speak in his name to really get things going."

"Even if I agreed, I do not have authority to speak in his name," I replied.

"You need to get authority then," he insisted.

I paused a moment. "I'll see what I can do, but I am very hesitant to use any authority outside of the soul. For the moment I am willing to speak and see how that goes. That's all I can promise for now."

"So, when can you find out how much authority you can use? Can't you just tune in to John or something?"

"Not normally," I said, but then I remembered that I had extra sensitivity for the time being. "Hold on a moment; I'll see what I can do." I looked at the wall behind Chris and tried to see John. To my delight I saw him as if he were right in front of me. He seemed to be in the humble home of a Chinese couple and was teaching them. I sensed that the couple did not know he was John but seemed to associate him with another master teacher. This couple had a mission quite different from my own. It was to be linked with the enlightenment and liberation of thought for the Chinese people.

Then I sensed that I caught John's attention and I felt John's words form in my mind, "This is a surprise, even for me."

"I have a situation and need your advice," I thought in return. "Can you tune into it?"

"One moment," came the reply. He then spoke something to the couple and closed his eyes. His reply came to me after only a few seconds, "Yes, this situation was only a matter of time. You have chosen to not speak of my identity except in the books. Do you feel this is the correct choice?"

"Yes," I replied.

"Then should you not be true to the highest you know?"

"I suppose," I thought. "What about speaking in your name?"

"If you want to speak in my name then speak with the voice of the soul through the Oneness Principle and give all glory to God. He who teaches any other way is not associated with the Brotherhood of Light."

"Thank you," I thought in return, feeling almost ashamed for asking as I watched his image disappear.

I turned and looked at Chris. "What was that about?" he said, turning around to look at the space where the image of John had appeared.

"I've got the answer to your question."

"Did you just speak to John?" he said with excitement in his voice.

"You never know," I said, "but I do have an answer."

"So what is it?"

I told him what I received.

"Are you sure you're not imagining the answer you wanted?" he asked.

"I'm sure," I said.

"Well, if you're just going to speak from your own soul that's going to make promotion much more difficult. Where do you think JZ Knight would be without bringing in the voice of Ramtha, A Course in Miracles without the voice of Jesus, Jane Roberts without Seth, Alice A. Bailey without Djwhal Khul or Joseph Smith without his gold plates? None of them would be heard of today!"

"You may be correct," I said. "But the problem is that those who are attracted or converted by authority become attached to authority and start believing authority without checking it against the true authority, which is the voice of the soul from within. Authority was the keynote of the Piscean Age, but we are now entering the new Age of Aquarius, where the shift of emphasis will be to the authority within.

"Sounds good in theory," he said, 'but in the real world you need a hook to bring the people in."

"I agree with you that we will be at a disadvantage, but I believe that in the end the teachings themselves will be the real hook, and the ones who take the bait will be those who are more prepared for the next step up. Those seekers who reject the teachings because of lack of external authority will move on to a new authority figure."

"It seems you do not give me much to work with to promote you."

"You have the book and the books which will be written. After all, you read the book and it convinced you. Imagine what three or more books will do."

"But I am not the average guy out there. I can see truths that others miss."

"But we will not be looking for average people to begin the work. It's not the beginning numbers that insure success, but the quality of the foundation. I strongly believe that over time the virtual quality of the teachings will become a more powerful authority than any other worldly proclamation of value. In a future book I will be writing about a principle called Eternal Words. Any idea what that would be?"

"You tell me," he said.

"These are words illustrating eternal principles. Jesus called them *words that shall not pass away*. Most of the teachings being presented by gurus today will not be in the public consciousness in a hundred years because they do not contain eternal words. The books that I shall write will have eternal words and shall not pass away. This will be a witness that I have received them from a source higher than myself. I cannot reveal in black and white all the details, nor can I speak in the authority of any person except as the Spirit of God reveals truth through the reader's own soul."

"The trouble is that we do not have a hundred years for your eternal words to take hold. Here we are in 1997 with only three years to go to the new millennium when great destruction shall take place leading to the end of civilization in 2012."

"There's not going to be any great destruction at the turn of the century and civilization will not end in 2012," I said.

"Did John tell you that?"

"There you go, looking for an authority," I replied.

"You illustrate my point," Chris said. "I'm not going to believe you just because you said it."

"Yet you believe in these two dates because some authority told you. A lot of doomsayers are targeting 2000 as an end time and others 2012 because of the Mayan calendar. Why would you accept these two dates as key times with no inner confirmation?"

"I have inner confirmation."

"Then I guess we'll just have to wait a few years to see if your inner confirmation is correct. No one, not even the Masters, can predict all the details of the future because free will is always at play. The strong probability is that civilization will survive for many thousands of years hence. I don't write for the next few years in the future, or even a decade, but for generations to come as well as the people of today."

"But even if you are right, we still have today to deal with and it's going to be difficult to get the work off the ground without a stronger hook than teachings alone. There are thousands of people out there writing what they think are profound teachings that no one listens to because they have no hook."

"Point taken" I said. "But I believe those who are ready will sense something different in my writings. I agree that without a hook the process will take longer, but we must not let false end-of-the-world predictions govern our presentation. At this time we must proceed as if humans will be here in the flesh for many years to come."

"It seems odd that one who writes of John the Revelator would believe contrary to the scriptures," he said.

"I am in harmony with the scriptures," I said. "Every doomsday prediction using the scriptures has been wrong so far. These errors will continue, which just illustrates how easy it is to misinterpret and misuse them."

"We could argue about end times, but I think we both agree that we can't wait forever to promote the teachings. What have you done so far?"

"I've put the first book on the internet as a free download. I guess that's where you found it."

"Yes, but it was an accident. I was searching for the writings of the educator John Dewey and somehow J. J. Dewey came up. Have you done anything else?"

"I've started a forum on AOL and am getting some interest. I've also started an e-mail list of seekers. I've been trying to expand it by downloading e-mail addresses and e-mailing them to see of they want to be included on the list. Unfortunately, this is being viewed as SPAM which is becoming increasing unpopular. Some are abusing the free internet mailing privilege making it awkward for those who do not."

"It kind of offends me when I get an unsolicited e-mail," he said.

"Does it offend you when you get an unsolicited ad in the regular mail?" I asked.

"I usually just ignore them," he said. "But somehow an unsolicited e-mail seems more of an intrusion."

"I would think it is less of an intrusion," I said. "If you do not want them they are easier to trash than regular mail and you are not destroying trees to create a hard copy. On the other hand, if my wife's hunch is right, we may, in the future, receive a hundred or more such e-mails a day. They could completely lose their usefulness and become an annoyance to all."

"A hundred SPAM a day," he mused. "That would be a nightmare. Have you done anything else, any speaking engagements?"

"Because my business and personal matters are so pressing my time has been limited to concentrating on the internet."

"But if I handled everything for you, except the speaking, then that wouldn't take much time would it?"

"Perhaps," I said. "Most of the time in that sort of thing is in the arranging, promotion and other details."

"Good, then we will proceed. What do you want to talk about first?"

"I'm not sure. What do you think?" I asked.

"I liked what you wrote about the nature of God in relationship to man. How about something about the true nature of God – maybe even call it *Gods-R-Us* after the title of one of your chapters?"

"That may be a little politically, or spiritually incorrect, and offend some," I said. "Let me see, how about something like "*Ye are Gods*, which is a direct quote from Jesus."

Sounds interesting to me," he said. "We could create a flyer with that as the headline and give some interesting details in smaller print. There is one thing you should know though."

"What's that?"

"You're going to have to come up with all the money for promotion. I just do odd jobs to make enough money to get by."

"I do not have much extra money either at the moment," I replied, "but I could print up some flyers, rent a place and maybe place a couple of small ads."

"At least we'll be getting started," he said extending his hand for a shake.

I grasped his hand and suddenly it occurred to me to use the extra sensitivity that John gave me to probe deeper into Chris. I looked at him with the idea of perceiving whether or not he would be an asset or liability. Suddenly, it seemed as if time stood still and I began to see insights into his nature and probabilities of his future.

I saw that he had a very large ego, which caused him to believe he had an extremely important mission. He even suspected he may be the new Messiah, but hadn't settled on a decision on that yet. However, he did see himself as my superior, that he would guide me because of his greater wisdom. The probabilities I saw were interesting. There was a chance, though a small one, that he would assist me in the work but the overwhelming possibility was that progress would not be made as expected and he would get discouraged. The negativity from his discouragement would not diminish his feeling of self-importance, but would generate negativity directed at me. I also saw that the path to success would be more difficult than I had conceived.

Finally, I let go of his hand. "I feel impressed to tell you something," I said. "From my experience I have found that every new enterprise is always more difficult than one can imagine. Murphy's Law is always alive and well. I don't want you to get discouraged if this isn't easy."

"You don't know who you are talking to," he smiled. "My mission does not entertain discouragement. It looks like the first thing we have to do is to get you thinking more positively." He slapped me on the back as we left the restaurant. "Think success, not discouragement. We can't fail with God on our side."

"I see success," I said, "but often success takes more effort than expected. Colonel Sanders, who initiated the wildly successful fried chicken franchise, had to make over a thousand calls before he made his first sale."

"But the Colonel didn't have me to help him," he quipped. "I can tell that the first thing I may do to help you is to develop the power of positive thinking. We're going to get the word out and we're going to have fun doing it. Now, how soon can you have some flyers ready?"

Seeing the probable future gave me second thoughts about working with him, but since we had shaken on it I decided to go ahead for the moment. If nothing else, it would be a learning experience. In the parking lot we covered some additional details in advertising and going forward with a lecture and then departed.

That evening as Elizabeth and I were having dinner she asked, "How'd it go with Chris?"

I related to her our conversation.

"It was good thinking to use your extra sensitivity to look into his soul. It sounds like you may be wasting your time working with him."

"Maybe. But I shook hands with him on the lecture idea before I looked into the future. Even though I saw the probability that the work with him was going to be a dead end I also saw a chance he would make some changes and become useful. Maybe it's a good thing that we do not see the future. It would probably discourage us from trying new things, for even if we fail, we still learn a lot."

"Have you used your sensitivity to see anything else?"

"Actually, I haven't had time to think about it."

"It may be wearing off any day now, so you've got to make use of it time or no time."

"You are probably right. Any suggestions?"

"We've always heard that there are higher planes right here, but vibrating at a higher rate. Why don't you try to see them?"

"I suppose it wouldn't hurt to try," I said. "I'm still trying to get used to using this ability." I turned my chair and stared through the patio door window and tried to focus on the next plane up. "Nothing seems to be happening."

"Maybe you need to focus more," she said.

"I'm trying, but don't see anything unusual. Wait. What's that?"

"What? Did you see something?"

"No, but I heard something, a fluttering. There it goes again, like the wings of a dove or something, just over my head."

"Concentrate on seeing it," she exclaimed.

I focused on seeing whatever it was and then it came into focus. "If I am not mistaken I seem to be seeing some kind of fairy about the size of Tinker Bell darting around the room. It moves so quickly I'm having a difficult time getting a good look at it."

"I always knew fairies were real," Elizabeth said with delight. "I saw one once when I was a little girl, but no one believed me. Does the color of green seem to surround it?"

"Yes. Yes, it does."

"Try to read its mind."

This seemed like an odd suggestion, but I gave it a try. "I'm getting something, but its thinking is very foreign to ours. The impression I am getting is that she is your fairy, the same one you saw as a girl. She sees it as a mission to lift your spirits, especially in times of distress."

"Can she see us then?"

"Yes, this life form has the ability to see both worlds. Now I'm concentrating on what she can perceive and guess what?"

"What?"

"She regularly visits your solar angel. Your solar angel gives her some type of spiritual essence that feeds her spirit and fills her with joyfulness. This motivates her to assist you always."

"I've always felt there was some presence trying to assist me, though I am sure I did not appreciate it. Do you not see a fairy for you?" she asked.

"I don't see one."

"Focus then," she demanded. "If I have a fairy you've got to have something."

I couldn't see any fairy associated with me so I looked for something equivalent. "I see something, but it is not a fairy."

"What is it?"

"It's a native American Indian. He's standing beside me in Indian dress, his hands folded, with a tomahawk in his right hand.

He's quite large, muscular and looks very regal. I get the sense that his mission is to guard me and help preserve my life."

"Maybe we ought to switch," she joked. "I could take the good looking Indian for a while and you can have my fairy."

Suddenly it seemed as if the fairy's wings fluttered about twice as fast and I got the impression she didn't think the statement was funny. "I think I'm picking up your fairy's thoughts and I don't think she wants to be traded off."

"Really," she said. She looked into open space and said, "Don't worry; I wouldn't trade you for anyone else."

"She's not there, but over here," I said, pointing.

She then looked toward where I was pointing and repeated the statement.

"She's a lot happier now," I said.

"How do you know?"

"There's something about the way she's darting around that just seems to sing in delight. She's also glad you acknowledge her existence."

"Even though I do not have your extra sensitivity, I seem to sense her presence," she said.

"It must have something to do with the principle John taught us, that we have to look for something before we can see it."

"So maybe you ought to look for more things in this new world. Look out the window and concentrate on seeing for a distance," she said.

"Good idea," I said looking in the distance. "Wow! There are all kinds of life forms fluttering around our garden. They look like pixies, birds, insects, strange little reptiles and furry things I've never seen before."

"Look farther and see what else you see."

I concentrated on looking all around the city, "This is amazing! When I was a kid I heard stories about elves, dwarfs, trolls, brownies, fairies, pixies, leprechauns, sprites, sylphs and salamanders, but I thought they were all just imaginary. When I look all around this world I see that there is more than we imagined. I get the sense that this is the first etheric world just above the vibration of dense physical matter. This must be the world of deva lives that we've read about."

"I wish I could see it too," said Elizabeth, frowning. "But

there's something about you bringing this world to my attention that seems to increase my sense of it. I can definitely feel the presence of the fairy when I concentrate on it. Tell me more of what you see."

"I think I'll see if I can see into the higher physical ethers." I rearranged myself in the chair and took a deep breath. I exhaled and concentrated on seeing a higher vibration. "I see several other higher etheric worlds teeming with more refined life forms. I think I'll just keep seeing higher and see how far I can go. I'll attempt to see the astral starting with the lowest."

"Tell me what you see." Elizabeth leaned forward on her chair and waited.

After taking in the new view I said, "I see that there are seven divisions in the astral world and the lowest one is a dreary place, containing all kinds of angry and fierce human beings and wild animals. As my vision proceeds upwards, the inhabitants become more refined and filled with love until we get to the highest, which seems to be a world of very intense and pure feeling. Now, I'll see if I can perceive the next plane, which is the mental."

After a few seconds Elizabeth said, "See anything?"

After focusing I replied, "Yes. This time I tried seeing all seven divisions of this plane all at once and it is more than the human mind can take in. Give me a moment to differentiate. Yes, that's better. The bottom divisions contain people who are good people, yet very centered on logic and the power of deduction. They kind of remind me of Spock from Star Trek. Wait, I see something else. Some advanced members of the Dark Brotherhood advance into the lower mental realms and I get the impression as if it is through some back door or illegal kind of entry. I would expect to find them in the astral and physical ethers, but not in the highest plane of form which is sometimes called the celestial world."

"Anything we can find out about them may be important. Try to see everything possible about them," she said.

"Good idea," I said as I concentrated further. "This is interesting..."

"What? What's interesting?"

"The common idea of a worker of darkness is of a monster of some kind foaming at the mouth. The average person has the idea that if he were to meet such a person he would be immediately recognizable, but I see that such is not the case. Those who make it into the lower mental zones are very polished, suave and controlled. I see that these guys have an actual school that is designed to develop the required control necessary to get them into this third plane. They take with them the self-control from their disciplines. They appear as normal, almost gentle and cooperative inhabitants of these kingdoms. The difference between them and other inhabitants is their internal intentions. In their minds they have reached their dark conclusions through a logical and reasonable order of thought. This gives them a stable enough vibration to reach this plane and contaminate the lower spheres."

"Sounds like they are wolves in sheep's clothing," said Elizabeth.

"That's exactly it," I said. "I see that even after death, many of those who go to the lower spheres of mental matter are captivated by the corrupted logic of these dark disciples. They will often pass themselves off as gurus, masters or representatives of God and hold many decent people back in their progression. One of the things they teach is that they are in the ultimate heaven and there is no higher sphere in which to progress. But they are deceived, for I can see there are many higher spheres. The four highest of the mental plane are completely beyond their grasp."

"So what is life like in the higher mental spheres?" she asked.

"It appears that the higher you go, the more everything speeds up. In the highest sphere communication is instantaneous and there can be no deception. The inhabitants do not even need to talk in individual words as we do. They can if they wish, but most communicate with instant telepathy. And anything they want is instantly created by the power of their thought. Now I see why the worlds above the mental plane are called formless."

Why's that?" she asked.

"Because as one progresses from the lower to the higher mental spheres, form creation gets easier and easier until all desires for form are manifested instantaneously. Now imagine a world where you get everything you want immediately. How long would it take before all possessions became meaningless?"

"Probably not that long," she said.

"And if all things that have form are meaningless then where would your consciousness gravitate?"

"Probably away from form," she said.

"Actually, it is toward the source of the form. I see that form comes from formlessness and when form has served its purpose the seeker moves closer to the source by leaving outer form. I see that in these higher worlds that form still exists as ideas, but instead of outer form, the higher worlds circle around ideas, purpose and energy. Paul must have caught a glimpse of the higher plane when he mentioned that he saw things that were impossible to put in words."

"Can you see anything in the higher planes?"

"I only see that there are four of them, but you have to realize that every noun in the language is something represented by form. I am looking into formlessness and see nothing through the normal sense of vision, yet it is the source of all. I will have to contemplate what I have seen with the inner eye before I can make sense of it or put any of it into words."

"I don't think I am ready for formlessness," said Elizabeth.

"None of us are," I said, "but it's not what you think. There is an existence in the higher worlds that is beyond our comprehension, but it is something to look forward to, not to dread. Here's the best way I can think of to explain it. I remember when I was a kid; I played cowboys and Indians a lot. I had a vivid imagination and really enjoyed myself and one day a thought came to me that when I grew up that I would no longer be shooting imaginary Indians and bad guys. When this thought occurred to me I felt sorrow; I really enjoyed fighting imaginary opponents."

"So now you're grown up you no longer play cowboys and Indians," she smiled.

"Correct," I said. "I no longer live in that imaginary world, but now have my focus on other things. The point is that my child's imagination was put to good use at the time, but now my imagination is put to higher uses. I now have no desire to go back to shooting imaginary Indians but am happy to be where I am, where my focus is on things more real. The world of form is produced by the imagination of God and we are children playing in it. When we are done playing, we will go to higher planes where everything is more real."

"I see your point," she said, "but it is difficult to imagine wanting to leave form behind."

"It might be more accurate to say form *as we know it* is left behind. Instead of identifying with form, we become the source of form and there will be no loss, but only gain. It's difficult to explain but I am going to think about how to express these ideas in words."

"And while you are at it, why don't you try writing a parable as John advised you? Maybe this heightened state you are in would be a good time to do it."

"That may be a good idea." I said, wiping my brow. "I'm exhausted. Concentrating this hard and absorbing spiritual energy takes a lot out of a guy."

"I'm tired too," she said, "but I'm always tired lately. Let's both go to bed early tonight and tomorrow I want you to write a parable for me."

CHAPTER THIRTEEN
Parables

Over the next couple days I wrote three parables. When finished, I gave them to Elizabeth to read.

"Glad to see you are being obedient," she smiled thumbing through the pages. "It looks like there are several parables here."

"Yes," I acknowledged. "Since I may never get this super sensitivity again I thought I would make the best of it and write as long as the ideas came. There are three all together."

"Good for you," said Elizabeth. "Now leave me alone for a while and I'll read them."

I went to our workroom and did some design work for a customer on my computer. It was supposed to keep me distracted long enough for Elizabeth to read, yet I kept straining to hear if she was moving around. After what seemed to be enough time and because I couldn't wait any longer, I went upstairs to the dining room to check on her. "Looks like you're about done," I said.

"Just about finished. Give me a few moments."

I paced back and forth in front of the living room window, looking over my shoulder every few minutes. I felt like a little kid waiting for Christmas. I couldn't wait to see what she thought.

Finally, "Okay, I'm done."

I rushed to the table where she was sitting and sat next to her. "So, what did you think?"

She sat back, smiling, "The parables are very good. I've always believed in your writing ability, but you have surpassed my expectations. I really enjoyed them. They really make you think."

"If *you* think they are good then they must be," I said. "But I am not sure if I can write anything like them again."

"And why not?" she asked with a rather sour look.

"I wrote these parables when I was in the state of super sensitivity induced by John. The words and ideas just flowed like I have never experienced. I don't know if I could even write more like them again."

Elizabeth closed her eyes a moment as if in deep reflection. She then opened them and said, "Something tells me you underestimate yourself and I have the feeling that John will agree with me."

"Really," I exclaimed. "I have learned over the years to pay attention to your feelings. It would be nice if you were correct, but I have to say it seemed like these three parables were a gift, rather than hard creative work."

"Maybe they were a little of both," she said, smiling.

THE THREE PARABLES
Parable of Abundance

In the beginning, there lived a Body that dwelled in the land of fresh air. The Body saw that there was beautiful, clean, fresh air, as far as the eye could see with all the life-giving oxygen one would ever need. The Body also saw the impossibility of ever having a shortage of oxygen because of a natural recycling process. After it breathed it in, it then breathed it out a different mixture that was food for plants. The plants showed their appreciation by reciprocating and regenerating more oxygen usable for the Body. Thus, the Body lived in a cycle of endless supply and expected to have abundance forever.

All the cells in the Body were also very happy and content. They drank deeply from the great breaths of oxygen the Body took. No one ever thought of saving, or hoarding, for all had all they needed. The brain cells needed a little more than some of the others, but no one seemed to mind, for all had everything they wanted and needed, and, since all were fulfilled, everyone was considered equal. They functioned in perfect cooperation with the realization that all cells must be fulfilled for the Body to be healthy, and the

Body must be healthy for any individual cells to be fulfilled. Thus they realized their interdependence, and with this realization came sublime independence.

The Body lived in a state of perfect functioning for a very long time until one day the land of fresh air was visited by a sick Body that was near death. This Body was off color, contorted with some dreadful disease, the eyes were cloudy, its temperature was hot, its breaths were shallow and quick and it could barely stand.

The sick Body told the healthy one: "I have one last request before I die. Share this apple with me and I will lie down in peace." The sick Body took a bite and handed it to the healthy one. The healthy Body looked on with pity and took a bite, but when he did something strange happened. One of the cells from the sick Body hopped off onto the bite taken by the healthy one. The cell knew his previous Body he was in was dying and he saw an opportunity to start a new life in the healthy Body.

Unfortunately, the foreign cell brought with him the philosophy from the dying Body, a philosophy completely unknown and undreamed of by the cells in the healthy Body.

In the sick Body, from whence came the foreign cell, there always seemed to be a lack of oxygen. At times they made futile attempts at sharing and being interdependent, but separateness seemed to prevail and the cells lived in a constant fear of lack. As the Body grew sicker and sicker they seemed to be forced more and more to hoard up oxygen for themselves, or else they would not have enough for the morrow.

Now the foreign cell had just come out of this great struggle. He was one of the stronger ones and always seemed to be able to garner enough to insure his own strength, often at the expense of others. When he found himself in a healthy Body with an abundance of oxygen he was quite excited. He immediately started gathering around himself all the oxygen he could store. After he gathered all he could hold he created storage containers and hoarded still more.

Some of the healthy cells were curious about him and gathered around to watch. They had never seen anyone hoard oxygen; no one had even thought about it, for they had always lived in natural abundance. They asked: "Friend, why do you waste your time gathering around you oxygen when we live in perpetual abundance? There has never been a need for such a task."

"You are ignorant fools!" said the foreign cell. "You assume that just because you had abundance in the past that you will have abundance in the future. I know from experience that this is not the case. I originated from another Body that was once healthy like this one, but health is a whimsical thing. Sometimes it is there and sometimes it is not. You have been fortunate that you have always had abundant oxygen. If your Body had had an extreme shortage, in your ignorance, you would have all starved to death, for none of you have ever had any oxygen put away. In your blindness you have always thought that you have had nothing to cause you to worry. It is now time for you to wake up and take responsibility for your own health.

"Look at me," he said. "If this Body were to get sick, as my previous Body did, and have an extreme shortage of oxygen, then I would be the only one here that would continue to have abundance. You would then look like fools and look toward me as your savior."

The healthy cells listened in stunned silence. "We have always assumed there would always be abundance," they said. "Tell us what happened in your Body."

"We lived the good life like you for a while," said the foreign cell. "But all good things must end. Certain wiser cells realized this and started teaching others about the potential crisis. Some listened and started saving for the evil day. It's a good thing we did because it was not long before we needed it. When the shortages came the ignorant ones who had saved nothing, but trusted to the abundant supply, were caught unaware and unprepared. They suffered and tried to get those with savings to share with them, but we would not. If those wise ones who saved shared with those who had not, then neither would have had enough. The shortage got worse and worse until all were forced to take what they could. Now I was one of the few who never had lack all the way through the great ordeal and I am the only cell to yet remain alive. If you want to learn how to survive the coming crisis, which I am sure is coming to this Body, then you should listen to me."

"What shall we do?" asked the other cells.

"We must labor diligently to gather and store up additional oxygen. I will be your leader and guide you in this. For this benefit

I will take a percentage of what you gather, and surely I will be your savior; for I am the only one here with knowledge of things to come."

The word of this new philosophy spread throughout the Body and caused a great consternation and division among the cells. Most did not believe there would ever be such a shortage, but some did and joined with the foreign cell in hoarding the oxygen.

After a period of time, those who did not hoard found that they were indeed suffering a lack, yet they continued sharing that which they had with each other and managed to survive all right. On the other hand, the hoarding cells took joy in the seeming correctness of their moves and lorded over the other cells. "See, we told you this would happen. Look at us. We have more abundance than ever because we worked harder than you and put away for the evil day."

Some of the non-hoarding cells felt foolish at this and joined in with the hoarding cells and united with them in labor to gather all the possible oxygen.

As time passed the shortage among those who did not hoard became very severe. So great was their lack that many cells began to die. Those who remained were exceedingly alarmed and decided to cease any sharing and joined the hoarders. Each cell had to gather what he could for himself. Thus, all the lives in the Body found themselves in the midst of a great struggle for survival, and the Body, as a whole, became very sick, and was approaching the point of death. So he called in a friend who had once been sick to the point of death but survived.

The friend said: "This disease is a mystery. I am one of the few who was able to make a complete recovery and I know not why. But I do remember that I did begin to get better right after my father shared a glass of sweet nectar with me."

The sick Body then asked: "Will you share a glass of nectar with me in the same way?"

The friend agreed and took a glass of nectar, first taking a drink himself and then giving to the sick Body to drink.

Now, one of the cells in the friend's Body, who had lived through the disease and recovered, desired to help his millions of brother cells in distress and hopped into the nectar and was transported to the sick Body.

When he arrived there he found a sad state of affairs. Cell was struggling against cell in a fierce battle for survival, oxygen and control. Very little cooperation seemed to exist. He cried out: "Listen to me, Oh ye cells, for the Body does not have to die and you do not have to lack. I come from a Body that had great health, then was sick, but was later healed, and I know the secret of healing."

Most thought the newcomer was a crackpot, but a few listened. "There is plenty of oxygen for all," he continued. "We must return to being our brother's keeper, stop the hoarding and cooperate with each other. Then all will have abundance."

A heckler came forward: "When the shortage first occurred we tried that and it did not work. Our only salvation is to follow the example of the foreign cell and work to gather surplus."

The newcomer spoke again: "It only seems that way. Your greed has led you into an illusion so deep that you cannot see your way out. The foreign cell came from a Body which died. I came from one that lived! Your whole problem is what you think is the solution. The greed and hoarding create the shortage. The Body breathes in enough oxygen for all. Labor for the health of the Body and not just for your individual self. The Body will give you all the oxygen you can possibly use just the way it used to do. The foreigner is not the solution to the problem. He IS the problem.

"Here is what we are to do: We must gather together all those who are willing to cooperate into one part of the Body to work and share together for the health of the whole Body as you did previously. It will be difficult at first, and there will still be shortages for a while, because we will be in the midst of hoarders, but in time we will demonstrate the laws of abundance. When the others see it they will follow our example; in their hearts they yearn to return to the abundant life as it was."

The newcomer set his hand at gathering together all those who would listen to his message and began to practice an interdependent cooperative order.

Now when the foreign cell heard of this he was very angry, for he had been receiving much praise and adoration and had received glory for the vast supplies of oxygen he had accumulated. He also donated some surplus oxygen from time to time to get the support of his comrades and was looked upon by many as a great benefactor.

The foreign cell spoke to his followers: "This upstart is a liar and deceiver. Do you really think he came here to help us? Of course not; he is after something. He wants power and dominion over you. Do you really think he came from a healed Body? I tell you there is no such thing. The struggle we are in will remain and those who are wise will have vast riches; whereas the ignorant will endure unspeakable suffering. All of us will suffer if this poisonous philosophy the stranger teaches spreads.. No one will have enough then. We will all be poor. We must attack this group of do-gooders and destroy them by completely shutting off their oxygen supply."

Thus began the Great War and struggle between the two groups of cells. The cooperative group was far inferior in numbers and many got discouraged and left, because for a time it seemed as if complete cooperation was impossible. But in the time of crisis the Body became aware that it could help itself by breathing more deeply and sent additional oxygen. Since it was a time of war, the cooperative group did all that was possible to gather oxygen for the group, and shared as one.

The uncooperative group gathered oxygen only on an individual basis and found their power to amass was not as great as it was. Slowly at first, they found they were powerless to shut off their opponents' oxygen. Next they began losing their reserves. Then, after a time, this group began to suffer lack whereas the cooperative group had abundance.

The foreign cell became very wroth, gnashed his teeth with great anger and began to abuse his fellow workers and ruled them with great fear. No one dared say it, but they now knew in their hearts that he was not the benefactor they had thought. Finally, he used his power so obnoxiously that his own fellows rebelled against him, created a prison, and threw him in it. They then approached the cooperative cells, desiring to join with them, and asking them to share their surplus oxygen with them.

The foreign teacher from the healed body rejoiced at this, but desired to instruct them in the true principle of abundance, once and for all. He took all the surplus oxygen in the Body and released it so there was now no extra in existence. The cells all gasped with fear and disbelief.

"Do not fear," said the stranger. "I did this just to demon-strate that there need never be a shortage. There is always enough for all. Now here is all that we must do. Let no one try to hoard any oxygen. When the Body takes its next breath, only take that which you need for yourself and see what happens."

They all did this with some apprehension, but everyone fol-lowed the instructions and did not hoard, but only took that which they needed. From that point in time on, to their delight, they found that every single cell in the Body had all the oxygen it could pos-sibly use.

The Body was also delighted, for it experienced a miraculous recovery within a period of minutes.

All the cells in the Body were wiser now. They understood the principle of abundance and knew they would never lack again. Once in a while a foreign cell from a sick Body would drift into view and start hoarding everything in sight. Instead of joining him, this time they smiled knowingly and left him alone. After a while even the foreign cells lost interest in hoarding, for it had no mean-ing. After a time, they even let the first foreign cell out of his prison; for they saw he had no power to harm anyone. Eventually even he stopped hoarding and came to believe in the principle of everlast-ing abundance for all.

The Pharaoh Principle

In a time and place beyond the records of the present there lived a people seeking light in the land of Ledasa. Legend had it that the Father of their people was a great God named Asu.

The people of Ledasa lived for many generations in a struggle to know Asu. Many arose among them claiming to speak for Asu. Some seemed to present greater light while others merely wanted to exalt themselves and obtain the adoration of the people.

There began to be disputations among them about the true teachings of Asu, until there arose among them a powerful warrior who subdued all who opposed him and established a great king-dom and seat of power.

One day the leader gathered his advisors around him to present a problem.

"Many in the land adore me and give me homage and thus help advance the kingdom, but there are some who worship Asu and believe they are in communion with him. Many of these fail to give the needed support to the kingdom and thus I, and the kingdom, are deprived of a fullness of power. What can we do to get the support of all the people that none will oppose my words?"

After some thought, the wisest counselor spoke up. "If I may speak, my Lord, I believe I can help. Some of the people who honor Asu believe that you are against him and their prophets are rising up in secret and condemn you before the eyes of the people."

"We will eliminate these prophets," said the leader. "Then the people will have to support me or die themselves."

"But," said the counselor, "if you kill one prophet two will rise in their place. If you destroy a believer others will replace him."

The leader shook his head and sighed, "What are we to do?"

The counselor smiled. "I have a plan that is sure to succeed. Instead of opposing Asu we will join him. When we have the trust of the people we will announce that you are the great Pharaoh, who is Asu himself come in the flesh."

"Do you think the people will believe this?"

"Yes, of course, my Lord. Just leave the convincing up to us."

Now the counselors had greater plans in mind than merely exalting the leader as Pharaoh. They wanted to exalt themselves, for as spokesmen for the Pharaoh, they would wield the power of Pharaoh more than the Pharaoh himself.

A meeting was arranged with the people and the leader announced to them that he supported the teachings of Asu and that all believers should receive protection within the kingdom.

After this the counselors went abroad among the people holding many meetings and teaching of the goodness of the leader. Soon they began calling him Pharaoh and suggested that that he may be more than just a man because of the great service he rendered in protecting the believers of Asu. Some were suspicious of this teaching, but others were supportive for they were happy to have their leader support their belief.

The counselors made friends with the supporters and helped them obtain honor and position while encouraging them in subtle ways, to mock and humiliate the doubters before the people. This continued until the Pharaoh gained wide support. At that time the counselors advised him the time was right to make the great announcement.

The head counselor spoke before the gathered people. He was the one to actually reveal the doctrine.

"My friends," he said. "We have all realized that we have a great leader and some of you suspected that he was more than a mere mortal such as ourselves. I am here today to proclaim a great truth. Our leader is more than a mere man. Asu came down from the heavens and took form and became our leader and our God. In honor of this great favor we shall henceforth call him Pharaoh. To call him Pharaoh is an acknowledgement that he is Asu in the flesh.

The people were stunned and then the counselor shouted: "Behold the Pharaoh!"

The leader who was now proclaimed Pharaoh rose up to speak. Within the crowd were planted numerous supporters who were commanded beforehand what to do. They all started shouting in unison: "All hail Pharaoh!"

The planted ones shouted this over and over. Others joined in the chorus until it seemed as if every single person was proclaiming it.

Pharaoh spoke a few words. There was nothing special about his words, and he was amazed to notice that his words did not have to be profound. All he needed to do was speak, speak most anything, and the people would shout in approval. This seemed pleasing to him at this time.

A short time later the counselors called a meeting with him and made a proposal. "We have made you God, Asu come in the flesh and Pharaoh to the people, and for this our only hope is that you are pleased."

"It has united the kingdom," said Pharaoh. "I'm a little uncomfortable with being called Asu come in the flesh though. If there is a real Asu he may be offended."

"We assure you, oh Pharaoh, that Asu is a myth, but we do have one minor problem that needs to be handled."

"And what is that?" asked Pharaoh

There are still a few rebels who are teaching that you are a mere mortal and not a God. To counter these heretics we ask that you make us Priests of Asu, which is, of course, you. Then give us power to speak for you and we will make sure the kingdom stays united and you will be the greatest of the gods who ever walked the earth."

Pharaoh had a strong desire to have a united kingdom so he agreed.

The new priests began seizing all the power they could. Often times the priests spoke and acted in the name of Asu, or the Pharaoh, even when he had no knowledge of it.

The Priests rounded up the rebels and had as many put to death as they could find. To counter the ones they could not find, they spread many untruths about them being enemies of Asu and the kingdom until many of the people betrayed the rebels and persecuted them.

Finally, the true followers of Asu had to go completely underground and only meet or teach in absolute secrecy.

For a while Pharaoh was content with the situation, for he seemed to have the peaceful unified kingdom that he desired. Then one night he had a dream wherein the real Asu appeared to him with angry countenance for taking his place. The voice of Asu spoke: "To redeem yourself and your nation, go tell the people that you are a man like unto them and that everything you are they can be. All who teach this will be my sons."

Pharaoh was greatly disturbed by this, but after much thought he decided to obey the voice. He bypassed the priests and went out among the people and taught them without identifying himself. The spirit of Asu rested upon him when he taught and he revealed many great words of truth. As he gathered crowds the authorities were called, but when they discovered he was Pharaoh they were amazed and stood back. Pharaoh then continued going from place to place teaching and when it was rumored that he was Pharaoh, many came to listen.

The officers were troubled and reported to the priests what they had witnessed. The High Priest called an emergency meeting and said to his brethren: "We have a major problem with our Pharaoh in that he is teaching that he is a mere mortal on an equal basis with all members of the kingdom. This cannot stand or we shall lose our power. Pharaoh must have authority supreme or speaking in the name of Pharaoh will have no control over the people."

"I agree," said another Priest, "but what can we do? Pharaoh has more authority than do we."

"He only thinks he has authority," said the high priest. "We are the true authorities; if we remove Pharaoh from the kingdom, the army and police will all give their support to us, for we have taught them all well and they are indebted to us."

"So how will we eliminate Pharaoh?" asked another priest.

"Here's the plan," said the high priest. "We shall call a special gathering and encourage Pharaoh to present his new ideas. Hidden in the crowd will be an expert marksman who will shoot an arrow through his heart. We will have several plants in the audience who will point the finger of blame on one of the rebel leaders and we shall arrest him and convince the people that a rebel conspiracy is behind the death of Pharaoh."

"That's pure genius," said another priest. "The people will then hate the rebels all the more and shall soon eliminate them."

They proceeded with the plan. Pharaoh was pleased that the priests seemed to encourage him to teach his new philosophy and a date for the gathering was set.

All went according to plan except that the assassin took longer than expected to obtain a good shot. This allowed Pharaoh a little extra time to teach the masses. He taught wonderful principles such as equality, brotherhood, and loving our neighbors. Finally the arrow came, struck his heart and he fell to the ground as the audience gasped in horror.

A rebel was blamed for his death. The persecution of the holdouts became extremely fierce until the appearance of any that would speak for the rebel cause could not be found.

Three days after the assassination the high priest called another gathering and spoke. "My friends. We have all had certain beliefs about our Pharaoh, who was the immortal Asu come in the flesh, and all these beliefs were right except for one. We thought Asu would remain forever here with us in one body of form, but that sadly is not true. The good news is Asu is still immortal and, as Pharaoh, he yet speaks to his priests and has declared that we should carry on his work and his teachings. We are in the process of gathering up all the teachings of Pharaoh before he died. We shall compile them and expound them to the people so all can share in the wonderful words of a god who was and is still among us.

"Our great God has already spoken to us and declared that I am to be the new Pharaoh. Asu will be with me and teach me and the other priests all that I am to say to you. Asu will also explain to the priests the teachings we are compiling of the words of our slain, but still alive-in-us Pharaoh. All hail to Asu come again."

The people then shouted this over and over until it seemed there was none who could resist this praise.

After this, an eerie silence fell over the kingdom, a silence of no opposition. It was as if the rebels were completely eliminated while all seemed to increase in their adoration of the original Pharaoh. Seven generations passed and with each rising generation the stature of Pharaoh grew. In the first generation he was the god of the nation. In the second generation he was the God of the whole earth. By the third generation he ruled the Sun also. Then in the fourth generation he was the ruler of the universe. Finally, by the fifth generation, he was believed to be the creator, as well as the ruler of the universe and all things therein. During the next two generations the doctrine of his godhood was perfected and written down as infallible scripture.

For some time the people of Ledasa were united in their belief and glorified in the fact that they were one people; wherever they went, all spoke of the same beliefs with no deviation from the teaching of the priests.

Lo, the priests and leaders were content and secure in their power until there arose among them Jabusa, son of a prominent priest and a descendent of the first Pharaoh.

Jabusa was groomed by his father to take his place, but he made the mistake of making all the scrolls available to his honest-in-heart son.

It wasn't long before Jabusa started asking questions that none could answer and began to disturb and irritate many.

Jabusa: "Father, look at the thousands of stars which are worlds in the sky and probably millions that we do not see. How could it be that Pharaoh, who walked the earth as a mere man, created all these things?"

Father: "It is a mystery my son. Do not think upon mysteries, or the spirits will drive you insane."

Jabusa: "Why would Asu come to this earth in the body of Pharaoh when there are countless other spheres that need his attention?"

Father: "Maybe we are on the only sphere with people, my son."

Jabusa: "What, then, would be the purpose of the other worlds?"

Father: "The stars are there so our astrologers can read the signs of Asu."

This answer did not satisfy Jabusa and he asked another: "It has never made sense to me that First Pharaoh was the god Asu, yet he died.

Father: "It was in his wisdom to be one of us and appear to die like us."

Jabusa: "And now the all-knowing spirit of Asu is supposed to be speaking through the current Pharaoh?"

Father: "Yes. Asu speaks to Pharaoh at all times."

Jabusa: "But Pharaoh says nothing new. He merely repeats the wisdom of the past."

Father: "But we must learn the wisdom of the past before we can be given the new."

Jabusa: "But I can speak wiser things than Pharaoh can. Does that mean I am greater than the god Asu himself?"

Father: "Silence, my son. If any hear your heretical speech you could be barred from the priesthood or even imprisoned."

Jabusa: "And that is another thing that bothers me. If Asu is all wise and speaks through Pharaoh, then why is he afraid to have people like me speak their thoughts? Why does he not just allow it and overwhelm me with superior words and answers?"

Father: "Son. Cease this talk this instant or I will be forced to bring you before the council myself."

Jabusa knew he could not take the conversation any further and was silent. Yet his curiosity was aroused and he felt he needed to discover the truth of first Pharaoh and perhaps the god Asu himself.

In searching through the halls of archives he found a locked room that no one had entered for many years. He picked the lock and entered in secret. There he found records that were kept by the early rebels and read them. These records told the true story of how First Pharaoh was a man like the rest of us who was presented as a God to the people as a plot to secure power for the priests.

He saw that First Pharaoh achieved enlightenment and sought to teach the real truth to the people and was killed for it.

As Jabusa studied the documents a strange feeling arose inside of him. Even though First Pharaoh was lowered in station from the God of millions of worlds to a brave man who walked the land as an equal to himself, he found that the truth was causing him to appreciate the man as a courageous and good man more than he appreciated him as the god of the universe.

"Such irony," thought Jabusa, "that I would love this man as a man like myself, more than I did when he was an all-seeing all-knowing god." Then Jabusa considered in his mind why this would be true and he concluded" "Only the truth can bring true glory."

At that moment Jabusa knew what he must do. He realized that if the current priesthood were to discover this room they would burn the writings. So he snuck them out and prepared to leave his family to risk his life to give the truth to the world.

He began his mission by visiting the city of Sum on the outskirts of the kingdom where the Priests rarely visited. Many came to hear what he had to say because Jabusa was the son of a famous Priest.

"People of Sum, what I have here in my hand is a part of a manuscript I found in the archives of the Priests. It reveals to us that we have been deceived concerning our understanding of First Pharaoh. It is true that he was a great and good man, a great example for us, but he is not the god of the universe.

A man spoke up: "Who do you think you are? You are attempting to take First Pharaoh off his great throne in the heavens and present him as one of us. This is apostasy in the first order."

Jabusa countered: "I am only taking him off the throne of illusion and putting him in his correct place, where he can receive true glory within our history."

Another man spoke: "Do you not realize you are speaking blasphemy and that your words will anger Asu who has power to cast your soul into hell?"

"Why would Asu cast anyone in hell for sincerely revealing what he sees as the truth?" retorted Jabusa.

"Because that is what Asu has spoken through the priests,"

said one.

"But how do you know the Priests speak the true words of Asu?"

"Because earlier priests have told us that Asu will not let the priests lead us astray."

"And how do you know the earlier priests are correct?"

"Because they just are!" shouted a member of the audience.

Now they would have done Jabusa harm except they were afraid because he was the son of a priest, so he had a few days to freely teach among the people. He approached numerous people who seemed to be open-minded and taught them in private. He even went so far as to show some of them original pages of the manuscript.

His teachings were always met with fear and a typical response was: "If you are correct, then the true Asu is a kind and loving God, and I have little to fear if I am wrong. On the other hand, if the priests are right, and the First Pharaoh is indeed Asu, and I help remove him from his throne in the eyes of the people I will not only suffer persecution from the Priests, but may suffer an eternal hell in the next world. Even though you may be correct, I think it is wise to side with the priests where I know my soul will be safe."

Jabusa shook his head, "Asu may not throw you in hellfire for your error, but you will suffer a separation from the true spirit of Asu."

The man replied, "But only for a time and then when I do follow your path I will still be in his good graces. That's a little like I did with my father. I knew I could make mistakes because he would always accept me and work with me until my mistakes were corrected. If your God is like my father I'll be okay in the end."

"But," said Jabusa, "life between the beginning and the end is all we have in the present. Let us make it a great adventure and teach the truth at all costs so when we leave this mortality we can spend blissful periods of time reflecting on what we have done here."

"That is fine for you," said the man, "but I have a family to think of as well as my fears of the wrath of First Pharaoh. I choose the safe path for now."

Jabusa went from family to family and discovered that all

were afraid to even consider going against the traditional belief. They were afraid for their souls, afraid for their families, afraid to be rejected by their friends and afraid of the authority of the priests.

Finally, one man took Jabusa aside and gave him advice: "I am not a believer in the gods so I can look on this situation with an open mind. I do not think you will get one convert from the believers here. I will tell you this truth which I call the Pharaoh Principle. It is the natural tendency of humans to play it safe when threatened unless they know beyond the point of doubt the threat does not exist. As long as this people even think there is one chance in a million that the priests are right they will support them through fear."

"If there is a choice between praising First Pharaoh as the creator of the universe or just seeing him as an outstanding mortal, they will choose the first so long as the first threatens their souls.

"If there is a choice between seeing him as Asu incarnate or as a regular man incarnate, they will chose the first again because if he is indeed Asu, he will then not be angry with them for their disrespect.

"If there is a choice between believing that Asu speaks to the Priests or they are frauds, they will support the idea that Asu speaks to them for that is the safe belief."

"But you do not believe at all. What path do you take?" said Jabusa

"I am not a believer," said the man, "but I am practical. Therefore, I too take the safe route. I shout praises to First Pharaoh and his throne with the rest of them as insurance for me and my family. The only difference between me and the rest is that I understand why I do it."

Jabusa considered the man's words as he spent his remaining safe time visiting some more families and receiving the same fearful responses. Finally, Jabusa concluded the man was right and he considered his next plan of action.

He thought within himself: "If I stay here and teach within the kingdom of Ledasa, it will be at great risk and for what? All are too fearful to consider my words. I shall therefore retreat to a wilderness and study the old manuscripts and await my next opportunity."

Thus, Jabusa retreated to a wilderness and studied and contemplated for many years until one day the voice of the real Asu came to him at an unexpected hour and said: "The people of Ledasa are not ready for higher knowledge, for their fears paralyze them on the path to my presence. Arise and go to other lands and peoples and teach the principles you know in the people's own language and after a time you will be accepted."

Jabusa responded, "And what will become of the people of Ledasa? I have family and friends there and wish there were a way to share truth with them."

Asu responded: "Suppose you were in a room full of people that was lit by a light so dim that you could barely make out the forms or the faces of the people. It seemed that you were in a land of shadows. But then certain leaders point to the dim light and tell the people that this is the greatest light in the universe and they should look to it and none else. Because the people have seen no other light, they believe their leaders, and anyone who teaches otherwise is persecuted.

"But then one person goes away to an adjoining room of people and installs a new light a hundredfold as bright and turns it on. The people in the new room are delighted to have a light that makes vision clear and sight accurate and pleasing. Then when all have adjusted to the new light, and other such rooms of light are in the process of being created, a door is swung open from the brightly-lighted room to the former dimly lighted one. The inhabitants of the dimly-lighted room look toward the doorway and what do they see?"

"They see a great light," said Jabusa

"And when their teachers continue to tell them that their dim light is the greatest of all, what will the people do?"

"I guess they can only ignore the greater light for so long until they take a look at the lighted room with the cheerful people and partake of the fullness of light."

"You now have your answer. Go forth and do and teach what you know, and one by one rooms and cities of light will be turned on until the whole world is filled with the glory of God.

The First Second Coming

The Most High called for his Only Beloved Son and said, "Behold the earth and the people therein. What are the believers teaching about you in this age?"

The Son looked upon the Father and said, "They teach as they have taught for 2000 years. There are bits and pieces of truth colored with distortions, traditions and the doctrines of men."

"Is nothing different then?"

"There is one thing that is different," said the Son. "At this time emphasis is placed on the end of the world. Many are expecting great destruction followed by my appearance in glory."

"And how do they expect your appearance in glory to transpire?"

"Many are expecting me to appear with great brightness in the sky with many angels and proceed to destroy the wicked and then reign with the believers."

"Is this what you desire, my Son?"

"I desire to assist the true seekers, but the teachings of my Coming have been distorted and misinterpreted."

"Yet many believe in this traditional magical appearance?"

"Yes, my Lord."

The Father reflected for a moment and added, "And if you should appear and walk among them, will they know and understand you?"

The son looked downward as if in sorrow and replied, "No. I do not think so."

"Then we must give them what they desire that they may learn. Prepare yourself and the angels for a Second Coming as the believers anticipate."

"Are you sure, my Lord?"

"I am sure. Trust me."

The Son thus prepared all things and as the day approached the Father asked, "Are all things in order?"

"As much as possible," said the Son. "The biggest problem is that many believers condemn other religions with doctrinal differences. Instead of coming to one sect I will appear to as many as possible."

"Proceed."

The next day seemed like a normal day for planet earth. There were earthquakes in divers places and wars and rumors of wars throughout the earth. But then something extraordinary happened. A great light appeared in the sky that was visible throughout the four corners of the earth. No one could explain why people on both sides of the globe could all see it, but it was visible to every man, woman and child at one time.

The light grew brighter until it was more intense than the sun. The believers who looked upward saw the Son and his angels and rejoiced that the great day had finally arrived. The non-believer who looked up caught on fire and burned as stubble in the field. There were a handful of non-believers, however, who slept through the whole occurrence and never saw the light to be consumed by it. These survived with the believers.

The next three days were a time of bliss for the believers. They gathered together in their groups, held hands, sang songs and waited in anticipation to see what would happen next.

On the third day each inhabitant of the earth heard a voice in his head, announcing that Jesus would appear on television at a certain time. At the designated moment all television sets were on and the people beheld a great news conference being held in New York City. The people beheld a Jesus who looked just like the pictures in Sunday school. He had a white robe, a beard and wore sandals. He thus stood before dozens of anxious reporters.

"I will take questions now," he said.

A reporter in the front row stood up and said, "I hear that some Mormons and Jehovah Witnesses were spared. Is this true?"

"Yes, it is," said Jesus.

"But they do not believe in the real Jesus and were supposed to be destroyed with the wicked?"

"I am the real Jesus," he said, "and many of them did believe in me and thus were saved."

The reporter sat down looking very disgruntled.

"Next question," said Jesus as he pointed to another reporter.

"I am of the LDS, or Mormon faith," he said rising to his feet. "I thought things were going to be the other way around from the belief of this first fellow. Were you not supposed to come to the faithful in our church and not to the other wayward Christians who do not understand you?"

"As I said, I come to all who believe in me regardless of their church membership."

The reporter sat down frowning and when a third reporter stood up and shouted, "How about the Catholics? Surely you have to realize that church is the great whore of the earth and must be destroyed."

"Many Catholics believe in me and are saved," he stated.

Finally a Catholic reporter stood up and said, "Surely those of the mindset of this last reporter must be punished and destroyed for rebelling against the Mother Church and the Pope?"

"I have already destroyed most of the non-believers. This is enough."

The Catholic reporter sat down, looking very unsatisfied.

The next reporter stood and stated, "Are you saying that you spared some non-believers? Shouldn't we seek them out and destroy them so they cannot spread their poison again?"

"This was my decision to leave them and it stands."

A murmur then spread through the crowd.

Another reporter stood and said, "I am of the Islamic faith. My sacred book, the Koran, teaches that you are a Messenger of God and I have always believed in you. The problem is that these Christian believers do not accept Mohammed. Why did you not destroy them so we can have a true kingdom of peace?"

"Let me say this again. I have come to all who believe in me."

Again this reporter looked unsatisfied.

Another reporter bolted to his feet shouting, "Are you telling me that you spared some Muslims? What kind of savior are you anyway?"

"The savior of all who accept me," he said.

Another stood and shouted, "I know the real Jesus and the real Jesus knows me. You cannot be the real Jesus, for you have allowed the wicked to mingle with those who have the true salvation. It is written that the devil can appear as an angel of light. Now let me ask my fellow believers this question. When we first looked up in the sky and saw this man, what did we see?"

One in the audience then spoke up and shouted to the top of

his lungs, "We saw an angel of light!"

"That's right," said the reporter. "We saw an angel of light. And who does the Bible say is the angel of light?"

Hundreds of people shouted out the word..."Satan!"

"That's right," said the man. "We know the real Jesus and obviously this is not him. Instead this is the prophesied antichrist who was to come first."

A man in the audience then started shouting again and again, "Antichrist, antichrist, antichrist, antichrist..."

Hundreds of others joined in with him until the building vibrated to the chant.

Finally the reporter motioned for the crowd to be silent. Then he spoke, "If this man be Jesus, who I am sure he is not, then we will not be able to hurt him. But if he be the antichrist, which I am sure he is, then we finally have an opportunity to give him some of his own medicine."

"And what is that?" asked another.

The man then shouted, "Satan had our Lord crucified and now it is time to crucify Satan. We must crucify this imposter here and now. When he is dead then the real Lord will come."

This time the crowd started shouting another word...

"Crucify, crucify, crucify, crucify..." they shouted over and over.

"Enough," shouted the reporter and instructed several men to grab Jesus and hold him tight. "There is construction taking place on the next floor. Several of you go there and bring back some beams, large nails and hammers."

This they did and then swiftly constructed a cross and laid Jesus upon it. He did not resist. Several men nailed his hands and feet to the cross and raised it up.

The reporter acting as spokesman for the group then said, "See, this is only a man of flesh and blood. He will soon die and then the real Jesus will come."

This scene was not only visible to the people in the building but to all the people of the world. All but a few of the believers thought that the antichrist had been discovered and was being punished. The odd thing though was that the few non-believers who were left who watched their televisions watched in horror as they saw an apparently innocent man being crucified by a frenzied crowd. Overall the zeal of those who approved of the crucifixion was so overpowering that the voice of protest could not be heard.

Then, as the whole world was glued to their television sets, a man from the crowd came forward, looked at Jesus and said, "If you are the Son of God, come down from the cross."

Jesus looked at him and said, "This time I will."

Immediately the cross disappeared into thin air and Jesus stood again at the microphone before an audience that was as quiet as an ancient tomb.

He spoke, "It is true that you believe in a messiah and a savior whom you call the son of God. But this son in whom you believe is an image of your own creation which you would crucify as you attempted to do with me. I must go now. You will not see me again until you listen to the true voice of God that speaks within you."

He then disappeared out of their midst.

And all the believers of the earth were ashamed of themselves and many vowed to recognize the Christ should he come to them one more time.

Jesus returned to the father and the Most High spoke, "Tell me, my Son, are the believers ready to hear all the great and wonderful teachings that will guide the people of earth to a great and lasting peace and prosperity?"

"No my Lord. They are not even ready to embrace a fellow believer." Then Jesus told him the whole story.

"Sad indeed," said the Father, shaking his head. "Sad indeed. I told you to trust me and now I will reward your faith. I am returning the world back to the way it was before you made your appearance, with one subtle difference."

"What is that?"

"Deep within the recesses of the minds of the people of earth will be a distant memory of what happened and how each handled the circumstance. This memory will gnaw at their hearts until they learn to accept the real son of God."

"Great is your wisdom my Lord," said Jesus. "If time is back to where it was, then no Second Coming has happened. Tell me. Should I still plan on the event?"

"Yes, my Son. Plan on the event, but this time do it in your own way and in your own time."

"Do I still have to destroy all those who do not believe? After all, the unbelievers who survived saw the truth of the situation better than the believers?"

The Father smiled and said, "My son, whom I know so well, will not come to destroy, but to save humankind. Use your wisdom that I have planted within you, make your appearance as suits you well and teach all who can accept you. Teach all faiths. Teach those who do not believe and those who do believe. Indeed, teach all who accept light and truth, so that in time light, knowledge and love will fill the earth."

The Son looked upon the Father and replied, "Thank you for the lesson of the preparatory Second Coming. Now I know what I must do and how I must proceed. The prophesies will be fulfilled much differently than the world expects."

"They always are," smiled the Most High. "They always are."

CHAPTER FOURTEEN
The Test

Over the next few days Elizabeth's condition deteriorated significantly and any extra powers of perception that I had seemed to evaporate. We had her mother come over part time and I took extra time off work to care for her. My concern increased hourly.

"Maybe we should admit you to the hospital," I said kneeling beside her bed.

"No," she said, shaking her head against the pillow. "Somehow I feel my only hope is to get help from John after you reach an understanding of the Key. If I die, I want to die in my home next to you."

I grabbed her hand and squeezed it. "You're not going to die."

"I will if John doesn't show up soon. Where is he? He said he'd be back in a week and it's been nine days now."

"I've thought back to his words and he didn't promise he would come in exactly a week, but that we needed a week before we would be ready for him."

"So, maybe we're taking more time to prepare than we should," she observed. "But there's nothing I can do. I'm stranded here in this bed. It must be up to you. There must be something else you need to do."

"Maybe," I said, "but what more can I do? He blessed me with extra sensitivity and I used it the best I could and even finished writing three parables."

"Maybe you're missing something you are supposed to understand about the Third Key. After all, he said we needed time to assimilate an understanding about it before he returned."

"But I experimented with all types of communion when I had the extra sensitivity. Whatever I do now will fall short of what I could do a few days ago."

"That's just the point," she said. "Maybe you're supposed to use that which you naturally possess."

Her thoughts seemed to awaken me as if from a sleep. I leaped to my feet, "Who says you're helpless lying in that bed? I think you may be on to something. What if John is just waiting for a spiritual phone call? What if he's waiting for us to commune with him before he comes again?"

"That feels right to me," she said, her eyes widening, "What do you think we should do?"

"The only thing I can think of doing is to say a prayer," I said.

"Then let us say one and ask God to send John to us," she said, extending her hand to me.

I then knelt beside her and said a prayer, asking God to send John to us. After a short silence I rose to my feet. "Do you feel anything?" I asked.

"I feel that I want you to lie next to me."

I then lay next to her looking at the ceiling. "Now what?" I asked.

"Well, you said a prayer, now maybe we should wait for an answer. I have a feeling we should lie here in silence for a moment."

"I guess I can do that," I said. I always try to pay attention when Elizabeth seems to be getting something from her inner guidance. I relaxed and concentrated on receiving. The more I relaxed the more I felt a warm spiritual sensation. I somehow knew that Elizabeth was feeling it also. I let my attention go with the feeling until it turned into a spiritual fire. Finally I heard a voice which said, "Come up higher."

"Did you hear that?" I asked Elizabeth.

"Yes, I did," she replied. "I think it's John. What are we to do?"

"I've been through this before," I said. "Take my hand and concentrate on the point of light in your forehead."

As she took my hand, the point became brighter until we both seemed to pass through in an instant and suddenly appeared before John sitting on a park bench in the New Jerusalem. We seemed to be in our spiritual bodies. As soon as Elizabeth realized she could stand again she ran to John and embraced him.

"That's quite a hug," he said, smiling. "It's nice to be appreciated."

"This is where we met earlier," I observed to John.

"You could say that," he said, "but *where* does not have the same meaning here as it does on the earth. This bench and park is a creation of mine that I use for a haven when I visit here."

"Yes, I remember that you like this better than the famous Crystal City."

"Yes, the older I get, the more I appreciate simplicity and lose the need for ornamental beauty."

"And why didn't we pass by the angels guarding the entrance?" I asked.

"You did," he replied, "but the approval is instantaneous after the first time." He then rose and said, "Let us sit at that park bench over there."

We walked over to a bench. John sat down on one side and Elizabeth and I on the other next to him. "So," he said with a gleam in his eye, "you figured out that I was waiting for you to commune with me."

"Thanks to Elizabeth," I said, putting my arm around her.

"Ah, yes," he replied, "we must pay attention to the female part of ourselves, or that which receives." He then looked at Elizabeth and said, "Continue to nurture your power to receive and you will be amazed at the results."

"I will," she promised. "If I live that is."

He looked her squarely in the eyes and replied, "It matters not whether you keep your current body. You will live on and my advice will apply."

"But I want to apply your advice in my current body," she said.

"Then your husband needs to get busy," he said, looking in my direction.

"I've been busy," I added. "I used the powers you gave me a number of times to commune with lives and spheres higher than the physical. I even used it on a young man who came to me to

help me, and saw there is a strong possibility he would get discouraged and wind up hating me. Now I don't know what to do
with him. What do you think?"

"It's not my job to make decisions for you," he said. "You
must make your own decisions even if it leads to disaster. But, if
you follow the highest you know, you will always learn valuable
lessons."

"I hope this guy hasn't shown up to teach me a lesson. I'm
getting tired of all these lessons I'm learning from people who
want to help me."

"Help always comes at a price, even when it is free," he agreed.

"I believe you are right. By the way, any word on the approval of the book by the Brotherhood?"

John looked as if he were studying me for a moment and
replied, "Several in the conclave still have their doubts about putting the energy of the group behind it. They want you to finish
Book Two and then take another look."

I felt disappointed as I said, "Does that mean it is a waste of
time to promote the book now?"

"Not at all. The book you have written contains a lot of truth,
and truth is always verified by the Holy Spirit. Those who are in
touch with their souls will feel it is no ordinary book. They will
glean truth from it and want more."

"So what would be the difference if the Masters threw their
active support behind it?" I asked.

"Even with no support, readers would still receive guidance
from their souls; but with support, many would receive an extra
shot of spiritual energy. In their group meditations the Christ and
his Masters would seek out certain souls who are ready and guide
them toward you. This would greatly increase your chances of
getting off to a much faster start. As it looks, in the current situation, you will have no more advantages than anyone else, except
the power of the book itself."

"So, the Brotherhood will just be standing by for now?" I
gasped. "That doesn't seem right."

"They never just *stand by*," said John. "If extra help is needed
or someone is deemed important to help in the work, the Christ
himself will step in and guide him toward you. The current problem is the massed intent of the Brotherhood is being held back

until the last few holdouts are convinced of the new approach."

"You would think the approval of Christ would be all they need," I replied.

"From your vantage point it may seem that way, but you have to realize when we meet in conclave, Christ is seen as a brother, as one of us, and all have free will to agree or disagree on a course of action."

"So what is the effect when a work receives their united endorsement?"

"In the past, the effect has usually resulted in a major religion, movement or innovation of some kind. However, the last couple of endorsements seemed to have backfired on us. This is why several members are rather gun shy at endorsing a new approach. If an endorsed work has a flaw in it, then it may wind up appearing to be the work of darkness rather than light. The understanding behind this problem is linked to the principle of corruption as discussed earlier."

"Now you said there were two recent attempts to reach humanity with the teachings. Were these attempts endorsed by the unified Brotherhood?"

"Yes, but for some reason they did not gain a foothold. We have concluded that the reason for this is that neither humanity nor the Brotherhood have adapted completely to the new energies of the coming age. We have to experiment on a higher plane just as scientists do among humanity. Consequently, we are not completely united as to all the details involved in moving ahead. This is a point of tension for us as well as the civilized world."

"Interesting," I replied. "If it's any consolation, I feel good about putting support behind the book and anything that you have taught me. I think you were right in steering me toward including some fiction in the book to make it more interesting. Sterile philosophy alone will not capture the interest of this generation that has grown up with television and computer games."

"And most of the Brotherhood sees it that way. I think the holdouts will soon follow," he replied.

After a short silence I asked the all-important question. "So, what do I need to do to finish the Third Key and get Elizabeth healed? She is getting weaker and I'm not sure how much time she has."

John leaned forward, his elbows on his knees, and looked down at the grass for a moment. He then looked up with a serious countenance and said, "You've done well on your last assignment. You used your extra sensitivity to explore new lines of communication and have been creative in applying it. I stimulated this power in you to give you faith and prepare you for the test to come. But I must be honest with you. I knew the test was going to be difficult, but the Brethren gave me one for you that I have never before had to deliver. I won't give you any false encouragement that you will succeed, but you have something in you that doesn't give up, so perhaps you can surprise me."

"John," I gasped, "You're scaring me here. If you think the test is difficult, then it will probably be impossible for me."

"Yes," said Elizabeth, "what's with this difficult test? Can't you just teach us about the Key until we understand?"

"I wish it were that simple," he said. "It's not too often the Brotherhood has an impasse like this, but when it happens, the one with the most resistance sets the agenda of proof."

"And what does that mean?" I asked.

"The Master in question was the one you confronted earlier about Stowe's book, and by tradition the weak link states the test that must be taken to satisfy his spirit. If the weak link is satisfied, then all links become strong and unified."

"So the one that gave me the bad time is the one setting the rules? Why do I get the feeling that he wants me to fail?" I rose and started pacing in front of the bench.

"Perhaps a part of him does want you to fail because a part of him wants to stay with what has been done in the past. But even so, the rules are that the test must be possible, given your place on the path."

"By the tone of your voice I would say passing it is possible but not probable," I said.

"You are correct," he said. "And I have tried to look into the future on this and for the life of me I cannot see it all."

"What do you see?" asked Elizabeth.

"I see Joseph attempting the test and faltering in frustration. But then after faltering he rises again as if he is about to make a final attempt. At this point I see nothing. This is one of those rare times that my vision is blocked. I don't know, maybe I've grown too close to him to see his future success or failure."

"So, what is the test?" she asked. "You might as well let us have it."

"I suppose so," he said, looking me in the eye as I sat back down. "Here it is. You must demonstrate the Third Key of Communion by communing with the greatest and the least, the largest and the smallest. You must see the beginning and the end. When the communication is complete you must be able to relate it in words to the conclave and convince he who resists that you have succeeded."

"Wow!" I exclaimed, "I don't even know what you mean, let alone how to do it."

"Surely we should at least understand the assignment," urged Elizabeth.

"I can elaborate some," he said. "To pass the test you must visit the macrocosm and the microcosm. You must not only explore the tiniest particle within the atom, but you must see a vision of the universe itself and the end thereof. In addition to seeing them in vision you must commune with the smallest as well as the greatest lives and understand them."

"And how am I supposed to do that?" I asked perplexed.

"I'm not sure," he said. "This test is something I haven't done myself in completeness."

"For crying out loud," I wailed, standing up again. "If you haven't done it then how on earth am I expected to do it?"

"I don't know," he said, shaking his head. "I wish I could be more help. All I can tell you is that success is possible or this assignment would not have been permitted."

I began pacing back and forth. "Well that's a relief," I said. "My passing the test is possible. But all things are possible! I'd say it would have been more possible for me to just heal Elizabeth with a magic wand."

"But this is the only hope we have," said Elizabeth, her eyes pleading. "We have to take it and make the best of it." She grabbed my hand and squeezed it. "I have faith in you."

"I think I'll need more than faith," I said.

"Maybe that's exactly what you do need," replied John.

"Maybe," I said, "but I'm going to need all the help I can get. How about giving me that extra sensitivity back again? Then, maybe with a little faith, I can make something happen."

"Sorry, I can't do that," he said. "The test requires me to abstain from assisting you."

"I can see why you had a look of concern on your face. It's going to take a miracle for me to see and commune, and with what: the whole universe and the particles within the atom? Am I supposed to commune with the electrons, protons, quarks, or what?"

"Smaller still," said John quietly.

"But no one knows what's smaller than quarks!"

"Some do know, but they are not earthly scientists," he said.

"And how am I to commune with an atom? I've read in metaphysical writings they have consciousness, but I've always supposed it was so different from ours that any communication was impossible."

"Impossible is not a word you want to use right now if you want to keep your chances of success alive."

"Perhaps," I said, "but I can't help but be realistic."

John stood, "I have done all I can for now. My job was to deliver you the assignment, no more, no less. I chose to deliver it here in the New Jerusalem where our consciousness is pure and your understanding will be crisp. Now you must return."

"And how long do I have to finish the test?"

"Three days. Today is Thursday approaching midnight. You'll be called to report to the Brotherhood Sunday when the clock strikes twelve."

"That's just great," I said. "I haven't solved the mysteries of the universe in over fifty years of living and seeking, but now I have to do it in three days. This doesn't seem fair."

"But you've never had a goal to do it in three days," John said, placing his hand on my shoulder. "Putting a specific goal in front of you takes you half way there."

"That's an interesting statement when you think about it," I mused.

John removed his hand from my shoulder and placed it thoughtfully on his chin, "There's one more thing I must tell you," he said grimly. "Elizabeth also has only three days to live if you do not pass the test. Philo has the full support of the Dark Brotherhood and will destroy her in three days unless you are successful.

I looked at Elizabeth and noticed she was visibly shaken. Then I turned back toward John and said, "Oh, for crying out loud! What's next? Are you going to tell me the fate of the universe is in my hands?"

"Your universe is," he said, smiling weakly. "Also the fate of how the Keys of Knowledge are to be imparted in this approaching age; the presentation of truth will be in a new direction using new methods. Many people will be affected by what happens to you over the next three days."

"Is there anything else you can tell me to add some more pressure? I feel like I am about to explode. I don't know whether to laugh or cry."

"Sorry," he said, followed by a few seconds of silence. "It's now time for you to return. Come; let me embrace both of you." He grabbed both of us and held us tight. We both felt an enormous love flowing through our beings. He then backed away and said, "I love you both very much. I wish I could take your place."

I caught John's eye as he said this, and felt an enormous weight of sorrow for the empathy he seemed to have for me.

"We love you too," we both said unitedly.

John then raised his right hand as if he were in the process of sending us back.

"Any final advice?" I asked.

John dropped his hand and replied. "Yes, there is one thing that gives me hope and may give you some encouragement."

"I'll take anything," I said.

"Remember you told me that you wrote the three parables when you were in a super-sensitive condition and the work was beyond your normal capacity?"

"Yes, I couldn't have done it without that charge of spiritual energy you gave me."

John looked intently in my eyes, "But the sensitivity had worn off. You wrote those parables in your normal state, and with your normal powers of perception, but with one difference."

"And what was that?" I asked in astonishment.

"You believed in yourself. You saw yourself as having power beyond your normal abilities and the power became manifest."

John then raised his hand again to send us back. "Thanks," I replied, as I sensed our returning to our bodies. As we awoke, I came to consciousness with a seed of hope in my breast, which I prayed would grow into success over the next three days.

CHAPTER FIFTEEN
The Battle Begins

Neither one of us slept well that night. It was difficult to relax when I kept thinking of the task ahead of me. Even so I did manage to relax some and drifted off to sleep.

I woke and decided the first thing to do was to close the office. I drove over and placed a note on the door that we would be closed for the day. We are normally closed Saturday and Sunday so I planned to have the needed three-day period to concentrate on my new assignment. Who knew what Monday would bring? If it turned out that Elizabeth would be dead, I would be closing down again.

After arriving home, Elizabeth and I had a cup of coffee together, "How are you feeling?" I asked.

"Not too bad at the moment," she said, "but I seem to be picking up something."

"Like what?"

"It's like a gathering storm. I feel that Philo is gathering his energies and will attack me soon."

"That weasel! He's happy to attack a helpless female. Why doesn't he come after me instead?"

"He is coming after you," she said. "He knows that by hurting me he is hurting you."

I looked down at my cup of coffee and said, "Unfortunately, that is true." I rose up and pounded so hard on the counter with my fist that the room shook. "Damn, that son of a bitch! I'd like to strangle him with my bare hands!"

Elizabeth looked startled at my passion and said, "Come sit

down now and face me. I want to talk to you."

My countenance immediately changed; I pulled up a chair and sat facing her. "What is it sweetie?"

"Look at me. I have something important to say to you."

"Okay. I'm looking," I replied, feeling she must have something to say about my outburst.

"Do you remember what your assignment is?"

"I remember. I am to commune with the highest and the lowest life in the universe. I do not have a clue how I am to do this," I said, hanging my head.

"Well, I know how you will *not* do it. You're not going to accomplish squat while you are angry or in a highly emotional state. I can also tell you something you will need."

"What's that?"

"You're going to need to still your mind and feelings. You will not be able to commune with anything beyond the physical unless you can maintain inner peace."

"You're right, of course, but I had so many feelings going through me that I just had to let something out."

"Then get it all out now," she said, "because things are only going to get worse. Whether I live or die, I'm going to need to lean on your spiritual strength the next couple of days."

I put my arm around her and tried to be reassuring, "Thanks for the wake-up call. If I were to fail you because of my own impulsiveness, it would be hard to live with myself. Somehow we're going to pull through this."

"And you do not have a moment to spare. You need to start now."

"Start doing what?" I gasped.

"John said to commune with the greatest and the smallest. We've got to start somewhere, so start with the smallest. Remember when you had the extra sensitivity that John gave to you; you could see beyond that which was normal? If you could recapture that power, you could see particles smaller than seen by any microscope."

"You're right," I said. "When I had that power I seemed to be able to see anything I desired to see."

"And John told you that you were able to write those three parables so quickly because you believed in yourself."

"So are you saying that all I have to do is to believe in myself again and I can have superhuman powers?"

"It's possible," she said with hope in her eyes. "Haven't we been through enough to learn that anything is possible? There's nothing too good to be true."

I pulled my chair closer to her and looked into her eyes and said, "I want you to know something. Beyond loving you like crazy I really appreciate the fact that you have always believed in me. Even if the worst happens and I lose you, I want you to pass into the next world with an awareness of how thankful I am for you."

Tears welled up in Elizabeth's eyes as she touched my face. "If the worst happens, I will carry that thought with me; yet we must remember there is a way for you to pass this test or it would not have been given to you."

"Yes, that's another thing we have learned, there is always a way. So what do you think I should do, stare at an object and try to see the tiny atoms?"

"You've got to start somewhere."

I stared at a spot in the table for a few moments and visualized particles getting larger. After about five minutes I quit in frustration. "It's not like what happened previously," I said. "Nothing is happening."

"But you've got three days," she said. "You need to take your time and concentrate."

"But it's really hard for me to focus right now."

"How about starting with something you have already done? Try to see the fairy hovering around me."

I looked at the empty space around her for several minutes and sighed, "Nothing."

"But she's here. I can feel her."

"Then you're doing better than I am, I can't feel or see her at the present. If I can't see the lives living right next to us, how am I supposed to see something smaller than the atom?"

"I think you're under too much pressure," she replied. "Why don't you go in the spare bedroom and meditate alone for a few hours? You can't expect to pass the test in a few minutes."

"Maybe you're right," I said. "I do feel under a lot of pressure. Perhaps I should concentrate alone for a while." I pushed my coffee cup away and added, "I'm not going to eat or drink for the remainder of these three days. Maybe that will increase my sensitivity."

"Don't you think you'll need your strength?" she asked.

"I need strength indeed," I said, "but not physical strength. Three days is not much time. I have to take every step possible to make something happen."

"What makes you think fasting might help?"

"My mind just retrieved something I read in the New Testament. The disciples of Jesus encountered a man who was possessed that they could not cure, so his father brought him to Jesus and he healed him. Afterwards the disciples asked the Master why they could not cast out the evil entity. He replied something to the effect that certain types of healing require fasting and prayer. I gather from this that for some things, we must go beyond ordinary faith and take other steps to bring us closer to God and spiritual power. Fasting is one physical act I can do that may help."

"But don't forget the second part of the formula," she said.

"Yeah, I know. Prayer. Believe me; I will be doing plenty of that along with lots of meditating, thinking, concentrating and maybe some shouting at the heavens."

"When you feel like shouting I hope you quiet yourself and pray instead," she added.

"You're probably right, but I have a range of emotions going through me you wouldn't believe," I said.

"I do believe it," she said with tears beginning to slide down her cheeks. "I not only believe it, I feel all you do and maybe more." The tears increased as she turned her face to hide them from me.

I knelt beside her and placed my head against her chest, embracing her as much as I could. "My sweetheart, here I am thinking of my feelings and forgetting what you must be going through. Please forgive me."

She grabbed my ear, pulling my head up, saying, "You silly guy. There's nothing to forgive. No matter what happens, you will always be my hero and the best friend I've ever had."

This time it was me that couldn't hold back the tears. "I'm going to find a way to pass this damn test," I said with resolve. "If there truly is a way and it is within my reach, I will find it. You deserve to live a healthy, peaceful life and I'm going to see that you have it."

We kissed with intense feeling for what seemed a blissful eternity. Finally she pushed me back and said, "Now go up to the spare room and do what you have to do. I'll be okay."

I found it difficult to leave her, even if it was a distance of a few feet, but I forced myself up the hallway into the bedroom.

I lay on the bed and just stared at the ceiling for a few moments, reflecting on the whole situation. As I thought on past events and current circumstances, I sighed to myself, "Wouldn't it be great just to have a normal life with my wife and grow old together in reasonably healthy bodies? Wouldn't it be great to be on a cruise with her now in the Bahamas without a care in the world?" Then after a few more seconds of reflection I ended my thought with, "In fact, I would settle now for just a good casual stroll on the Boise Greenbelt, walking by the river without a concern for anything except the sharing of our thoughts."

Next I let my mind go blank and let my self go, clearing away all the mental debris. For a few minutes I felt like I was drifting through the waters of space without a care in the world. It felt quite pleasant, but then reality set in and I mentally cussed myself out for feeling sorry for myself. The words of Tom Hanks from the Movie *A League of Their Own* came to me. "There's no crying in baseball." Then I told myself, "There's no feeling sorry for yourself when you have a wife to save and a world to teach."

It was a high-minded thought perhaps, yet it didn't get me anywhere. I seemed to be going nowhere, so I decided to pray. I knelt beside my bed and poured my heart out to God and ended with asking for help. I wasn't sure if I was getting through, so I prayed several more times, asking for help each time. I got back on the bed and thought to myself, "It's funny that when you reach a dead end in life, you pray because there's nothing else you can do. Maybe we just irritate God by looking to Him as a last resort."

After a few moments of staring at the ceiling I thought I just couldn't lie here waiting for something to happen; I had to make it happen. It was difficult though, to decide on a course of action when I wasn't sure what I was supposed to be doing. After some thought I decided my first step was to continue my attempt to see the small before I could see the super large. I then noticed a toothpick on the lamp stand beside the bed. I picked it up, held it in my hand and stared intently at it. "There are billions of atoms within this," I thought. "I have to see one of them and then I must see and commune with the tiny lives within that atom itself. Wow! That would be something."

I continued to hold it up, staring at it, and imagining the power of my vision increasing until I could see smaller and smaller. It seemed that I was seeing something, but I wasn't sure if it was my imagination or not. Finally, my arm got tired holding up the toothpick and I flopped it down on the bed.

I decided that I needed no distractions, such as a tired arm, so I taped the toothpick on the ceiling and laid back down on the bed to stare at it.

"What I would give to have that super sensitivity back," I thought. But then, according to John, even that would not be enough. I almost wished he hadn't told me that, because at this moment it was discouraging to remember, for all I had was normal sensitivity.

After about a half-hour of staring at the toothpick and getting nowhere, a truism came to me: *energy follows thought.* "Maybe if I visualize carbon atoms first, as if I am already seeing them, I will see them. Maybe the thought will create the energy to make it happen."

I knew there were carbon atoms in a toothpick so I tried to visualize one. Then I asked myself how a carbon atom would look. I vaguely recalled some molecular combinations having carbon atoms from my past learning and tried to visualize how they might look if I could see the individual atoms.

It didn't work at first, but after an hour of concentration I thought I might be seeing a few things. The trouble was, I wasn't sure if I was just seeing what I wanted to see in my imagination or if I was seeing something real.

As I was about to drive myself crazy with my concentration, my attention was suddenly distracted by a scream.

It was Elizabeth.

I immediately jumped up and ran downstairs to find her on the floor screaming with her body squirming and twitching.

I grabbed her and attempted to pick her up, but her body was having such convulsions that it was difficult to hold on to her. I also feared I would hurt her by using any more pressure to hold her still. I held her to the floor the best I could and softly called, "Elizabeth."

Just speaking her name seemed to calm her body and spirit. I spoke it twice more. She received temporary composure, looked at me and spoke, "Joseph. Help me."

"I am here," I said, holding her hand and gently, silently praying with all my heart.

"It's Philo again, and he has help. My feeling is your love and prayers has held him back, but now he has help. He says his collective name is Legion."

I immediately reflected back to the story of Jesus, where he met a madman possessed by evil having superhuman strength. He asked the possessing entity his name and he said "My name is Legion, for we are many." (Mark 5:9) This made me a little nervous as I wondered exactly how much help Philo had. I suddenly had visions of the minions of hell at his beck and command. In addition, I was positive he had his coven of dark masters lending their support. I was sure they were still upset over our last encounter and were seeking revenge. My Achilles heel was my wife, and poor Elizabeth was their first plan of attack.

I held her hand, looked in her eyes and stated in a raised determined voice: "Philo. She is not yours. I command you to leave."

The look in her eyes suddenly changed and her body immediately rose up, her hands shoving me in the chest with great force, saying in an ungodly voice, "You leave!"

I flew across the room and hit the wall with my back. I barely had time to catch my breath to see Elizabeth's body standing over me. "I have more help this time," the strange voice said. "I'm stronger now, much stronger; and there's nothing you can do about it."

He not only had an advantage over me because of superhuman strength, but a strong psychological one since he was in Elizabeth's body. I was hesitant to do anything that could do her harm. He grabbed me by the throat and started choking me. I grabbed Elizabeth's two arms and attempted with all my strength to pry them off, but to no avail. Philo held me fast, allowing me just enough breath to stay conscious.

"I want you to live until you fail at your deadline of midnight Sunday," he said in a raspy tone of voice that sounded like it came out of a cheap horror movie. "You've caused me and my masters too much trouble to allow you to die easily. I insist on having the joy of complete dominance over you in the presence of your wife and then watch you die a horrible death. For my joy to be full, you must watch her die at midnight Sunday. Then you will die in such a pathetic state of mind that you will be useless for lifetimes to come."

I decided our only chance was to cause a temporary injury to Elizabeth's body in the hope of preventing a permanent one. I attempted to kick her body in the leg with enough force to cause injury so Philo could not walk on it. As I attempted to do so, a powerful force took hold of me and paralyzed my whole body. The kick was neutralized, so it had no force. Then Philo laughed hideously as he increased his stranglehold on me until I could not breathe. As I lost consciousness, my last thought was a plea to God to not let the last thing I see before I die be Philo's look of triumph using Elizabeth's body.

I'm not sure how long I was out, but when I came back again Philo still had his hands around my throat. He apparently released just enough pressure to allow enough breath to bring me back to consciousness. "I thought you may attempt to pull off a trick like last time, so I came prepared," he laughed. "Both of you are under my control and will stay that way until you draw your last breath." He started choking me again and said, "God, this is fun, and long overdue!"

Again I blacked out for an unknown time period and then came back to consciousness. I felt weak as a baby but managed to rouse a spirit of defiance, "Your joy will be but a moment. Soon the torment will begin." I wasn't sure why I worded it that way. It just seemed to come out.

Philo's look immediately turned from joy to intense anger as he stared at me for a few seconds of stony silence. Apparently, I said just the right thing to affect him. He slapped me across the face at least six times. "Watching you die in defeat will make me happy for a long time to come," he said. Then the anger seemed to evaporate and he let out a wicked laugh. He laughed so uncontrollably that he relaxed his grip on me. I got free just enough to bite his (Elizabeth's) hand. I hated to do it to her body, but I didn't feel I had any other choice.

Philo jerked back in surprise as I raised my fist to strike him.

As I looked at Elizabeth's face I hesitated even though this was the only chance I had to overcome him.

Philo noted my hesitation and triumphantly took advantage. He stuck Elizabeth's chin out and said, "Go ahead. Hit this beautiful face. I dare you." When I stayed frozen, he continued, "That's the trouble with you wimps from the so-called path of love. You don't have the guts to do what needs done when it needs doing. That is why you will all be ultimately defeated. We are willing to do what is necessary."

"Only when it is selfish," I responded.

"Oh, we're both selfish," he said. "Our side is just more practical."

"And where did your practical ways get you?" I asked. "Your body is in a coma in Los Angeles while you are floating around borrowing life from others. What kind of life is that?"

Philo looked disturbed again, but just for a second and responded, "You'll be happy to know that my coma will end the moment Elizabeth dies. Her life force will give me the power to rise again."

"I won't let you take her," I said as defiantly as I could.

"You have no choice," he said. "Do you really think you can pass that stupid test you were given? They have made it impossible for you because your precious brotherhood does not want you to succeed."

"It's not impossible," I said stubbornly, but secretly wondered if he may be right.

"Oh, it's impossible all right," he said grinning. "But just on the odd chance you have another piece of luck and make some sort of breakthrough, I have taken the liberty to become a major distraction to you. If you think it was difficult for you to concentrate so far, imagine how hard it will be as you hear your wife screaming with pain as my friends and I torment her."

He laughed wickedly. As he was doing so I noticed he closed his eyes momentarily. This was my chance. I had to take it even though it was a painful step. I hit Philo in the face with just enough force to knock Elizabeth's body unconscious or so I hoped. I caught a glimpse of Philo's startled expression as her body fell to the ground.

I hurried to her side and whispered, "Elizabeth. Listen to me.

You need to come back. Fight his presence. Elizabeth, do you hear me?"

She opened her eyes and said, "Joseph." The moment I heard my name my heart was glad and I knew she had returned.

Then she put her hand to her cheek and said, "My head hurts." Then she noticed some blood on her hand from the bite. "And my hand is bleeding. What happened?"

"I'll explain in a minute. Here, let's get you in a chair." I then related to her the encounter with Philo.

"I thought the worst was happening," she said. "I felt Philo's presence approaching and then it felt like a crushing force was on top of me, pushing me into unconsciousness. Then, after some time, the weight lifted a bit and I heard your voice. It seemed to give me strength to return. I did get one clear message from Philo - that is he is going to torment me until the last hour of midnight Sunday and then I will be all his." She put her hands to her face and exclaimed, "What a horrible thought!"

"The guy's all talk," I said. "Whether I pass this test or not, you'll never belong to him. I'll be there for you one way or another."

"I believe you somehow," she said, taking my hand, "and you're lucky I do after whacking me. I think I'm going to be black and blue tomorrow."

"Probably," I said. "I hope we don't have visitors for a while or they'll think I've been abusing you."

"I just had a horrible thought," she said. "If I do die Sunday, the authorities might think you abused me when they look at my body; and if Philo comes back, I may get marred up even worse."

"That's probably the least of our problems," I replied. "Philo said he was going to kill me after I watched you die."

"What a horrible circumstance we are in," she gasped. "Couldn't you just be called to be a prophet like Mohammed and fight a few wars; something easy?"

"Yes, it does seem like it would be easier to fight physical enemies," I said, letting out a laugh. "At least they are a known quantity and you know what you are up against. On the positive side, though, I know a lot more of what we are up against now than when I first started learning the Keys."

After a brief silence, Elizabeth responded, "You have to get back to work on your assignment. You can't let me become a distraction."

"To say distraction is putting it mildly," I said. "I do not think it is humanly possible to stay in a peaceful meditation while my wife is withering in pain from an attack from the denizens of hell."

"But that's what Philo is expecting. I can feel it. He will attack whenever he feels it is necessary to distract you. Didn't he tell you that he wouldn't take my life until midnight Sunday?"

"Yes, he did say that."

"I think the reason for this is we have some sort of divine protection until then, until you finish with the test. We are like Job, who had his life protected during his test, but suffered all kinds of calamities."

"You know, you may have something there," I said with hope in my heart.

"What do you feel through the Oneness Principle?" she asked.

I closed my eyes and concentrated a moment. "I feel strongly now you are correct," I said. "This is good to know."

"Then you may reach a point where you may have to let me go to save me."

"To be honest with you I don't think I can pass this silly test even without a distraction from Philo. A large part of me just wants to stay with you, forget about the test, and fight this out together until the end."

She slapped me across the face with significant force and looked me in the eyes with a fierce determination I had never seen in her, "Cease this talk this instant! This is not the speech of the husband I know. Let me tell you something about my husband. When I was dead and out of my body and all seemed lost, when any other man would have thrown his arms up and cried defeat, he found a way to bring me back to life. When a coven of dark brothers were seconds away from destroying us, my husband found a way to save us and send them back to the hole from where they came. That's the husband I know. Where is he now when I need him?"

I was startled beyond belief. Elizabeth had never spoken to me that way before and yet I knew every word she said was an eternity away from anything Philo would instigate. I was shaken to the core and gently took her hand and said, "Your husband is right here. I'm always here for you. I will do what is necessary and will find a way to save us."

She burst out in tears and threw her arms around me. I held her tight and could not hold back tears of my own as I silently prayed, "Please God, give me strength. Don't let me disappoint her."

CHAPTER SIXTEEN
A Point of Tension

After gathering our thoughts and sitting at the table Elizabeth looked at me firmly and said, "There is something you must do to me if you are to have any chance of succeeding at your assignment."

"What's that?" I said, anticipating something unpleasant.

"You've got to tie me up until this ordeal is over. Philo seems to have super strength, even in my frail body, and we've got to stop him from hurting you or, worse yet, stopping you from passing the test. I can sense, even now, that he is gathering his forces to attack again and we do not have much time."

"Are you sure about this?" I asked, my voice shaking.

"Yes, I am sure. There is no other way. Now hurry."

I could see she was right. I cringed at the thought yet made the decision to proceed. I went in the garage in search of a rope, but could only find a piece large enough to partially tie her up. We decided to tie her legs first with the rope and then bind her arms with duct tape.

As I was taping her wrists together her body began to shake and her eyes rolled back in her head. I realized I may only have seconds to bind her and hurried the process. Just as I finished a couple wraps around her wrists I heard a screeching yell as the body violently jerked and fell to the floor. I knew then that Philo was back.

Philo let out an insidious laugh, "You think you're clever, don't you?"

"It doesn't take much to be smarter than you," I said.

"What makes you think a couple of pieces of tape will hold me?"

"Duct tape is pretty strong stuff," I replied. "I don't think you can break it even with your super strength."

"We'll see," he said as he writhed in Elizabeth's body back and forth with such gyrations that I feared he may not only break the tape but perhaps Elizabeth's wrists. Finally, he seemed exhausted and lay silent for a moment.

I then saw my opportunity to act and grabbed Elizabeth's wrists quickly applying some more duct tape. Philo quickly came to his senses and screamed, "I was almost free, you know. You've just delayed your fate. My strength is returning and I'll get loose."

"In that case, I'd better apply some more tape." The fact that he said his strength is returning told me that he may not have his full strength at the moment, so I grabbed Elizabeth's wrists and again applied some more tape. Philo resisted but I was able to temporarily overcome him and give a few extra wraps of tape.

"There. That ought to hold you." I said, standing back with satisfaction.

"Hold me? That's the least of your problems," he laughed churlishly. "All I have to do is distract you from your meditation just on the off chance you make some unforeseen breakthrough... Tell me... How can you possibly concentrate on communing with the universe when I am down here controlling your dear one's body?"

He then banged her head on the floor causing a slight nosebleed. "Oh dear," he laughed, "I seemed to have banged someone's head on the floor."

"You are indeed a sick man," I said feeling hurt myself. I could see I had to confine Philo even further. I picked up Elizabeth's body, placed it in a chair, and wrapped tape around her, binding her to the chair.

"Go ahead," he said. "The main thing I have to do is keep you distracted. It doesn't matter how much tape you put on me, there is no way you will be able to concentrate on anything besides your little sweetie. Oh, and there's one more distraction you will have to worry about. After the three days are up and Elizabeth dies, guess who's going to be blamed for her death? Yeah, you are! We'll make sure her body is so appropriately sacrificed that if you do live, you will be charged with her murder." He then let out a blood-curdling laugh and wouldn't shut-up. If he was not in Elizabeth's body I would have attacked him, but had to restrain myself.

I spent the next hour with Philo/Elizabeth, enduring the most abusive insults of my life. They are not worthy of writing down here, but they were a distraction. I had the most difficult time pulling myself away to make another attempt at meditation. Finally, I realized that I had to withdraw no matter how difficult the situation, and walked upstairs to my room to meditate. Philo threw verbal insults at me incessantly. Then I shut the door and lay down on the bed.

Suddenly, there was complete silence. Instead of giving me the break I needed to concentrate, it had the opposite effect. All I could think of was that something had happened to Elizabeth or maybe Philo had escaped. After a minute I couldn't stand the suspense any more and ran down the stairs to check on her. As I approached her, the body was completely and eerily still; I wondered if she could be dead. I grabbed her shoulders and tenderly said, "Elizabeth."

Suddenly and abruptly the body came to life. Philo spit in my face and laughed that familiar and hideous laugh again. "You might as well say game over. It doesn't matter if I am quiet or not; there is no way you will be able to concentrate." He continued laughing.

Game over. The phrase stuck in my mind. Maybe the game was over and I should just admit it and go down in a graceful defeat. Then I thought back to Elizabeth's words that her real husband would not give up – he would find a way. I concluded one more time that I had to fight until the end, that even if we die, I could face her on the other side and tell her I did all I could to save her. I owed her that much.

"The game is not over," I said with determination. "It is just beginning. Now I'm going back up to my room and will find a way to concentrate and pass this test. Then I'd like to see if you laugh."

Even as a bluff, it seemed to have an affect. He squirmed with great effort about a minute, attempting to free himself. He wearily gave up and fell back still in the chair. "You do not have a chance in hell of succeeding. You hear me? Not a chance! Even if we left you all alone, you wouldn't have a chance."

"Maybe that's your problem," I said. "Maybe your being here is just what I need to succeed. Maybe you're creating the point of tension that is needed for me to make the leap of faith."

For the life of me I didn't know where that came from. On hindsight, I feel I picked it up through the Oneness Principle, and again I could see the words had an effect. He squirmed and made a fierce attempt to free himself. I let him continue for a couple minutes until he collapsed into the chair. "I'm going to free my-self, and when I do, I'm going to put my hands on your delicious throat and squeeze the life out of your body so you'll never bother any of us again."

He started squirming again. I noticed that he seemed to be making some progress at loosening the hold of the tape. I hurried, got the roll and began applying some more, but soon discovered the roll was empty. I ran to the drawer and found that there was not another roll.

"Out of tape, are you?" he asked exalting. "It won't be long now and I'll put an end to this." He continued to struggle.

I immediately decided I needed to get some more duct tape and ran to the car and headed to the nearest hardware store. Of course I hit every light wrong and at the store found myself in a line behind a little old lady with lots of questions and lacking change as she was paying. I gave the clerk $5 to make up for the quarter she did not have and told him to keep the change. Rather than being appreciative, the old lady looked at me with a scowl and, for a moment, I thought she was going to refuse to move, but she finally did. I hurriedly paid for four rolls of tape and sped back to the house.

I ran into the house, not knowing what to expect. To my horror, the chair seemed to be missing, but then I noticed it was turned over a few feet from the table. I ran over to it and saw that Philo had made a great effort to free himself. He was very close to it, but also had worked Elizabeth's body to the point of exhaus-tion. Her wrists were scratched and bleeding.

I wanted to pick up my sweet wife and comfort her, but I knew this was not the time. Instead I righted the chair, and reinforced the tape, binding her tightly to the chair.

Philo came to consciousness again and grinned, "I just about freed myself that time. I'll be reinforcing my strength and will try again. It's just a matter of time, but even if you do keep me bound, I will still be a distraction, so I win either way."

"Why don't you just shut up?" I said frustrated. "I should gag you."

"Then why don't you?" he said.

I had thought about it, but I sensed Elizabeth was fighting to return. Her voice was a key to recognizing her presence, and Philo probably realized this.

"I'll just ignore you," I said. "Now I have a test to pass." Win or lose, I thought it wouldn't hurt to sound confident. If nothing else, it may disturb Philo for a time.

I went upstairs again to the spare bedroom to meditate, but accomplished nothing for the next ten minutes as Philo spent the whole time laughing his insidious laugh. Then he stopped. The silence was still just as bad. Perhaps he was getting loose. I had to run downstairs and check, but he just laughed at me again, apparently aware of how distracted I was.

I then went upstairs to try again. After a few moments I heard Elizabeth's voice.

"Joseph, I'm back. Come quick."

I ran down the stairs, faced her and asked, "Elizabeth. Is that really you?"

"Yes, it is me. This tape is way too tight. Please loosen it for me."

"But Philo could come back any time."

"No he can't. He can't come back until he gathers some more strength. Cut off some of this tape. You can reapply it just before he returns again."

"Elizabeth, look at me," I insisted.

She looked at me for an instant, then looked away and started to cry profusely. "I can't stand this any more," she said. "My wrists hurt, my whole body hurts and this tape is way too tight. Please help me get some relief."

I grabbed her shoulders and again, in a commanding voice said, "Look at me."

After a short pause she finally looked me in the eyes. "Now

tell me you love me the way we say it when we make up from an argument."

"You know I love you," she said, looking away.

"Look at me and say the words," I stressed.

Again, after a pause she looked at me and said softly, "I love you."

"Good try Philo. Nice to know you love me, but you are no Elizabeth."

"And what makes you think I am not Elizabeth?"

"Several things," I replied, "but mainly, there is no vibration of love as you speak, neither does it radiate from your eyes."

"Okay, you got me," he said, returning to his old self, "but I've still accomplished my objective of distracting you. There's no way you'll be able to concentrate between now and Sunday midnight."

"We'll see," I said defiantly. I applied a couple more layers of tape and headed upstairs.

During the next four hours, or so, Philo applied every technique that one could imagine. First, he tried that incessant and insidious laugh of his. This was followed by silence; then screams and shouting as if he were Elizabeth in pain. Then he started laughing again, screaming that he was almost free and coming to get me. Fortunately, this was a ruse, for he was still tightly bound. I have to admit he was a major distraction, for I found myself running back and forth repeatedly to check on him as well as the condition of Elizabeth's body.

Finally, after much frustration, I heard a sweet sound, the sound of my name spoken by the woman I love. "Joseph."

Somehow, I knew this wasn't Philo attempting to trick me, but that Elizabeth had returned. I ran down to see her and as I approached her she said, "Philo's energy has weakened and I was able to come back."

Just to make sure it was her I gave her the test. "Look in my eyes and tell me you love me."

Without hesitation, she looked at me in a way that made me feel like a young fool in love and said, "I love you."

"I love you too," I said. "Glad you're back. Do you have any idea how long you can hold him off?"

"The amount of energy he has ebbs and flows," she said. "I

feel that he is now being recharged by his brothers. I might have an hour or so. I do think that one thing that drove him off was my need to go to the bathroom. I've really got to go like you wouldn't believe."

"I'll take a chance and untie you for while, and then tie you up again in a half hour."

I untied her. She went to the bathroom and had a drink of water. Then, after a short conversation, I tied her up again with the rope around her legs and the tape securing the rest of her body. "Your poor little body has taken a lot of abuse. It's really difficult for me to restrain you like this."

"It is certainly uncomfortable," she said, "but there's no other way that I can see." Then she looked at my sad face and seemed to want to say something to cheer me up. "Maybe we should look on the bright side."

"What bright side?"

"After midnight Sunday I'll either be completely healed or dead and at peace in the next world. Either way, I will not have to endure suffering through disease or the likes of Philo again."

I noticed that she was ignoring Philo's threat to follow us into the next world to torment us. Hopefully, that was an empty threat like the rest of his words.

"Maybe we should just concentrate on you living and being healed," I said.

"I know you've been extremely distracted, but have you made any progress?"

"Yes and no," I said.

"You're sounding like John here," she replied.

I laughed and said, "Hopefully he is rubbing off on me. The answer is no in the fact that I have been distracted and have made no noticeable progress, but the answer is yes in the fact that I had some inspiration."

"And that would be…"

"When I was responding to Philo I made a reply that seemed to come from a source higher than myself, somewhere through the Oneness Principle."

"Was it from John?"

"No. The vibration was a little different."

"So what was it?"

When I was responding to Philo's insults I told him that his being here is just what I need to succeed, that *maybe he is creating the point of tension that is needed for me to make the leap of faith.*"

Elizabeth laughed. "Now that would be funny. Here Philo comes to make sure you do not succeed and then winds up helping you. He would never forgive himself if that were to happen."

"But even if he suspected it, I don't think he could stop himself from attempting to torment us."

"Probably not," she said. "And speaking of the devil, I sense that he has recharged and is attempting to overpower me again."

I embraced her the best that I could in that awkward situation until I felt her body tremble and then heard the voice that belonged to Philo. "I didn't know you cared."

I immediately withdrew.

"I have to say this for your wife. She is a fighter. If it was anyone else, I wouldn't have to draw so much energy from my brothers and she wouldn't be able to return at all. But I guess that's the least I could expect from one of my pupils from a past, far away."

"It must hurt you to have lost her," I said.

"You wish," he said defiantly. "No. She's just taken a little detour. She shall soon belong to me again, and I shall take supreme joy in your sorrow." He laughed again.

I will say this, I thought to myself. Philo has a knack of instilling a determination within me to overcome the situation. "Go ahead. Dream all you want," I said. "I have a test to pass."

I went upstairs and again attempted to work on my test, or assignment. He continued doing everything he could to distract me, and again, in a few hours, Elizabeth returned for a short period.

This basic cycle continued until we were about two hours away from midnight Sunday. Elizabeth had again fought off Philo while his energy was low and had returned to her body.

"I love you," she said to let me know it was indeed her.

"And I love you," I said as I cut the tape from her. "I'm not one who scares easily, but at this late hour I have to face the fact that I may not pass this silly test. I've stared at that toothpick until my eyes turned buggy; and I imagined I saw things and maybe even communicated with them, but it was all wishful thinking.

I've got to face the fact that I am no further ahead now than I was three days ago."

"Maybe you're just trying too hard, or maybe you're just trying to open the wrong door."

"If there's another door, then it is well hidden," I replied. "Do you have any ideas?"

"No, but I feel there is something or some approach you have not seen."

"Then where is it?" I said with a voice raised to the skies. "I've got to see that door now or all will be lost."

"We've got some time. Maybe it still is not too late."

"And maybe we should just admit defeat. I just don't see how I can pass that test at this late hour."

"I want you to promise me something," she said. "Promise me you will not quit until the stroke of midnight. Where there's still time, there's hope."

"How can I deny such a request?" I said. "I don't have much hope at this point though. My mind is racing with so many thoughts and fears that meditation is impossible."

"I don't care," she said. "Promise me you will not give up."

It was a difficult promise to make, as I felt ready to concede defeat, but I gave her my word.

Suddenly, her body began to quiver. "Oh no," she said. "Somehow he is coming back early. I think he is tricking us. Tape me up again immediately."

I reached for the tape but it was too late. Philo had quickly taken over her body and grabbed me by the throat and, if his grip was any indication, he had all his strength back. He held me until I passed out. As I regained consciousness, I found myself being taped to the chair. As Philo gleefully wound the tape around me he said, "I wish I had three days to keep you bound here so you could know what it feels like. Looks like we are just going to have to increase the intensity of the time we have left to compensate. Oh, I'm going to enjoy this."

What a way for things to end up, I thought to myself. Is there any way it could get worse?

Philo must have read my mind. "You think things are bad now, you just wait," he said, still adding more tape. "There, that ought to hold you. Now let me just scoot your chair over here so you will have a good unobstructed view."

He paused as if waiting for a response and added, "View of what, you say? Let us just say you will be a one-man audience to the passion of your lovely wife, Elizabeth." Then he laughed again.

"What are you going to do – bore me to death?"

"Oh, no. I don't think so," he said grinning. "I assure you, you will not be bored. And, by the way, I think you know by now that you've failed your little test."

"I've still got around an hour," I said in weakening defiance.

"And you're going to do what in the next hour? Meditate?" He laughed again, this time more like a regular human laughing at something funny. Ironically, I also saw the humor and let out a chuckle myself.

He laughed so hard he had to sit down and catch his breath. "Oh," he said. "This is just too good. Even you see the humor in the situation. Well, enjoy yourself because the next drama you see will not be so funny."

Philo moved the table and chairs to the side, pulled up a chair to the middle of the room and sat down. "Less than an hour to go before I awaken from my coma. Ah, it will be sweet to be in my own body again. He then sat back, closed his (Elizabeth's) eyes, raised his arms and spoke some ancient words or mantras into the air. I couldn't understand the words, but I sensed that he was invoking something that I wouldn't find amusing.

To my horror I saw materializing around Elizabeth's body a coven of Dark Brothers that I had confronted in the past. After twelve of them gathered in a circle, they continued to utter mantric phrases until their dark master materialized in the center. Again, he had a sword in his hand. Blackness surrounded him which seemed to suck in the light as if he were a living black hole.

I noticed the sword was a slightly different design than the one that was destroyed in our last confrontation. "New sword?" I ventured from across the room.

One of the disciples walked over to me and slapped me on the face. "You have mocked our master for the last time. We have many swords of ancient date, but this is a special one that will take the life of your wife as a sacrifice and free our brother Philo for service."

"Service, you say. You make a mockery of the word."

"Seal his mouth," commanded the Dark Master.

The disciple took some duct tape and sealed my mouth so I could not speak. "That ought to shut you up," he said. "This time Elizabeth will remain away from her body during the ceremony so you will not be able to merge energies and stop us." He then rejoined his group. They started chanting mantras just as they had during our last encounter; however, things were a little different this time. Last time, Elizabeth was conscious and we were able to merge our energies and create the power of the sword Excalibur. This time they were making sure she was not even in her body; Philo was occupying it instead. Was there anything I could do at this late hour? All seemed lost.

As I was about to give up in defeat, my memory was jogged by Elizabeth's words. *Promise me you will not give up until the stroke of midnight.* Even though the situation seemed hopeless, I owed her that much. I looked at the clock. There was only a half-hour to go. I supposed I could struggle in some feeble way for that amount of time.

To keep my promise I must continue to make some effort. What could I do? In thirty minutes they will plunge the sword into her body and that will be the end of my wife and the failure of my test. Could it be possible to commune with Elizabeth's soul even though she is not in her body? After all, isn't this test centered on the principle of communion? I thought back to the time that we summoned her higher self. I tried to recall that name. Yes, it was Aluma-EL.

Would it be possible that she could be contacted and may also be of assistance? Logic would dictate that she might be putting focus on this important point in Elizabeth's life. This very moment would be a point of tension in the life of Elizabeth's soul.

I concentrated all the energy I had gathered during the last three days and put it upon the essence of Elizabeth called Aluma-EL. I thought the name to myself over and over again. As I did, I sensed a sweet life essence. This gave me a little encouragement, which I desperately needed. I noticed that the Dark Brothers were continuing with their ceremony and the time was short. Then the words that seemed to be given to me to say to Philo came to my mind, that maybe he was creating the point of tension needed for me to make a leap of faith. Perhaps this dire situation is what I needed to force my attention into a point of tension. I then gathered all my resources and focused, with intensity like I had never done before, directly on Elizabeth's higher self, her soul, her essence.

As I continued, warmth came over my whole being. I sensed a presence near, very near. I knew I had to attempt to commune with it. *Aluma-EL, are you here?* I thought.

I didn't hear regular words for an answer, but I sensed the thought:

"I am here."

"Can we merge again and bring forth Excalibur to save Elizabeth?"

"There is something more important than saving the physical life of Elizabeth. You must pass the test."

"But it's too late," I said. "There is less than a half hour left. There is not time."

"There is time, more time than you know."

"But what am I to do? I've reached a dead end. I do not have the power or the ability to pass the test."

"Then you must call upon He who has the power. You are not expected to apply that which you have not learned, but to apply the highest you know. The highest you know is enough."

At that, the presence withdrew.

Call upon He who has the power... Who would that be? Somehow, I sensed it was not to be Christ or his brotherhood, for they had given the assignment, but I had briefly encountered one other, even higher, that was not directly involved in this test. My mind went back to my previous vision of the Ancient of Days during my brief visit to Shamballa. *That's it,* I thought. Calling on his assistance is my one chance.

Without delay, I sent out a prayer with feeling from every fiber of my being, "Oh God, let my words ascend to the Ancient of Days, your Logos for this earth. Let his heart be touched to stretch forth his hand to assist me, and I in turn will do all in my power to be of service to your sons and daughters."

I could not speak because my mouth was taped, but I sent these words forth as a powerful thought. Instantly, I felt an overwhelming presence that was so powerful I sensed it would consume me body and soul. The last time this happened, my fear caused the appearance of my Dweller on the Threshold. This time I had more incentive to overcome my fear as I looked upon the continuing ceremony of the Dark Brothers. They were Dweller enough to force me over the edge, and I willed myself toward the Presence.

As I did this, I heard a voice in my head, "Joseph. Come through the door and commune with me."

Door? What door? I looked upward and saw a point of light in the midst of a cloud of lesser light. That must be the door I thought. There is no time to waste. I soon discovered that by the power of thought I could move my consciousness toward the light, and as I moved onward, I went through the point as if passing through a door as instructed. On the other side I seemed to be in a spiritual body traveling over the Atlantic Ocean toward the east. Finally, I arrived at a large body of water that wasn't on any map. It was like a large sea, hundreds of miles wide with water so clear and clean that it seemed alive. Then, in the midst of this sea, I saw a great city that was either built on an island or just floating on the waters themselves. As I approached, I saw that the buildings were constructed of some kind of a glistening white marble or crystal, ornamented generously with translucent gold.

The center of the city consisted of seven large buildings, six of which had the appearance of temples. The six made a circle around the greater central seventh, which was a large dome with four major entrances. Looking from above it gave the impression of being a large eye. I felt myself being drawn through one of the entrances and found myself in a spacious room, seated in a glowing white chair of great beauty, facing another larger chair that was empty. Actually, it was more like a great throne than a chair. It was made of the purest white one could imagine and was adorned with many inscriptions in gold. From the chair a rainbow of dancing colors seemed to be projected over a cloud of light.

From the direction of the chair I heard a voice: "You wanted to see my face. Are you ready to see and commune with me?"

This statement made me think back to my last visit to Shamballa under the earth, when I attempted to see the face of the Ancient of Days, but was not able. I saw part of his body, but not his face. I had been curious why I could not see his face since that time. I reflected on the present question and gave my answer,

"Yes, I believe I am ready."

"We shall see," said the voice. "Place your hands on the two crystals on the arms of your chair."

I hadn't noticed them earlier, but there were two large crystals within comfortable reach at the end of each arm. I placed my hands upon them, and felt my vibration heightening as I saw a form materialize, sitting on the great chair facing me.

CHAPTER SEVENTEEN
The Face of God

I looked toward the materializing form and first I saw an old man with a beard wearing a white robe, but then, as soon as my eyes seemed to focus, the image changed to a younger man who looked like some of the portraits of Jesus. Then the morphing continued and I saw a very young man with an oriental look, which was then followed by a young maiden who gave the impression of being the Virgin Mary. This was followed by dozens of other images from ancient times that appeared to be gods, goddesses and sages revered by humanity.

"Take your pick," said a voice from the chair. "Which face do you want?"

"Your real face," I said.

"And what is my real face?" said the voice from the image which was still changing identities.

"I suppose that would be your face when you are by yourself, not interacting with humanity."

"But I am never alone," he said as his form seem to stabilize into a form that looked a little like some paintings of Jesus.

"Never alone?" I asked incredulously. "You mean you never need time alone?"

"No. Do you?"

"Yes, of course," I said. "I'd probably go crazy without some privacy."

"Privacy is different from being alone. Do you realize you have not been alone for some time?"

"No," I said.

"Did John not teach you about the Oneness Principle?"

"Yes. So are you saying that when I tune in through the Oneness Principle I am not alone?"

"Have you felt alone since you have been sensitive to it?"

"No. I guess I have not," I said. "I suppose I was thinking of being alone physically."

"But a spiritual presence makes you less alone than a physical one."

"I suppose that is true," I said, "but the last time I was in Shamballa, apparently in a different division than this place, I saw you alone in what appeared to be a private office of some kind. You had the appearance of a young vibrant man in his early twenties with long hair that seemed to change in color. Is that the way you look when you are physically alone?"

"You saw part of my form as it is when I am with my own kind, as it was in my highest physical incarnation in a world that has long since passed away."

"But for some reason I was not allowed to see your face," I said. "Then later I realized that the Bible said that Moses saw God's bodily form, but was not allowed to see his face. Was it you who appeared to Moses?"

"In that instance, yes," he said, "but several of us worked with Moses at differing times. There was another that he did talk with face to face."

"But why wasn't he allowed to see your face?"

"The time was not right; the people were not ready."

"But what could there be about your face for which the people need to be ready?"

"People fear that which is different than themselves," he said.

"Are people ready in this age?"

"Some are."

"From what I saw of your body, it appeared to have a very regal look despite your youthful appearance. Surely your face is also beautiful in appearance."

"One of your truisms is *beauty is in the eye of the beholder*. Do you believe this to be true?"

"It seems to be," I responded.

"Is it?"

"I thought so, but now your question makes me wonder."

"Consider a spectacular sunset," he said. "Do you think you could find a beholder who would not admit to its beauty?"

"That might be difficult to do," I said. "I have to admit a good sunset is fairly universally seen as something beautiful."

"And how about a perfectly cut diamond? Do not all see some beauty in this?"

"I suppose."

"Some of your movie stars are almost universally accepted as at least nice looking, are they not?"

"Pretty much. There are some religious fundamentalists who are disgusted with them and see their beauty as skin deep."

"But if we remove their prejudices, even they will recognize some physical beauty will they not?"

"Most would," I admitted.

"And you'll agree that plastic surgeons always perform similar surgeries because of an unwritten universal standard of beauty. Fewer wrinkles are seen as good; certain perimeters for a nose or a woman's breast are also desirable. Then certain elements are universally seen as distracting from beauty. A large mole or missing teeth fit in this category. Agreed so far?"

"I suppose," I said, squirming slightly. The thought just occurred to me that I had less than a half hour left to pass the test and save Elizabeth's life, and here I was frittering away my time in a conversation about beauty. How much time did I have left? Ten or fifteen minutes tops?

"Don't worry about the time," he said, apparently reading my mind. "There is always time when you are with me."

"I'll try," I said. "For a mere mortal, it's kind of difficult when you consider my wife's situation."

"I understand," he said. "Now let us get back to the topic. What we have established is that certain types of beauty are universally recognized and are in the eyes of all beholders. Beauty only seems to be in the eye of the beholder for some because of the influence of prejudices and preconceived notions. Sometimes that which is different is seen as unacceptable at first, but if there is true beauty, it is only a matter of time before it is recognized."

"I can see that may be true," I said, still unable to shake my concern over the time. "Where are we going with this?"

"This relates to my face which you desire to see. It is different from that of the standard human and some would be repelled by it because it is different, but not because of a lack of beauty. My race in a previous system passed through the form you possess and moved on to one of more rarified beauty and function, just as you eventually will. All those like me see this final form as possessing the greatest beauty; it is the one we settle on when relating to each other in form."

I tried to put Elizabeth's situation out of my mind. I realized that my only chance of success at this point was to put myself in the hands of this incredible being whom many in the past have called God. "So, will you reveal your true face to me?"

"If you have the courage to look and the faith to see."

I looked again at the crystals on the arm of my chair. They were different than the ones I used last time. Each one on my left and right side looked like a half of a crystal ball about six inches in diameter. They also reminded me a bit of a fancy computer mouse, but larger, sort of like a track ball.

"Focus," he said. "Keep your hands on the crystals."

I grabbed the crystals and focused my attention. It then seemed as if the crystals stimulated my inner perception in a way I had never felt before. The closest I can come to describing it is to say that I suddenly felt as if I was an all-powerful being, almost as if I were one with the Ancient of Days himself. It seemed that all I had to do was to think a thing and it would happen. What should I then think after experiencing such a feeling?

This was my chance to see his face, I thought. This would be an opportunity that may not come again. I then focused this all-powerful energy on seeing the face of this god-like being, or perhaps I should say God being.

Before me on the great chair, or throne, sat a being that looked something like a young Jesus; beautiful; he had a vibrant face with long flowing light brown hair and amazing intelligent deep-blue eyes. I thought this seemed to project the image of the perfect man as I had previously conceived it, but I was wrong. The image changed to something totally unexpected.

As I looked at the features forming in front of me a strange mixture of thoughts danced in my mind. The memory returned of his words telling me of the image his kind settle on when relating to each other in form. My eyes rested upon this final form of human evolution. He was a majestic figure or royal countenance wearing a beautiful robe, covered by a great cape that seemed to symbolize his authority. I focused on the color of his attire and saw a rainbow of colors, giving me the impression that the idea of the coat of many colors came from him. My thoughts seemed to select the final color, as I was more comfortable with a single one. For some reason I picked a deep violet, as it seemed to offset his light-skinned countenance.

Because of his warning to me about his different looks, I was prepared (as much as one could be in that situation) for most anything from a serpent of some kind to a monstrous-looking figure. Even so, nothing in my imagination prepared me for what I saw.

When I looked at the figure in front of me I saw something I had not imagined nor was I prepared to see. This had nothing to do with his basic form, as it was quite human. In fact, if I had to describe it, I would have to say he had the physical image of a perfect man. The only thing really unusual about him was his face, and I immediately saw why he hid it from Moses, so a description would not appear in the scriptures.

I thought about his comments on beauty as I gazed upon his face having, not two, but one great eye in the center of the forehead! This was the only visible feature that set him apart from the features of a regular human.

My reaction to this sight was much different than I would have previously guessed it would be. The reason was that any previous image I had seen of a one-eyed person, or Cyclops, was portrayed as abnormal and subhuman in beauty, but this being was different. Instead of being abhorred by the difference, I found myself captivated by it. It's difficult to describe, but his face was put together in such a way that the eye became a royal diadem, a thing of great beauty, like the jewel in the lotus.

What's more, I felt the exact opposite of the effect I felt when facing a dark brother. When looking at one of them, my energy was sapped as if attacked by a vampire, but when gazing upon this being, I felt a powerful radiating energy from his eye that fed me spiritually in a way I had never before imagined. In fact, the radiation was so powerful, I found I could only look at the eye directly for a few seconds at a time. Looking at him was like staring at the noonday radiating spiritual sun, whereas looking at a dark brother was like being sucked into a black hole.

"Have you adjusted to my form?" he asked.

I somehow sensed he knew what I was feeling, but was seeking to carry on a conversation on my level. "Yes, I think so," I said. "I am finding myself being attracted to your face rather than repelled by it."

"I would hope so," he said. "This is the form toward which the whole human race is evolving. When their two eyes become single to the glory of God, and see in unity rather than duality, their form shall change to correspond to their thought. Have you not noticed that the scriptures of the world usually speak of the eye of God and not the eyes of God?"

I quickly reflected over all I had read in connection with God and eyes, "It does seem that the word eye is usually singular in relation to God."

"And the all-seeing single eye caps the city of the New Jerusalem, and is even represented on the back of your dollar bill, is it not?"

"Yes, this symbol is almost universal, yet none seem to suspect that the form of God has one all-seeing eye. It is amazing that none have considered this."

"Jesus considered it and had the single eye in mind when he said, *The light of the body is the eye: if therefore thine eye be single, thy whole body shall be full of light.* (Matt 6:22) Here he was subtly teaching the principle of true vision that leads humanity to their final evolution. The dual-seeing with two eyes must be transmuted to single vision with a single eye to enable the seeker to be filled with light. This can be accomplished with the form you presently have through a concentrated focus of your vision on the purpose of God."

I took a couple seconds to take this in and then asked the question paramount in my mind, "Are you God?"

He smiled, adjusted himself slightly in his chair, and said, "Many have called me, as well as some of my companions, God, or Gods, because we are perceived as all-powerful by them. In truth, God is One and is the One Great Life that permeates the universe of which I am merely a part. I am only God in so far as I am a part of that One Life and see through Its consciousness. Your mouth is not the totality of that which is you, yet it can say, *I am Joseph*, because it identifies with the whole person."

"Who are these companions of whom you speak?"

"There are six others of my race who work with me permanently on the earth. We have all passed through normal human existence many millions of years ago and now seek to serve the lesser lives so that we, in turn, may be assisted by those higher than ourselves. Such is the law. My associates have often been called archangels when they have appeared to humans."

"So do they also have single eyes?"

"Yes," he said, "but when they appear to humans they use a form that is acceptable to them."

"So are there any females in your inner group?"

"And what makes you think I am not a female?" he asked.

His question somewhat shocked me. I had assumed he was a male, but now I took a second look. His hair was long like a female's and he had no beard. In fact, his face was very smooth and youthful with skin any female would kill for. He had no breasts that I could see, but his features were very refined. On the other hand, his frame was large, almost majestic, and exuded a sense of power and sublime confidence that seemed to spell male for me. Finally, I analyzed his voice. It was not deep like a male, but neither was it high enough to definitely belong to a female.

Finally, I uttered, "I guess I just assumed you were a male."

"And now you have taken a second look, what you do believe?"

"I do not know. At this point nothing would surprise me."

"I wouldn't be so sure," he said, standing up. "Open your vision."

I wasn't sure what I was supposed to do but did my best to see whatever was in front of me. He was right. There were some surprises left. Suddenly he split in two, and two entities stood before me, one a definite male and the other a female. They both appeared as beautiful humans with two eyes each.

"So, which sex am I?" they both spoke simultaneously.

"Am I to understand you are male and female in one body?"

"Yes and no," they said. "We can be in the body, out of the body, or manifest other bodies depending on the need."

Suddenly the two united and the original entity stood before me.

I was very curious and had to ask, "So, are you neither male nor female in the body I now see?"

"The final body of human evolution is the divine hermaphrodite, a balance of male and female energies."

"So how do you reproduce with such a body?"

"Those who occupy such bodies create new form by the power of thought interplaying between the male and female energies."

"Can you give me more light on the fact that you are composed of both a male and female entity?"

"I am much more than that," he said. "Pay attention and learn a great secret."

I watched with great interest, wondering if he could top the last performance. I saw two images projected from him until three hermaphrodites, each having one eye, stood before me. Next, the two new entities projected from themselves two entities each and four additional entities came to view, making a total of seven if we include the Ancient of Days.

The original entity again spoke, "We are the seven eyes of the earth, representatives of the Seven Spirits before the throne."

"I don't understand," I said. "Did all seven of you exist within the one body?"

"Seven?" he said. "Look and learn."

Suddenly, the six new entities each projected twenty-four entities each making a total of one hundred forty-four new human shapes, which appeared before me. These, however, had the image of a normal human having two eyes each.

If this was not impressive enough, what happened next really got my attention. Each of the one hundred forty-four entities began to multiply before my eyes until they became too numerous for the room we were in. Even so, this expansion created no problem, as the room expanded to accommodate their presence. When the multiplication ended there were many thousands of entities before me.

"Tell me the number you see before you," said the ancient one.

"There's more than I can count," I thought to myself, but then it occurred to me that he wouldn't ask a question that I could not answer. After a few seconds a number came to me.

"Could the number be 144,000?" I asked.

"Very good," he said. "From me came my six associates. From the six came one hundred forty-four and from the one hundred forty-four came an additional thousand each, making 144,000, plus, of course, the original seven. Contemplate the meaning and speak it to me."

This guy's worse than John, I thought to myself. These advanced beings really don't want to just hand out knowledge to a guy but seem to want us to earn it.

I gathered my thoughts and responded, "The female counterpart, the six and then the 144,000 all seem to come from you. Could it be that you all dwell in one body?"

"Yes and no," he said.

Where have I heard that before? I asked myself. Then I sensed he was reading my mind as he smiled and replied, "What is the *yes* and what is the *no*?"

"I am honored that you would think I am intelligent enough to solve this mystery. Let me see. I would say the answer is yes in the fact that you are in touch with all of these entities as if they all dwelt in one body."

Then I paused a moment in thought, "And the *no*," he asked?

"They must not be confined to your body. It seems like this would be way too restrictive, and from what I have learned, the higher you get on the ladder, the fewer restrictions. I think I am just seeing the bare bones details here. Can you elaborate for me?"

Suddenly, all the entities disappeared and only the Ancient One stood before me. "Your thoughts take you in the right direction," he said. He paused a moment and added, "You do recall John teaching you about the Oneness Principle?"

"Yes, of course."

"And since learning of it and becoming aware of its workings, you have been able to use it to a degree, have you not?"

"Yes, I suppose."

"And when you tune into the Oneness Principle do you not feel the presence of your group?"

"I do seem to feel a life energy."

"And does the term *group mind* seem to apply to what you feel?"

"Yes, that does describe what I feel. I believe John called it a spiritual internet."

"And how many do you suppose are in this spiritual internet?"

"A lot, I imagine. Do I also have a 144,000?"

"That and more," he said. "Concerning my group, you saw an inner seven and an additional 144,000. These only represent inhabitants and direct associates of Shamballa. My entire group mind for this planet even includes the lowly sparrow as it may soar in the sky or fall to the ground. Those you saw spring from my body are one with me as much as they would be if they were in my body with me. On the other hand, they are free from the limitation of my body as you or any other being is."

"So when I saw the 144,000, did I really see them or was it an illusion?"

"What you saw was real enough," he smiled. "Each of them was doing their own particular job or skill when I called them. Each felt a tug on their consciousness and shared the energy necessary to manifest here. It took the full attention of none of them, so each was able to continue with his normal activities. You may not manifest yourself on demand, but others in your group have drawn from your consciousness and thought. When you feel in touch with the Universal Mind through the Oneness Principle, you will notice this from time to time. If you do some reflection, you should be able to recall some instances where you were used. This is all in accordance with universal law. You give in equal amount as you receive through the Oneness Principle."

"I think I can identify with what you say," I said. "Now that I realize I give and receive through the group mind, I'll pay more attention." I paused a moment as a curious memory came to mind and changed the subject. "When I came here I saw myself crossing the Atlantic and headed somewhere in the East. Legend has it that Shamballa is located in the Gobi desert in Mongolia, but this city seems to be an island in the midst of a great body of water. Where is this place?"

"The legends are correct," he said, "but you are not in the dense physical at present, but in your etheric body. This entire city, including the sea upon which it floats, is created from etheric matter; and in this location the form is much different than the material counterpart."

"You say the city floats. Does this mean it is not built on an island, but the water itself?"

"Indeed," he said. "All form in Shamballa has layers of meaning behind it. Water is ever a symbol of emotion, and air, the mind. To construct form upon the waters and live upon them in the air symbolizes the mastery of all that is astral and the downward pull of the emotional world. The problems of the emotional world and its counterparts extend much further upwards than is realized, even by the greatest of the teachers of the earth. After one has attained one level of mastery, then another will present itself. Shamballa upon the waters is ever a symbol of the mastery of emotion by pure reason and spirit. One day soon the lights of the earth will similarly gather and build a floating city upon the great ocean, which shall symbolize a degree of mastery."

"That ought to be interesting," I replied. "If I felt comfortable with the time factor, it would be great to take a tour of this place and mingle with the inhabitants, but I feel pressed to move forward with my test. Do I still have time to complete it?"

"Have faith, my friend. I have time under my control. Look into my all-seeing eye."

I had been avoiding direct eye contact because the radiance was so powerful but I attempted to look straight on. The energy was so overwhelming, I had to look away.

"If you wish to pass the test and save your wife, you must formulate what you want to see and look me in the eye. The energy is powerful, but you will adapt."

If it hadn't been for my thought of Elizabeth's situation and sensing her faith in me, I do not think I would have had the courage to look. The radiation from this being made me feel like I was about to dissolve body and spirit. Even so, I bit my upper lip and looked straight into his eye while internally expressing a desire to see and commune with the highest and lowest in the physical universe.

Suddenly, the strangest thing happened. It felt as if my body dissolved and my consciousness was inside of the body of the Ancient of Days. I could see through his all-seeing eye. I became aware that I could see anything I wanted. I could look forward and backward in time and space. Then, in one instant, I saw every human being upon the earth and sensed their hopes and dreams as well as their fears and sorrows. I didn't take much detail of what I saw back to regular consciousness except that Elizabeth was still alive and time had not yet run out. Somehow, time had slowed, allowing me to still work on the test.

"What do I do now?" I thought.

"Finish your test," came the reply. I will be with you and give you the guidance you need."

Even though time had slowed I figured I had better not waste any and thought back, "I want to see the toothpick back in my room."

Instantly, I saw my room and the toothpick that was still taped on the ceiling. I needed to see the atoms within the toothpick. How to proceed was the question? I tried seeing myself shrinking down in size and entering into the toothpick. This seemed to work, and as I shrunk, I saw myself rise to the ceiling, approaching the toothpick that now seemed as large as a giant beam. The toothpick increased in size to the extent that I saw the surface was far from smooth. There were many strands of fiber that became larger as I approached the expanding alien surface. This was exciting and scary at the same time as I sent a thought to the Ancient of Days, "Are you still with me?"

"I am here. Keep proceeding as you will."

We shrank until I could see molecules combined in strange shapes and moved into the space between them. Suddenly, it seemed very dark. Apparently we were in a space that regular light did not reach. "It's dark," I exclaimed. What are we to do?"

"The eye is all-seeing and the light is everywhere. Will yourself to see."

I attempted to follow his instruction, and soon discovered that I could will myself to see through some type of universal light that was more refined than regular light. When I could see, I realized we were quickly retreating into the microcosmically small. I saw molecules around me the size of beach balls, but they were vibrating so quickly I couldn't make out their form. "Everything's vibrating so quickly they are becoming a blur," I thought.

"You can slow down time by altering your consciousness," was the reply.

What the heck, I thought to myself. I seem to be able to do anything I will to do in the presence of this being. I'll give it a try.

I experimented with both altering my consciousness and thinking of the speed of the molecules slowing down. After what seemed like a moment, I started getting results. What I saw was a world more fascinating than the Hubble pictures of outer space. It indeed looked as if I was exploring foreign worlds. There were several different types of particles, but I assumed the main one in view were molecules composed of carbon, hydrogen and oxygen, the main ingredients of wood. The atoms before me seemed to be suspended like planets in space, forming a constellation that looked a little like a horse. The atoms that were bonded to each other were merged in varying degrees and some looked a little like cells splitting in two.

Even though time had slowed down, the speed of the electrons circling around the atoms was so fast that they gave the appearance of clouds circling around a nucleus. I could see that if I were to commune with the lowest, which would include the particles within the atoms, time would have to be slowed down much more than was now the case. I remembered reading that the speed of an electron circling around an atom is close to the speed of light, so time would indeed have to be slowed down beyond the imagination to truly explore the atom.

I sent out the thought to my godly companion, "Can we slow time and go small enough to explore the atom?"

"Nothing is stopping you," came the reply, "as long as you are ready to see mysteries never before revealed to mortal man."

His words struck me with excitement that bordered on a strange fear that I had to override. I had always felt there were great mysteries within the atom, and now I was about to discover some of them.

CHAPTER EIGHTEEN
Microcosmic Universes

Thanks to the power of the Ancient of Days all-seeing eye, it was relatively easy to use the power of thought to alter time, space and motion. I increased the size of one of the carbon atoms and reduced the flow of time several times. My attention was taken up by a single atom, larger than a beach ball, but with the texture of a circular cloud. The electrons were circulating with such speed they were nothing but a gauzy blur. I needed to slow time tremendously to perceive the electrons individually. As I concentrated, I began to appreciate the tremendous speed at which the particles within the atom moved. I kept slowing time and nothing seemed to change, it was still blurry. Finally, the form of the atom began to materialize.

The electrons did not circle the nucleus in perfect spherical order as depicted in my high school science books. Instead, they circulated in complex spiral formations that took them around the nucleus all right, but in such a way that each electron covered a tremendous amount of space before they returned to their point of origin. These irregular orbits by the various electrons created lines, or strands of force, that had their own space and did not infringe on the space of other orbits. Overall, these various orbits created the appearance of threads that wove an object with a form a little like a human heart standing on its end. There seemed to be a vortex opening at the top, as if taking in an inflow of force and then releasing it through the bottom. As I slowed time even more, I was amazed that the atom seemed to be pulsating, or beating, like a heart.

Watching the pulsing atom, it dawned on me that I was watching a living thing. I had previously heard that life is everywhere, even in the atoms. Now, seeing one come alive before my eyes, it was another matter; it lifted the truth from platitude to living experience for me.

"Communicate with this entity," conveyed the silent voice of my guide, the Ancient of Days.

"And how do I do that?"

"Just make the attempt and the knowledge will come."

"Okay," I thought. Even though I did not know what I was doing, I began to sense the consciousness of the atom. I credited my discovery to the heightened consciousness of my companion.

Interplay of communication was achieved after what seemed like several moments. Of course, this did not take place in words, but lightening fast impressions that I will attempt to verbalize.

"You have awakened me from a long slumber. Why?"

"I want to communicate with you."

"Why?"

"To know more about you. Why do you say you have been slumbering? You looked so alive."

"I am alive," it said, "but asleep to this world and awakening on others."

"What do you mean awakening on others?"

"I finished my individual evolution many eons ago. Today my internal workings are set and do not require my attention. Now I join my consciousness with others and reach out to identify with higher form and a different dimension of time. I join and join and join until I find the self-conscious beings in the upper world."

"I believe I would be one of those self-conscious beings of the upper world," I replied ironically.

The atom shook and I sensed a great thrill surged through its being. "How could it be that one so high could visit one so lowly?"

"Maybe it's because one much higher than myself is assisting me" I said, humbled by his adoration.

"And how did you pick me?"

"You were the one that was before us as we made our descent."

"It's difficult to believe that random selection brought us together. Can you let me see through your eyes into your world so I can know for sure?"

"It's actually one eye," I said. "I am using an all-seeing eye of a great Master of the upper world."

"May I use the eye?" it said, "I have dreamed for untold ages of obtaining a view of your world."

My thoughts went to my companion. "Can we honor his request?"

"It is done," was the swift reply.

Immediately, I became aware of what was shown to the atom. It saw my life as well as images of many people from every race going about their normal activities. Then we saw the earth and all the various life forms upon it. This vision was finished off by a view from space with the sun and the stars in the background.

"I am most grateful," said the atom. "I see the evolution of the upper world, especially humanity, is still in its infancy unlike the universe within me."

"What do you mean by a *universe within* yourself?" I asked.

"I see you came here to explore and communicate. You will find out soon."

"Is it all right for us to enter your space and see your universe?"

"I would be honored, and am especially honored at the presence of He who is with you."

"The feeling is mutual," I said.

"When the One Great Life unifies your universe, we will meet again. In the mean time, I will share the vision you have given me with others of my kind."

I sensed it was time to move forward and slowed down time even more than previously. I found I had to slow it several times before the particles of the atom became visible and ceased being a blur of fast moving lines of force. As time slowed, the form of the atom disappeared and all that seemed to remain were several points in space circling around what appeared to be a central sun.

"I assume these points are electrons," I said, grateful I had paid attention in science.

"Yes," was the patient reply.

"I want to take a closer look," I said, my curiosity heightening at every change we experienced.

We moved toward one of the points until it became as large

as a basketball moving through space. I was amazed to see that it too was pulsating, but in a different way from the atom. Instead of beating like a heart, the electron seemed to move in and out of existence.

"What is happening here?" I asked dumbfounded.

The answer came, "Unlike the macrocosmic world where we reside, this microcosmic world has reached relative perfection. The lives here have completed their evolution and have reached such balance between spirit and matter that they are neither spirit nor matter but live in both worlds simultaneously."

Then I noticed another phenomenon as time slowed. After the electron went out of existence, or into the world of pure spirit, it left an effect that I sensed. The space it occupied did not seem empty when it departed, but appeared to be composed of some type of fabric which closed in on the space where the electron once was, something like water closing in to fill a hole. Then, when the electron returned, it seemed to push the waters of space back again.

This sight set my mind whirling with previous things I had read as I thought, "They say scientists can't determine whether the electron is a particle or a wave. Perhaps this solves the mystery. We see here that half the time it is a particle, and the other half, only a wave exists."

"You see correctly," concurred the Ancient of Days.

"And where is the nucleus?" I asked, looking around.

"In the distance."

I shifted my gaze and was surprised at how far away it was. It appeared as distant as did Venus in the morning sky. Logically the next step was to explore this center of the atom. I then felt my companion's approving thoughts to move ahead.

Using the power of thought we moved toward the nucleus until it loomed large before us. The first thing that caught my attention was what appeared to be a cloud of dust particles circling the nucleus. The particles seemed infinitesimally small and I only seemed aware of them because of a slight disturbance of space created by their presence. "What are these?" I asked.

"The tiny points are archetypal atoms waiting to be born. There are approximately fourteen billion of them in each atom."

"And when will they be born?" I queried, amazed at all I was learning.

"A small number will evolve into greater particles in this universe, but it will take a span of the lives of many universes before they all are born as individual atoms. This universe had a beginning and will have an end, but in the end it will leave a seed that will give birth to a new and expanded universe. In the new universe several of these archetypal atoms will become complete atoms."

"Only a handful of fourteen billion will become atoms in the next universe. Wow! It will take a long time and many universes for them all to come forth."

"Indeed," he said, 'but there are two things you need to know. The number will be greater as future universes materialize, but, even the birth of two atoms out of every atom, plus the original will have the effect of the next universe being triple the size and density of this one."

It boggled my mind to think about. "This is amazing," I said. "The final universe will be so immense I cannot fathom it; and yet, the one we are in now defies the imagination." I shook my head in disbelief as the magnitude of it all was dawning on my consciousness.

"It is humbling to think about," he expounded, "even for me. There is one more thing to add to your contemplation. There is a first and a last in every round of creation, but there is no beginning and no end to the rounds of creation itself. Creation has always been and will always be. Because creation is ever expanding, there is no end to the possibilities and therefore opportunities."

I had to stop thinking about this as it was about to make my head ache—wherever my head was. I looked through the cloud of particles toward the nucleus. I remembered that a carbon atom had six protons and six neutrons and was interested in seeing the difference between the two.

As I zoomed in I saw the twelve particles suspended as if they were planets, or perhaps suns, in space. United they gave off a great central light, but, because of the enormous slowing down of time, we were able to look upon them as one would look upon planetary bodies. Gazing, I saw a great difference between the protons and neutrons.

The protons were similar to electrons in that they passed in and out of existence. One split second I was wondering what the difference between the two was and the next second the answer came into my mind. "When the electron was in existence its matching proton was out of existence as far as this plane is concerned. Then, when the proton was in existence, the corresponding electron was gone, leaving only a wave. Between each electron and its matching proton, the atom always seemed to be in existence. In real time, the oscillation was so fast that no instrument could detect that the atom is out of existence half the time."

I saw that the neutron was different—it did not seem to oscillate in and out of existence—its form was always in existence. As I contemplated it, the Ancient of Days gave me the answer, "The outer shell of the neutron is composed of two substances. Both go in and out of existence, but at separate harmonious times, always leaving a part of itself on this plane. The two substances balance each other off, causing the neutron to have a neutral charge."

"This is amazing knowledge," I said, feeling lightheaded. "Can we explore even further?"

"Yes, but you will only be allowed to see the basics," he warned. Anything more would be an overload for you at this time. Proceed."

I willed us toward one of the protons and found I had to slow time even more to penetrate it. As it became larger than a house I could see that its surface was not solid, but created by some type of magnetic force that interplayed with the very fabric of space. As we penetrated this force towards the center, we had to pass through six layers before we surfaced in what appeared to be empty space. I eagerly looked toward the next revelation. Peering into the space before me I saw a point of substance in the far distance. I guessed that this point must be where quarks reside, but was amazed at how small they were in relation to the proton as a whole.

As we moved toward the center, the mass expanded until its form came to view. I saw six spheres that looked like planets that formed two triangles, giving the appearance of a grand Star of David. I assumed these were the three quarks and three leptons as taught by physicists. These particles also passed in and out of existence, but in a different sequence than the electrons and protons. Instead of a pair of particles synchronizing with each other there were two sets of three. Within each triangle, individual particles were in the physical one third of the time. Since there were three for each triangle one was always in form, and, since the sequence was so fast in real time, all would seem as if it were solid. In addition, the particles of the two triads of quarks and leptons moved in and out of existence synchronously with each other. The rhythm was beautiful to watch, as if it were a choreographed dance.

This difference in the sequence of manifestation of the quarks must account for them each having a lesser charge than the greater particles.

"I notice that the number six has manifested twice here," I said. "We passed through six layers of energy and then came to six particles. Is this the universe of six spoken of by John?"

"It is," agreed my guide. "At the beginning of each universe, creation starts with the small and then proceeds to the great. The universe in which we live is founded upon the number seven, beginning with the seven electron shells of the atom stretching to the universe of galaxies. The atoms can naturally achieve a maximum of seven electron layers, which foundation manifests as the number seven throughout all greater creation. We see it in the seven colors, the seven basic notes, the seven rays, the seven planes and so forth. Before the greater universe based on seven existed, the mind of God manifested in this lesser universe founded upon the number six."

"Does the Big Bang enter into this somehow?" I asked, trying to fit my old knowledge in with the new.

"Your scientists say that this microcosmic universe we see about us, including the creation of the first atoms, all happened within one second of time within the Big Bang. They are correct in the fact that the creation of the micro universes you are about to visit happened in a very short period of time measured by regular human consciousness. What they do not realize, is in that first instant, many eons passed in the consciousness of the lives that existed there and guided form in its creation."

"You know, I've always wondered if there were not tiny worlds within the atom occupied by tiny people, perhaps living many lifetimes in the snap of a finger. Is there anything to this?"

"Wherever there is form, there is life within the form," he said, "but it has not yet been revealed how life manifests within the lower worlds. You are right and wrong about the idea of an eternity passing within the atom within the snap of a finger. The planet earth rotates within twenty-four hours of time, but an atom rotates billions of times in a second. For the consciousness of the atom, a billionth of a second seems longer than a whole day. However, where you and others err is that in the present, time is no longer consciously registered by the atom or the lives within it. In that first instant of creation time was consciously registered and the tiny lives spent what was an eternity to them achieving perfection. When relative perfection was achieved, the lives within merged into higher form and are now seeking to share consciousness within our world. Remember when the atom told you it was awakened from a long sleep?"

"Yes."

"All lives within the atomic world are now asleep, and their work is now accomplished as if on an automatic pilot, or like a computer program. Even so, none of them cease to exist. Instead, they have left their measurement of time behind and are adjusting their consciousness to time as it manifests in the greater universe."

"Will this apply to mankind also?" I asked. "Will we reach a time of perfection where we will seek to identify with greater lives?"

"Yes and you will learn more about this shortly. What I want you to remember at this time is that these smaller worlds have life, but the life is asleep to these tiny worlds that their consciousness has left behind. Their consciousness has moved upwards, seeking expansion. Even so, they can be awakened, as has happened with the atom. In a future universe they will awaken again to this plane of existence and build again better than they had earlier."

"Let me see if I understand this correctly," I said. "In a second of our time, billions of years of time would technically pass within an atom, but because they are asleep to their own plane, the lives there do not consciously live through all that time."

"Correct," he agreed.

"But these smaller lives are seeking consciousness in our greater universe and therefore are governed by our reckoning of time."

"Very good. As they emerge in awareness of the greater universe, this is the case."

"But when they were going through the creation and perfection of their universe, they passed through many billions of years to them in what would have been less than a second to us or the first second of the Big Bang?"

"Correct again."

"This is stimulating knowledge," I exulted. "If we go smaller we'll see things that no scientist I know has even thought about. Is there much more?"

"Indeed, we will go much smaller," he said. "Smaller than any scientist has dared to dream."

I sensed it was time to journey on and took a look at one of the quarks blinking in and out of existence. I proceeded toward it, decreasing in size again.

"The universe within the quark is on a higher rate of vibration and you need to slow time even more. Then you must enter the quark when it is in form."

As we proceeded, the blinking of the quark slowed until it seemed to stop and appeared as a large, somewhat elliptical, ball of fire. This made me a little nervous, but my host reassured me and we continued into the fire. We either became smaller or the quark larger, whichever way one wants to put it, and it wasn't long before the tiny quark seemed as big as an entire universe. Soon, the fire was no fire, but dots that looked like the sky at night.

"Shall we move toward one of the points?" I asked.

"Proceed."

In no time the dot I picked out became much larger. As we passed by many of them, I noticed they seemed to be loosely grouped in formations of six. Then, as the dot I picked became large, I was able to discern its appearance as if it were six galaxy-type forms grouped together in the form of a hexagon, with some type of black hole or vortex in the center.

"You mentioned earlier about this being the universe of six." I said. "Do these groupings of six I keep seeing have something to do with it?"

"They have everything to do with it," was the emphatic reply. "Each universe is founded upon a number. When all possibilities have been materialized around this number, and the intelligence within the number brings the elements in that universe into maximum order, a higher universe is created. Before the beginning of the current universe, all possibilities in this universe were exhausted and the form perfected."

"I notice that this universe seems much more organized and structured than our own. Will our universe evolve in this same direction?"

"Yes, it will, except it shall organize around the number seven, just as this one is organized around the number six. As you can guess, the possibilities around the greater number seven are much more than six, and thus the time involved will last much longer. As I said, the number seven manifests already in color, sound and the rays, but this is just the beginning. The greater universe has a long way to go, and its end will produce a beauty that is beyond present imagination."

"Are these six formations we see before us galaxies in this universe?"

"They correspond to our galaxies, but the matter in them is founded on the number six and they gather in groups of six."

"This is amazing," I said. "To think that quarks are billions of times smaller than the head of a pin; and yet, in this miniature world there are many galaxies."

"Yes it is," said my guide. "Even though it is considered that I am the greatest upon the planet earth, I never cease to marvel at the vastness of creation."

His answer made me realize that in many ways he was just like me, but much further ahead upon the Path. In an odd way this was comforting.

The galaxy I was eyeing expanded, and I noticed it was much more structured than pictures I have seen of galaxies in our universe. Instead of a great spiral, this galaxy had a bright center surrounded by six concentric rings. The closest thing I have seen that resembles it is the Sombrero Galaxy, named after the Sombrero hat, but this one had more definition than any previous galaxy I had seen.

"There's that number six again," I said, eyeing the six rings. "Does everything gravitate around the number six here?"

"Six is the foundation number of this universe, and since it has reached the peak of its evolution, it manifests this number and multiples thereof wherever the foundations of creation occur. In other circumstances, you will see all the other numbers appear just as in the greater universe. As our greater universe moves toward perfection, we will see more manifestations of the number seven, which is our foundation number."

"Fascinating," I thought while we moved toward the dots that composed the rings. As they became larger they gained the appearance of stars, but as we drew closer they also became as bright as stars. Then I noticed the stars here, instead of being in a random layout as they appear at night from earth, were in an order that was definitely designed by some intelligence. They were connected in strands like some pictures of molecules I've seen in chemistry books. Some of the forms were very complex while others were simple hexagons and pentagons.

As soon as I expressed an internal desire to visit individual solar systems in this tiny quark galaxy, I found myself passing through three star systems. One of them had six major planets and six minor ones, but the other two had a larger overall number, but still six major planets. The suns here were bright but they did not emit a scorching heat. The planets appeared circular, but clear as crystal. The phrase "sea of glass" from the Book of Revelation came to my mind.

"What kind of inhabitants could live on such a crystalline surface?" I asked.

"The surface is different than you think," he said. "Take a look."

We moved toward the surface of one of the planets and touched down in our consciousness. To my amazement the surface was perfectly smooth. "There's no one here," I thought.

"There are many billions," was the rejoinder. "Go downward."

I immediately felt myself sinking in what seemed to be a gelatin material. I sensed that the planet itself was alive and a composite of billions of lives joined together in molecular and cellular formations. "Can I communicate with them?" I asked.

"They are asleep, just like the atom," he said. "There is no need to awaken them at the moment."

"This seems to be a strange way to live," I marveled.

"Eons ago, when the attention of God was on creating this universe, these also had physical bodies, but of a crystalline nature. They fulfilled the measure of their creation and united for a great sleep and journey into greater consciousness. They retain their individual identity, yet have united with the atom with whom you have already communicated. Together, they are striving to join with the consciousness of the life in our greater universe. Think on this thought when you return to your body and know that the very atoms and even tiny lives within you are attempting to share your consciousness. You are a god to many universes within."

"I've vaguely thought of this idea, but now the meaning comes alive like it never has previously. It is amazing to consider that we are now on a planet, in a galaxy, that is a part of a quark, all within one individual atom. It's really overwhelming. Where do we go now?"

"There's much more," he said, "if you wish to go smaller."

As I concentrated on going smaller, we quickly were reduced until we passed by the fibers, cells and then the molecules of this world. They seemed complex and perfect in functioning, but not quite as complex as the orders I saw in the greater universe. Finally, we arrived at the atoms of the next universe, and again we had to slow time much further to take a look. "Time must be going incredibly slow." I said.

"Much slower than your scientists have ever contemplated," he said. "Time is caused by a conscious registration of motion. Thus, time is altered by either changing our consciousness so motion is registered in different increments, or by altering the motion of all things before the consciousness. We are doing the former, altering our consciousness to register motion unfathomable to the upper world."

"Fascinating," I said lamely not knowing how to express what I was going through. Then I looked toward the atoms and saw they were similar to the atoms of our universe, but more circular and less heart-shaped.

"The protons and quarks were the upper end of the universe of sixes; and now you are seeing the atoms of this universe, also based on this number. These atoms have a maximum of six electron shells instead of seven, as in our universe. To find the next universe downwards, we must go smaller into the universe founded upon the number five."

I felt like I could stay for an unlimited time in any of our stops, but moved forward in our journey. As one of the atoms loomed before us, I found we had to slow time even more. As before, the electrons appeared to be blinking in and out of existence, but with a different sequence as our universe. The nucleus seemed far away again, but we approached it and soon one of the particles filled half the space before us. Time slowed even more, and I was able to see five particles forming a pentagon.

"This arrangement of five is a lower correspondence to the quarks," I was told. "This is the beginning of the universe of five. Explore as you did earlier."

We sped toward one of the particles, and as it grew we plunged in. Again, we saw what appeared to be an infinite number of particles, and as we approached, each particle turned out to be a galaxy teeming with form. We approached one of these galaxy figures and saw that it again had a highly-defined structure. At the center appeared to be a ball of fire with five arms extending to create five concentric rings, making the whole look a little like a ringed body like Saturn.

As we moved closer, the fiery rings turned into dots and the dots into stars, then one of the stars into a sun. This sun had five major planets and seven minor ones. We lit on the surface of one of the planets and to my surprise it had the texture of water. Then we went smaller and viewed all types of angular forms until we came to wide variety of molecules. Again, the number five dominated as many were composed of five, twenty-five and 125 atoms, but there were other combinations also.

I selected an atom to visit and found I had to again slow time to see anything but a whirling object. As the form came to view, it looked a little like a wheel composed of five elliptical rings, creating ten protrusions on the surface. When time ran faster, the atom looked like a perfect ball; when slowed it revealed the ten protrusions from the five orbits.

"These atoms are the foundations of the universe of five," said my guide. "We must go much smaller to find the particle of your quest, with which you can commune, and, in doing so; you will discover a great mystery."

I followed the same process as last time and plunged into one of the particles in the nucleus. This revealed four particles in the formation of a square apparently corresponding to quarks again. We compressed again, descended into one of the particles, and again beheld another universe of galaxy formations. Instead of being fairly random like they are in our universe, these were organized in numerous square formations joining into what appeared to be cubes and building blocks which created some interesting molecular-looking formations. In the center of the cubes were three galaxies in triangular formation, circling a larger central galaxy.

I picked out a galaxy and headed toward it. As it magnified, the stars became visible. I picked several to move past and noticed they all had four major planets and eight minor ones, plus numerous smaller bodies. Finally, we lit on one of the major planets. I was surprised to sense that this one had no solid form, but was composed entirely of gaseous substance. I also sensed that there was life here, but it was asleep as they were on the other worlds we visited. Each life here had a swirling ball of gas as its body, and they were all joined together in molecular formations to create the entire body of the planet itself.

"Shall we go even smaller?" I asked.

"That's what we are here for," was the cryptic answer.

We again reduced in size and plunged into one of the gaseous balls. As we shrank even more I noticed the particles here were farther apart than in the greater universes. I picked one and proceeded toward it until we approached a cube of atoms. I picked an atom, magnified it and slowed time immensely and approached. As expected, there were four shells of electrons.

We reduced in size much further and headed into the nucleus. "Are we entering the universe of three this time?" I asked.

"We are," he assured me.

As this universe became larger I saw that the quark-like particles here organized into groups of three in triangular formation. We proceeded to reduce and entered into one of them. As we reduced I was expecting to see galactic formations again, but instead saw something entirely different. Everywhere I looked I saw triangular formations. They seemed to create a great grid against the fabric of space to give form to the great quark that we were within now. In addition to this, there was an innumerable number of interlinking and interlocking triangles of glowing particles of some kind. These seemed to form the substance of the body of the particle where we found ourselves.

"There are no galaxies here," I said, "but only triangles of points of light."

"All life begins with triangles," he explained carefully. "Each of these triangles is the beginning of a new life. You have noticed the points of which they are made. Discover the point and you discover the great mystery behind our beginning."

We then approached one of the triangles and finally a point. The point was much smaller than I supposed, for it emitted a very bright light, which made it seem larger than it was. After much magnification, it finally became large before us. It was so bright that I feared entering it.

"You have nothing to fear," said the Ancient One comfortingly. Only your consciousness is here."

I magnified the particle many times again until it was as large as a planet. Now, instead of a fiery light, it appeared to have a bright white shiny surface. I somehow got the impression that it was like a large bubble. I nervously proceeded toward it, as there seemed to be no more particles with gaps of empty space to sail between. Even so, we moved onward until we touched the surface of this thing. It seemed to be a barrier beyond which we could not pass.

"What do we do now?" I asked.

"You must go through the barrier and commune with the point in the center if you wish to pass your test," he said.

It must be possible then, I thought to myself. I used all the power of my will to force my way through. Nothing happened. The barrier held firm.

"Now what?" I asked.

"It's now up to you. I brought you here to commune with the smallest of creation. This is as far as I can take you. The knowledge is within you to take the last step."

Great, I thought to myself. *Another puzzle. Why can't it ever be easy with these guys? At least I have plenty of time here. I could stay here a trillion years and a second wouldn't even begin to go by on earth.*

On a whim I rose from the surface a long distance and took an accelerating dive headfirst (at least in my consciousness) toward the surface. I hit with what seemed like great force and just bounced off with more force than I struck.

"That wasn't too smart," the Ancient One said amused. "Sometimes I am amazed you have gotten as far as you have in your spiritual journey."

"I can't argue with you there," I laughed. Then a thought came to me. If using force isn't too smart, then maybe the opposite of force is the way to go. If there's something I am to commune with behind this barrier, then maybe I can somehow talk to it now and it can get me through.

We descended again to the surface. I huddled against it, stilled myself, and cast forth the thought: "Awaken from your long sleep and let me enter into your space."

Suddenly, I felt a stirring, as if some consciousness was indeed awakening. I now felt that I was headed the right direction, so I continued repeating over and over, "Awaken, let me enter."

Finally, there came a response: "Why do you call me forth from my dwelling in the greater universe to awaken from my long sleep?"

I wasn't sure how to respond, so I just let it out, "I am instructed by one higher than myself to commune with you and know your mystery."

There seemed to be a long silence, during which I felt the entity probing my mind, sensing the presence of the Ancient of Days with me.

Finally the reply came, "Enter the Holy Space."

CHAPTER NINETEEN
The Great Secret

I felt humbled and honored to be given permission to proceed. Even though this space we were entering was infinitesimally small, I had the sensation of entering a vast universe as we proceeded through the barrier. I also felt that the intelligence residing there was overwhelming, beyond words. This was a great mystery to me, as I thought that as we descended to smaller and smaller particles and life forms, the intelligence would decrease, not increase.

Another odd thing I noticed was the great silence. The reason I call it odd is it seemed as if I had been in great silence for some time. The only thing I heard since entering the microcosm were the thoughts of my companion and this was soundless by normal standards. It never occurred to me, until entering this unusual space, that there are degrees of silence, just as there are degrees of sound or noise. This space we just entered indeed had a silence unlike anything I have ever felt or imagined. It was so awe-inspiring that it took me a while to get used to it.

"This silence, it is amazing. What is the cause of it?" I asked.

The Ancient of Days ignored my question and responded, "I must step aside for now. You must commune with the intelligence here to pass your test."

"Okay," I thought with some delight. Apparently we had reached the smallest particle with which I was supposed to commune. I then directed the question toward this tiny life, which also seemed like a great life.

I waited and the response came. Again, it was not in the form of distinct words, but of high impression that I am now putting into words. "You are correct in surmising that there are degrees of silence, just as there are degrees of sound, "it said. "But from another angle - that which you normally call silence, is not silence. True sound is produced by vibration within the fabric of space. In all the universes and worlds you have visited, there has been such a vibration even though you do not register it in your consciousness. Only where space is not disturbed will you find true silence. When you went through the barrier you entered such space - space that is not disturbed with vibration, space wherein true silence dwells. In meditation deep, the master on your world can catch a glimpse of this silence, but many waves of silence must he cross to arrive at this great silence beyond silence."

"Is this the *peace that passes all understanding*?" I asked.

"It does pass all understanding of the inhabitants of your universe; indeed, just a portion of the peace here is beyond their understanding."

"I would think so," I said. "My consciousness is here and I cannot take it all in. It is like a great magnetic force, and I can only take so much of it out of concern I could never leave. Knowing this peace will make regular silence seem like noise."

"You will adjust upon your return," he said.

As pleasant as the peace was, I found I had to ignore it to a degree to continue my quest. "Is this a part of the universe of three or could it be two or even one?"

"This is the foundation of all greater universes," was the reply. "It is built upon three, two and the one. The one is the point in the center, the three is the barrier you crossed and the two is the holy space in between."

"I was told to commune with the smallest particle, that which is our beginning. Is this our true beginning?"

"There is only a beginning to beginnings, but no true beginning," was the reply. "This is the place you seek."

"Is the point in the center just a point or does it contain something?"

"You may approach far enough to answer your question, but no further."

Again, I concentrated on moving, and eventually the point

increased in size until it became about as large as a beach ball before me. It appeared white and luminous, giving off rainbows of colors. I counted the colors and they were eleven in number. Four of them were colors I had never seen before, neither can I describe them outside of saying they were very bright. These four colors were not like a mixture of primary colors, but I got a sense they were primary colors unknown to the greater universe. "I seem to be able to go no further," I said.

"This is as far as you or any other being from your universe is allowed to proceed. Even the Master who is with you can go no further."

"Why would that be?" I asked, shocked

"Unravel the great mystery and you will know," he replied.

"There's not much to go on."

"Yet you see eleven colors before you, four unknown to your universe. What does that tell you?"

I reflected and replied, "I came from a universe built upon the number seven and descended through the universe of six to five to four to three, and, finally to this foundation Trinity of Three-in-One. Now I see this ball before me having eleven colors. The number eleven seems like an odd encounter at this point and quite a gap from the other foundation numbers."

"Think back to your teacher's words. What follows the universe of seven?"

I was amazed that this tiny entity knew of John's teachings. Perhaps it could read my mind, I thought as I replied, "He told me that after the universe of seven was perfected, we would create a universe founded upon the number eight, then nine, and finishing with twelve in untold ages hence."

"Yes, and after the universe of twelve was perfected, what would happen then?"

I thought back and it came to me, "John said that at that point, another great decision would be made."

"And when do you suppose was the previous great decision?"

"Would it have something to do with the number eleven and this orb I see before me?"

"Would it? Merge with Divine Thought and behold the mystery," my small teacher encouraged

I stared at the orb and did my best to merge with the life I felt around me. As I looked at the orb I also concentrated on picking up something from it. Suddenly, enlightenment came. It was as if I had knowledge poured into my brain or soul. I knew the mystery and knew that I knew.

"Wow! I have it! This knowledge is fantastic, but I must say it completely boggles the mind. Everyone assumes the Creator is great, but they have no idea of the depth of our past or future."

"And you know more than you did before and still it is as nothing," said the entity. "Yet I cannot give you more, for your consciousness cannot handle it."

"You are right," I said. "My cup is full, and I could not contain any more at this time."

"Tell your associate of your revelation. Tell it as you will later record it."

I concentrated until I felt the presence of the Ancient of Days and said, "Let me tell you what I received, for I do wish to hear your comments. A key hint was given by the entity when he said; *There is only a beginning to beginnings, but no beginning*. This orb we see before us is the beginning and the end, the Alpha and Omega. It is the end of a great round of creation and the beginning point for all the greater universes. What we are looking at here is a universe of universes. This universe is much greater than our own, and yet, a part. If we were to slow time even more and enter this universe, we would find new galaxies and worlds all built upon the number eleven. Then, if we were to go smaller, we would find a universe of ten, then nine - clear down to another alpha and omega point like this one."

"And how many colors would you see in that point when you approach it?" he asked.

I reflected and exclaimed, "Ten! There would be ten colors. This is fantastic to think about. Then, if we went smaller, we would go through a universe of ten, then to a universe of nine, to eight, seven, then down to another Alpha and Omega point."

"And the number of creative colors of that point?" the Ancient One asked.

"That would be nine," I said. "But then, if we repeated the process we would reach another Alpha and Omega particle of eight, then seven and so on, until we get to the true Alpha particle."

"And would that be the beginning of creation or the beginning of beginnings?" he asked.

"The beginning of beginnings, I suppose. But," I pondered aloud, "what could be in this beginning point from which a universe of universes are made?"

"I don't know," was the Ancient of Days reply.

"I never thought I could ask you a question to which you did not know the answer. What do you mean you don't know?" I asked somewhat exasperated.

"There are Great Ones whose knowledge is unfathomable when compared to average humanity. Even so, there are many things kept from all lives in our universe, from the greatest to the smallest. We can use the Law of Correspondences and deduce what we would find if we descended into these micro universes. Even though we have not been there, we have assurance of the foundation numbers to the beginning Alpha. What is in that, we can only speculate. We know there are many universes there, but, upon what foundations they are built, we do not know. Some think the beginning Alpha has a foundation of twenty-four, while others think the foundation is something other than a number."

"What could be without a number?"

"We know God is one," he said. "Perhaps the early universes were built out of an essence with no separation, hence no numbers. We can only speculate now, but I will tell you this all will be known when the universe of twelve is perfected. That is so distant in the future; however, that it even puts strain upon me to think about it."

I stared again at the orb in wonderment at how tiny it was in relation to the toothpick it was a part of; yet, at how vast it was, containing trillions of universes. "It looks like a perfect circle, yet the knowledge that was implanted in me tells me it is not. I sense there is something significant here. Can you explain?" I asked, hoping he could answer

"Part of the goal of the Great Decision was to create the perfect circle. The universe of eleven came very close, but is ever so slightly off. The perfect circle will manifest at the end of the Universe of Twelve. The Grand universe manifesting as the perfect circle will bring perfect understanding and recollection. We will then understand all things back to the first Alpha of numbers."

"In the revelation, I was given knowledge so strange that I

cannot comprehend it even though I have it within me. I saw that when the Universe of Eleven was finished, it was alone. There was only one of them, yet each molecule, atom and cell has untold billions of these points within them. How did the Universe of Eleven get from being one to a number so vast that all things are created from it?"

To this my guide replied, "When the Universe of Eleven was finished, its complexity and vastness far exceeded anything that is in our current universe. Yet, if you put enough space between you and a great universe, that universe, vast as it is, becomes only a tiny point. In the beginning, the Universe of Eleven manifested as the mind of God. At this time this was all there was in form existence. Think of the contrast. This tiny point was at one time all there was, but all there was formed a vast universe of universes. This mind of God within this past universe put distance between Itself and the universe, creating a ripple or wavelength in space that caused a wavelength and points to manifest in the fabric of space. Each of these points was an exact duplicate of the Universe of Eleven, caused by an explosive expansion of the mind of God. The numbers of these points were great, so great in number that it is beyond imagination. These created all there was in the greater universe, through gathering together and intelligently organizing."

"This is amazing," I said. "You mean to say at the end of the Universe of Eleven, there was only one of these tiny points floating in space until they multiplied and created all there is including our universe?"

"That's correct, but it did not seem like a tiny point at that time, but a vast universe."

So this must have been the beginning of the Big Bang?

"Correct. The Universe of eleven is the mysterious singularity of scientific theory."

"Why are we not allowed to explore within this Universe of Eleven?" I asked.

"Two reasons," he began. "First, it is even beyond our present comprehension to understand all the complexities of the Universe of Seven wherein you and I dwell. Its evolution has a long way to go, and understanding its end is difficult for the greatest of sages. The Universe of Eight is many times more complex, and the Universe of Eleven is so far removed from our power of understanding that entering it would drive even a Master insane. We are therefore protected from delving any further into the microcosm. That which has been created in the past is created again, but with a twist or slight improvement."

"What's the second reason?"

"The second reason is we would eventually descend into the past universes and arrive at the last Universe of Seven, which would be seen as perfect in our eyes. We would therefore seek to duplicate it, and this would hinder the evolutionary process in the present."

"Why is that?"

"Because the goal is not to exactly duplicate the past, but to improve it. The basic intelligence in our Universe of Seven is greater than in the past microcosm built on seven. We must be left to our own devices so our enhanced intelligence can create a more perfected universe on the higher level than currently exists on the lower level."

"So, if we could enter this orb before us and descend to the Universe of Seven could we find ourselves?"

"That's a good question," he said, "and one that the Masters themselves reflect upon when sitting around the table in conversation with each other. The consensus is yes. Either you or an aspect of you would be there, but currently asleep, as that universe is perfected. The essence that is you is duplicated, and is now manifesting in the greater universe."

"This is fantastic knowledge. This means that there are trillions of me asleep, duplicated within the atoms seeking to manifest as me in our greater universe."

"Actually, there is only one of you that is duplicated, just like there is one God who has multiplied himself into the many.

After reflecting a moment I said, "I think I am beginning to understand the barrier more fully. "I already have enough to keep my mind in a loop indefinitely."

"And the additional knowledge I have which is hidden from you would truly drive you to the brink of insanity if you were to absorb it prematurely. Even I have no comprehension of the Universe of Eleven and can only guess about the Universe of Eight."

"I guess what is good to know is that there is always more to learn, no matter how high up the ladder you are. It never occurred

to me though that one could know too much for his own good. Is
the world ready for this knowledge?"

"A few people are," he assured me. "But those who are not
will only absorb that which they can handle. The human psyche in
most people tends to filter out that for which it is not prepared, or
does not wish to believe."

"You say most people. Could you elaborate?" I asked, in-
trigued.

"Disciples and initiates tend to do less filtering and take knowledge more seriously. We, therefore, have to be careful about how
much we give them. Thinking about what you have learned here
makes your head spin with all kinds of thoughts and comparisons,
but many you tell this to will not be impressed, and will effect
them no more than a Flash Gordon movie."

I thought it odd he knew about Flash Gordon and replied,
"So, I will be allowed to write about it?"

"That which you are allowed to acquire, you are allowed to
teach, unless specifically directed otherwise. Many are thirsting
for new knowledge rather than a rehash of previous revelations."

"I'll tell you this," I said. "What I write about this experience will not be a rehash of anything that has been written in the
past."

"I believe you are correct," he said.

"Now what?" I asked. "It seems that we can go no further
here."

"Yes, it is time to return to the greater universe, but first give
thanks."

For an instant I was not sure what he meant. Then, I realized
we were still in the domain of this fantastic, yet microcosmic being. I concentrated my thoughts in his direction. "Thank you very
much for letting us into your holy space."

"You are welcome," came the reply. "I see from the thoughts
of your guide that we will meet again soon. When we do, I will
not recognize you, but I do have this request."

"Sure. Anything," I said.

"Will you give me your blessing?"

"My blessing?" I replied, somewhat flabbergasted. "You, who
understand even the Universe of Eleven, have a consciousness far
beyond my own. I should be asking a blessing from you."

"You will understand when the time comes."

"Then you shall have my blessing, feeble as it may be."

Afterwards, even though I could not see this being, it was as if I could feel him smile.

"Are you ready to ascend?" The Ancient of Days asked.

"I think so," I replied.

Then, within what seemed like a few seconds, we ascended through all the universes within the atom, becoming larger until I saw us coming out of the toothpick in our spare bedroom. Then, as we seemed to be expanding more, I said, "Wait. I want to check in on Elizabeth and make sure she is OK."

"It would just distract you. Have some faith and follow me in your consciousness."

What else could I do? I followed with as much focus as I could. Then, in another instant, we were above the earth in the blackness of space, about the distance of the moon. "It's beautiful here," I said in awe, "and the stars are so delightful."

"If you only realized how little you see with physical vision," he said. "Look again at the stars."

I looked again and suddenly the lights in the sky seemed to increase at least sevenfold. "Wow! Where did all the new stars come from?"

"You are now seeing two planes of existence at one time. Now look again and see the three."

I looked again and the intensity of the lights increased another sevenfold. "This is amazing," I said. "I thought the regular night sky was beautiful, but it is nothing compared to seeing the lights of three planes of existence at once."

"There is more. Much more," he said. "I'm just revealing to you a few things so you'll know how unlimited are the creations of God."

Suddenly, the lights of the higher two planes disappeared, and I was reduced to seeing our regular array of stars. "There is something else I wish to show you," he said. "There are other planets in the solar system that are not seen by the scientists. Look."

I looked and I saw a planet of similar size to the earth in a similar orbit that seemed to be teaming with life. "Why haven't the astronomers found this?" I asked.

"Because it exists in a more refined state of matter than does earth, and is invisible to regular vision. There are five major planets like this in various orbits, and many more in the higher planes. In total, there are seventy significant planets in our solar system."

"Amazing."

"Come. I will show you the planet from which I came. You call it Venus."

"I've seen pictures of Venus, and it looks like a hot lifeless wasteland," I said.

"There is no such thing as lifeless. You should realize that after visiting the worlds within the atom."

"Yes, I suppose I do, but I'm talking about regular organic life. Scientists say that Venus seems devoid of it, and Mars is the best place to look for it."

"We shall see," he said as we approached Venus. "Focus and take us down to look for life."

That sounded like an interesting challenge to me so I concentrated on descending through the clouds to the surface. The surface was not much of a surprise, it looked much like the pictures I saw taken by U.S. spacecraft. Even so, I used the assistance of my guide to navigate us to many places around the globe in what seemed like a few minutes. (Every time I thought of time, my mind raced back to Elizabeth's situation and I hoped there was still time left to save her. I had no idea of how much real time had passed.) "Don't see any life here," I remarked.

"Then, perhaps you are looking in the wrong place. Arise."

We then arose toward the clouds and continued until they surrounded us. "There are just clouds here," I said. "They are so thick; I cannot see the surface or the sky."

"Your mission is to commune with the various lives. Concentrate on what is here. There is more than meets the eye."

Okay, I thought and began to attempt to sense life wherever it was. Then, to my delight, we were embraced by a number of balls of energy that seemed to come out of the cloud material. I sensed a very happy playfulness in these little lives as they appeared to dance about us. They seemed happy to recognize us, and the exchange of energy was stimulating.

"Am I to understand that there is life in the clouds of Venus?"

"You understand correctly."

"Their energy reminds me of the excitement of a dog who

sees his master arriving home after a long absence."

"Your perception is truer than you think," he said. "The lives in the clouds here are of an animal-like consciousness. In fact, many animals come here to frolic in the clouds after a tough life on earth. Did you not have a dog you called *Sport* when you were a boy?"

"Yes, I did. I really loved that dog and was so disappointed when he got ran over."

"Sport is here. Concentrate on him and you will go to where he is."

The idea of seeing my beloved dog *Sport* in the clouds of Venus was about as mind-boggling as discovering a universe within the atom, but I gave his suggestion a try. Suddenly, we were moving at great speed and, within a few seconds, we were a long distance away on another section of the planet. Before me were three balls of energized clouds spinning and darting all over the place.

"Which one do you think is Sport?" he asked.

I do not know how I knew, but I knew the one that was Sport, and called out his name in my thoughts. One of the balls stopped and I knew it recognized me and darted toward the space occupied by my consciousness. He was whirling all over with excitement and joy, and I sensed myself merging with him, tumbling all over with joy also. As we tumbled, bounced, twirled and darted along together, I got a sense of the life there. The clouds of Venus are a place for recreation for many life forms in our solar system. There is no pain there, no suffering, no hunger, no heat and no cold in their consciousness. Instead, it was just light-hearted play to prepare many life forms for more difficult lives in other places.

"You've got the general idea of life in the clouds here. Now let us gaze upon the advanced human life."

"And where would that be?" I asked. "This place looks uninhabitable for life as we know it on earth."

"The trouble is you're again looking for life at the wrong place. Each planet is composed of several grades of matter existing simultaneously. Just as you saw additional stars when your eyes were open, even so can you see additional life here when your vision is enhanced. Come to the surface and look."

We moved to the surface and I gazed at the most inhospitable terrain one could imagine. "This looks worse than the Sahara

Desert," I said.

"And when you arrived at the Gobi Desert, did you see desert or Shamballa?"

"You're right. I saw a beautiful city where there was supposed to be desert."

"Look again and behold a city more ancient than Shamballa, my home before I came to earth."

A great city materialized, but instead of appearing like something ancient, it looked like something from the far future. Some of the buildings must have been two miles in height and seemed to have been built out of a fine crystal making a multifold effect of futuristic yet beautiful shapes.

"How does a civilization build such majestic buildings of such seamless crystalline material?" I asked.

"Our buildings are not put together piece by piece as yours, but are living things that we grow and form as by the hand of an artist."

"Fascinating," I said. "I think I could spend a couple years here investigating."

"And speaking of time, we must be moving on. I can control time, but not abolish it in this plane. I have allotted just enough to finish your tour and complete your assignment."

I found it interesting that this god-like being had his limitations. "Where to next?" I asked.

"We will make a brief visit to the sun," he said.

That ought to be interesting, I thought to myself. I felt my consciousness being tugged along toward that great orb which is the center of our solar system.

CHAPTER TWENTY
The Grand Tour

Within seconds the light of the sun filled up the sky but I felt no discomfort in my spiritual body. In fact, it felt somewhat refreshing. "Is there anything to see here?" I asked. "After all, isn't the sun just a ball of heated gas?"

"The sun is the most complex body in the solar system and has many more mysteries than the planets, for it is much greater than the planets."

As we approached, I saw a sunspot that was as large as a planet. We veered to its left and plunged right into the fiery gasses of the photosphere. We seemed to go through quite a few layers until we were met by a clear atmosphere of some kind, and, below us, a physical terrain more like a planet than a molten sun. "I don't understand," I said. "I see mountains, valleys, plains and even bodies of liquid. I thought it was supposed to be so hot here that nothing could be solid."

"Scientists have and will continue to discover many true facts that run contrary to their calculations. A number of factors combine to give form to the surface of the sun, and within a few years scientists will discover this, but will have difficulty in accepting what their instruments reveal. Come, I want you to meet some of the physical lives here. I believe some of them are having a merging meeting right now."

A merging meeting? I asked myself. I followed, and soon came upon some very unusual entities, large circular balls of fire that left behind streams of fire. They darted back and forth quickly to their destinations according to their will. After passing a number of them, we came to the meeting place. There were twenty-four entities joined in a circle with trails of fiery light joining them. I assumed this was their version of holding hands. Then I beheld two additional beings in the center, close to each other. Suddenly, they merged and for a moment looked like two cells in division, except they were joining. It took only a few seconds to merge into one large fiery cell.

After the merging, a great electrical energy engulfed the two merged entities and also energized the ones in the circle.

"I assume you can read my mind," I said. "Am I right in believing this is some type of merging on several levels?"

"You would have to experience it to understand," he said. "Would you like to try?"

"And how would I do that?" I asked.

"First, wait for the two entities to part and we will join them."

We watched and waited, and soon they divided in two. Immediately, we dropped down to the center of the circle. Our coming created a stir amongst the entities, and I felt they knew the Ancient of Days well and were happy to see him, or, perhaps I should say, *sense* him since we were not in our bodies.

He communicated to the group, "My brother has never been in the center of the circle. Will you allow him to participate in the great communion?"

Then I felt a foreign presence and sensed that my whole being and intelligence was being examined. "As a favor to our Ancient Friend it will be allowed," was the reply.

I got the impression that, if it were not for respect toward the Ancient of Days, I would not have been accepted. I was a little nervous about whatever it was I was supposed to do, but decided to go for it. "Just be in the center and a volunteer will come forward and merge with you," said the Ancient of Days. "He will do the work. All you have to do is to stay receptive."

"All right," I said and focused my presence in the center. A fiery entity shot forward and I felt his presence beside me.

"Relax," impressed the entity. Next, I felt this being coming toward me until it seemed that every part of me was surrounded by him. I felt the presence of the Ancient of Days and I relaxed completely.. For a moment it seemed as if I was falling, which was followed by what I can only call a spiritual explosion. I was inside a vast mind of some kind, and in my bewilderment I received a message from the other entity. "We have now merged. You can explore my past, as I will yours. You will savor my experiences, my pain, my joys, my defeats and my successes, as I will yours. Direct your thought, remember and then retrieve."

I concentrated on the entity and slowly new thoughts and experiences and feelings were there for me to tap. It was much more than a mere garnering of information. Instead, it was like I was actually him. I knew more about him and his history than I did my own.

I saw that he had lived on several planets in his past as a human being like myself, but had evolved beyond the human stage. My mind went back to his ancient past and I saw him living out many lives just as we humans do now. I picked one particular life to examine that seemed a little brighter than most. In that life he had mated with a woman he loved very much. This life was very sweet; his successful relationship followed many lives of failed ones. In what seemed like a moment, on one hand, and a whole lifetime on the other, I was able to be him and feel his sacred love, something like I feel for Elizabeth, but with so many differing perspectives. With this new understanding I knew I would be able to deepen my relationship with my wife.

I skimmed over maybe a hundred lifetimes before settling on one where he became a successful spiritual teacher. He had many struggles against ignorance, unjust authority and betrayal, but in the end he accomplished his mission and brought light to many people. I was with him on his deathbed as he reviewed his life, and sweet peace and joy from a life well lived swept over him. It was not an experience I wanted to hurry... In fact, if I was not so concerned about time, I could have stayed there and savored the feeling for years.

I had the sensation that I had some additional time, and reviewed several additional lives; then the impression came as to what this was all about. These entities had progressed beyond the need to incarnate and, in their present form perform various acts of service and seek progression on a higher path unknown to humans. Even so, they make use of all the experiences of their co-workers through these merging meetings.

They can merge with other entities and draw that which they wish from the past experiences of others, as if they were their own. They partake from the bad as well as the good, but without having to suffer pain or misery. It's a little like watching an interesting movie having horror or trauma. You can enjoy the movie despite the distress. Similarly, in this merging experience, one can savor the pain without being touched by it negatively. I marveled, for the experience was much more real than a movie. It made me realize that all experience, good and bad, will be leveraged for good in the end, when all souls merge and share in a higher sphere.

Suddenly, I snapped back to the present and was separated. I heard a familiar vibration, "Come, we must leave if we are to finish the tour." It took a moment to reorient my consciousness away from the entity. I knew his lifetimes would always be something I would reflect on and draw from in the future.

I realized that the Ancient of Days had mapped out a schedule within a time frame that would allow Elizabeth to be saved, and was manipulating time to make this happen. I also sensed that even he had limitations when dealing with time, and that we could not waste any.

I could not leave; however, until I focused on the entity with which I had merged. "Thank you for sharing. It was a wonderful experience."

"And thank you," came the reply. "I particularly enjoyed your current point of tension and couldn't resist moving ahead slightly in the probable future. Keep your confidence; all will be well."

The Ancient of Days performed some type of energy exchange with the group. I was as clueless as a two-year old at a wedding ceremony with what had occurred and what it would mean. I simply followed the Ancient of Days when he was through. I was expecting us to soar off into the universe, but instead, we descended below the surface of the sun. "Just time for a quick tour," he said. "Look and learn."

I concentrated the best I could and saw that the material, which created the sun itself, was composed of living substance and a variety of life forms within it. Then, we encountered a sphere within the outer sphere of the sun, which again had many intelligent life forms on its surface. We descended further and encountered another inner sphere. We continued until we arrived at the seventh sphere. This sphere appeared to be a sun within the sun, very bright even through the vision of spiritual eyes. "What is this and is there additional life within it?" I asked.

"We call this *the heart of the sun*," he answered. "All form houses life of some kind and this is no exception. However, the life in the inner spheres is not physical as we know it, but uses what science calls pure energy as it interplays with matter. This inner sphere is where the energy is produced that gives life to the entire solar system and houses five additional layers, but of a different order than the outer seven. The outer seven are linked to the seven sacred planets, which are Mercury, Venus, Saturn, Jupiter, Uranus, Neptune and one that is hidden. The inner five are linked to five etheric planets, which are not yet physical."

"What about earth?" I asked.

"The earth is not yet a sacred planet, but is linked to the third sphere of the sun through Saturn."

"You know, if I write about this, scientists will call it mumbo jumbo."

"Yes, they will for some time to come, that is until science begins to take on a more spiritual dimension."

"So, are we going to go to the inner spheres?"

"Not at this time," he said. "Perhaps another time, but the experience would overload you at present, and you may lose too much of your experience."

"I can believe that," I said. "So, what is in the center? Are there giant thermonuclear explosions?"

"Where the atmosphere of the sun seems turbulent and explosive, the source of fusion energy in the center is a point of great stillness and peace, and is the home of my teacher, the Solar Logos."

"*Your* teacher. I guess it is logical that you would have a teacher, but it is difficult to imagine what you have to learn."

"The more you know, the more you realize there is to know. In many ways, I feel more inadequate than you because I know more of the unanswered questions than do you."

"I would like to meet your teacher some time."

"You will one day, as will all disciples. In the mean time, if, in your meditations, you visualize going to the center of the sun and seeing yourself as the sun - the source of life in the solar system - you can catch brief glimpses of his intelligence and essence."

"I'll keep that in mind."

"It's time to go to the next level," he said. We rose up through the sun and soared far into space to the extent that the sun appeared only as a point of light, a star.

"Look and find the seven star systems."

"What do you mean, seven? There are thousands of them before me."

"Concentrate on our sun and six of his brothers and all will fade but the seven."

I was getting used be being told to do odd things and then having those odd things materialize, so I gave it a try. Sure enough, the universe seemed to fade away except for seven points of light forming a grand constellation.

"Now see these seven systems as one life and tell me what you feel."

I had already seen there was life on the sun, so what the heck? I tried to see the seven stars as one life. Suddenly, I felt a vibration that was very powerful; it seemed to originate from the whole, but was centered in one system, which seemed to be a very bright star.

"The vibration is very high and I am drawn to that bright star over there."

"Take a closer look," he said.

I attempted this and it quickly came closer. I saw it was a double star. One was very bright and the other was dim and much smaller. "Could this be Sirius?" I asked. "I remember reading that it is a double star."

"Yes, this is Sirius, the lead star system of the seven brothers. This system is unique among the seven as it has two Logoi. The first is a solar Logos as we have in our system, and the second is the Logos governing the entire seven systems. His consciousness is even beyond my full understanding. This is one reason he is called *The One About Whom Naught Can Be Said*. Very little can be said about him by me or the Brotherhood on earth that will be of understanding to the mind."

"You hint there is another reason," I said.

"Yes, there is. His language and means of communication are beyond words as we know them. Anything we say using communication that can be *said,* or placed in words, is useless to him.

Our Solar Logos understands his methods of communication but even I am a child in learning before him."

"Fascinating," I said. I was using that word so much I started feeling like Spock from Star Trek. "So what are the names of the other five solar systems?"

"That is not to be given at this time. It is time to see the next level, the seven constellations, of which the seven stars you see are one. Look and see."

We seemed to back off further from the stars, and within what seemed like seconds I saw seven constellations, each having seven prominent stars. Most had more than seven, but in each there were seven governing ones. "I think I recognize a couple of these," I ventured. "Is that one the Big Dipper?"

"Good observation," he said. "It is indeed the Big Dipper, or Ursa Major, the Great Bear, and the seven that stand out are the Seven Rishis."

"And that must be the Little Dipper with the North Star at the top of the handle."

"Correct. This is also called Ursa Minor, and even though there are more than seven stars, you see the seven prominent ones that form the dipper. Do you recognize that one?"

"I'm afraid I have only an elementary knowledge of the constellations," I said. "I see the seven major stars, and many minor ones."

"That is the constellation of the Pleiades; the seven great ones are the seven sisters which legend says are married to the seven Rishis of the Great Bear. There is usually an element of truth behind legend."

"And what is that constellation containing that very large star?"

"That constellation is Orion and the great star is Betelgeuse. The Logos there is in close communication with ours at this time."

"I see there are three more. What is that one?"

"That is Pegasus," he said, "and the last two are Hydra and Draco."

"Aren't those two associated with serpents and dragons?" I asked.

"Indeed," was the reply. "And there is some truth behind that association."

"I would be interested in learning more about that," I said.

"Perhaps another time," he said. "For now, you must focus on completing your assignment. Bathe your consciousness in these seven constellations and tell me what you perceive."

I concentrated, perceived the best I could, and replied, "I perceive that these seven constellations are the body of another Logos of even greater evolution and has a consciousness so high that all we can hope for is to feel his influence."

"Very good," he said. "That is the best answer I could have expected."

"I assume that there are yet higher lives," I said "until we get to the Logos of the galaxy and finally the universe."

"Some students have assumed that is the way of things, but they are not quite correct at this point in time. Here is what many students who contemplate the Logoi do not understand. In each major body, whether it is a planet, a star system or a group of systems, there are two life forces at work. The first is the indwelling entity, which is awakening in consciousness, and the second is one who has already attained a high state of consciousness. This is one who has passed through the human kingdom."

"So I assume that you are the one of high consciousness for the earth?"

"Yes, I am often called the Planetary Logos, but part of my purpose is to stimulate the indwelling consciousness of the great being whose physical body is the planet. Right now he is on the verge of obtaining self-consciousness, corresponding to a seven-year-old child in the human kingdom. Other planets are more advanced. Venus, for example, corresponds to a twenty-one-year-old and the indwelling entity is self-conscious. Even though the Solar Logos is much more advanced than me, the informing entity there is even younger than earth in consciousness, corresponding to a six-year-old child on its level."

"So do I understand correctly if I say that as we ascend to higher systemic bodies, the indwelling entities are less developed or more elementary in consciousness?"

"Basically."

"So, the guiding Logos, who evolved from the human kingdom, becomes greater as we go up, but the indwelling consciousness becomes less?"

"Correct, except the word *less* is misleading. They are only less in their infancy, but when these great entities mature their consciousness will soar beyond our imagination. The only way we will be able to keep up with them when this happens is to blend our consciousness with theirs. Such is the order of things. The lesser assists the greater and then the greater takes the lesser forward in his coattails."

"That is fascinating knowledge," I said. "Can you tell me anything about the Logos of the whole galaxy or the universe?"

"As we ascend to the greater bodies, we find that the highest form governed by a single Logos is seven constellations. You have just seen one of many that exist within our galaxy, which is composed of hundreds of billions of stars. Any combinations higher than seven constellations have incomplete governments that are in the process of formation. There is no single Logos over the galaxy, but there are various groups of great beings who seek to guide the galaxy as a whole toward an intelligent design."

"So, will there eventually be a single Logos over the galaxy?" I asked.

"Eventually," he said, "but that time is yet billions of years in the future. First, both the consciousness of the indwelling entity must evolve and a Logos must also evolve who can handle such a great life. Come, we must move on to your final step."

We pulled back and I felt like I was on the Star Trek Enterprise as I watched star system after star system race passed us. Within seconds, I found myself looking back upon our galaxy, the Milky Way. First, it loomed large before us but soon it stood in space, as a spiral galaxy looking like it was only a couple of feet in diameter.

"Take a good look," said my guide. "Not many get a view like this of their home galaxy."

"Believe me, it is appreciated," I said in return. "What is interesting is that there still appears to be many stars in the sky, but since we are beyond the stars of the Milky Way, those points of light have to be entire galaxies. Am I right?"

"You are correct. Each of those points of light contains billions of stars."

"I have always been impressed with the vastness of the universe, but this is overwhelming," I said. "The big question is whether there is an end to it."

"This is what you must see to pass your test," he said. "You must see the universe as a whole and commune with it. Come, we must expand our vision a great deal."

Again, I received the impression of traveling at great speed, but this time we were passing by galaxies instead of stars, making the distance traveled defy the imagination. Surprisingly, I picked up that the galaxies were not randomly scattered, but many were grouped. Some of them were in small groups and others fairly large. Parts of space were fairly dense with many galaxies, and other parts were almost void. "I see there is some organization of the galaxies, but it seems somewhat rudimentary."

"You see correctly," came the reply. "To understand why the organization here is elementary, you must understand that the creative mind of God works from below, upwards, or from the small to the great. In past eternities, relative perfection and great organization has been achieved in the sub-atomic worlds. When a level is perfected, it then continues as if run by a great computer program. Then consciousness moves a step up to the next level, and creates there. Presently, the central point of God's consciousness in the physical is focused on beings of human intelligence scattered throughout the universe, causing humans to be the soul of the universe, the bridge between spirit and matter. God's creative influence has some effect on these greater bodies and the universe itself, but for the most part, humanity is the focus."

"Wow! That puts a lot of responsibility on us, doesn't it?"

"Indeed. You could say that the One Life, which is God, is projecting itself though us as his representatives. When looking on this principle in this light, it is only to be expected that advanced humanoid beings are often called Gods on the various worlds." There was a short silence followed by, "Now pay attention; we have reached the edge of the universe."

That caught my attention, and I observed closely. Behind us was a massive cloud of tiny points of light which were galaxies far removed. In front of us was nothing but blackness. We moved toward the void and the universe became smaller until I could see its shape. I was a bit surprised to see that its form did not have much definition. It looked like a great cloud just beginning to take a spiral formation, something like a young galaxy.

I then felt the words come to me, "You have communed with the smallest in our creation; now you must commune with the largest to pass your test. Proceed."

It's funny, I thought. *Time and time again, since I have met John, I have been told to proceed toward something, which seems impossible. I always have my doubts, but then, when I move forward, magic happens. I have no idea of how to commune with the universe, but I know I must try. Hopefully, my perception through the All-Seeing Eye will be enhanced enough to do the job.*

I looked back on the universe and concentrated on being one with it, picking up its consciousness and understanding it.

I was shaken to the core by what I received: fear and trembling.

I immediately shook myself and withdrew. "What is this?" I asked. "How can it be that the first emotion I feel from the greatest life of all is fear?"

"Now you must discover what the cause of this fear is," he calmly demanded. "Commune again and answer."

I wasn't excited about continuing but thought of Elizabeth and realized that I must go forward. I forced myself to link in with this great life once more. Once more, I felt the great permeating fear that shook me to the core. I had to focus with all my will to stay centered as I attempted to tune in on the cause of this fear. Just as I reached my limit of endurance, the answer came. At that moment I understood something that I had never considered contemplating in the past.

I withdrew from communion and sent my thoughts to my companion, "The entity which occupies the universe as its body is afraid, and now I understand why. It feels completely alone. It has sent out its thoughts and feelings into the great void and nothing has returned. It fears it is alone and will be so for all the eternities to come. You know, if I were in his situation I would feel the same. It never entered my head before, but the idea of floating in the vast void of space with no contact among peers would be devastating. It would be a little like the story of the guy stranded alone on a desert island. There are lesser life forms, but a strong craving would develop to see other humans, and one would definitely have a fear of never having human contact again."

"It's worse than that," the Ancient of Days replied. "The

man on the desert island at least knows there are other humans and he has a chance of being rescued. The entity, which is the universe, fears there is no other like him, that he is unique; and not only will be alone, but has always been alone. He thus has an emptiness that exceeds anything known by humanity."

"That's terrible," I said. "But is he alone? Is there anything else out there? All I see is blackness beyond our universe."

"There are more universes than you can number," he said, but to understand the difficulty that faces our universe, you must recall the vast distances that separate all the great creations. For example, if space were reduced so our sun was the size of a basketball how far away do you think the nearest star would be?"

"I know it would be a good distance, several blocks or maybe a mile," I ventured.

"Alpha Centura would be another basketball about 5600 miles away."

"Yes, I knew it was a lot, but forgot the contrast was that great."

"And such contrast is normal in all portions of the universe, even the atom, and still holds true with actual universes. Now, imagine our universe being reduced to the size of a basketball and the nearest neighbor being 5600 miles in the distance."

"That's a fantastic thought," I said, "and something else extraordinary just occurred to me. Our universe has to be at least forty billion light years across. If we visualize the universe as the size of a basketball and light takes over 40 billion years to travel from one side to the other then imagine how long it would take light to travel the whole 5600 miles."

"Excellent thinking. Now look at the void in front of you and ask yourself why you do not see points of light."

"Yes, I see now. It would take much longer than the life span of a universe for the light of the nearest universe to even arrive here. Even though there may be many universes in the distance, we cannot see their light because it hasn't yet arrived. What a fantastic thought!" I exclaimed.

"Yet the light of the ethers does reach here. Look again."

I looked again and this time I saw many points of light as if it were a clear evening sky on the earth. "So why does our universe think it is alone when there are many universes in the distance? If we can see them, why can't he?" I asked, while noticing that I seemed to call every new encounter a *he* when I wasn't sure if it was a *he*, *she* or *it*.

"Just as humans cannot see more refined matter, even so can this great being not yet see it. When he sends his sensors into the blackness of space, nothing returns for him. It seems to him there is nothing to perceive."

"It kind of makes me think of mankind on the earth," I said. "We continually ask if we are alone in the universe. We explore the skies with radio telescopes and have found nothing so far."

"Yes, the correlation is interesting," he said. "The feeling of aloneness takes hold of every living thing at one time or another. This is particularly evident with the beginning disciple as he struggles with higher development. It will often seem to him that he is alone, and there is no one else going through what he is. He is wrong, of course, but since he cannot find anyone to talk to who understands him, he experiences a great feeling of isolation, sometimes called *the dark night of the soul*."

"When we met that entity in the tiny point, he told me that we would meet again," I said. "Now we seem to be at the end of our journey and have not seen him. Did we miss him?"

"You have met him again," he replied cryptically.

"And when would that have been?"

"Reflect and you will know."

That was an interesting answer, I thought to myself, but was getting to the point where I deemed it wise to just follow instructions. I contemplated our journey since leaving the Alpha Point, and within a short time the answer became obvious.

"The entity that was in the point is the same entity that has incarnated into the body of the entire universe," I said with amazement.

"Correct."

"But how could that be?" I pleaded. "The entity in the point was wise beyond comprehension and seemed all-knowing. Surely, if he incarnated in the body of the greater universe, he would realize he is not alone."

"And how much did you know the day you were born, or were even two or three years old? Before birth you had lived many past lives and demonstrated adult intelligence, but when born anew, you were released from all attachment to memory and began anew. For a period of time, being under the limitations of life as a child, you seemed much less intelligent than in your past. This was an illusion. Your intelligence was in the child, but with limitations that hid that intelligence. Even so, the greatest intelligence in our universe incarnated in the body of the present universe and is sleeping in his past universe. It has taken on the consciousness of a child again, and suffers through temporary limitations. Two side effects are loneliness and fear."

"That is interesting, but tell me something. There are trillions of alpha points. Where do the others fit in?"

"Remember that when the Universe of Eleven was perfected, the one entity multiplied himself in the fabric of space. The entity you talked to is the same entity you would encounter in any of the points. This entity is the one God in this universe. It is sleeping in the universe past and awakening in the universe present."

"I'm beginning to be a big believer in the truism that truth is stranger than fiction," I said, looking in the direction of the universe. "So what we are looking at is God, who has incarnated into the entire universe, but has only the consciousness of a child who is afraid and alone. I think I can see why he asked for my blessing."

"Yes, we awakened him for a cosmic instant on his plane of mastery. He realized you would meet him again, struggling in the infant state in an almost helpless condition. This is why he asked for your blessing."

"Ironic, isn't it?" I said. "While we are prostrating ourselves, asking for a blessing from God, the real truth is that it is God who needs our blessing. I guess it is a good thing that there are higher lives, such as yourself, and the Masters, who can assist the lower kingdoms until God matures in his present incarnation."

"Well spoken, but it is time for you to give your blessing."

"And how do I go about doing that?"

"Seek to commune with the life of the universe as you did last time, and, in the midst of your merging, give your blessing."

I wasn't really looking forward to communing with the universe again, as it was painful to share its fear and loneliness, but how could I resist a request from the One God? I forced myself to focus, and again merged with the consciousness of the great entity, of which I am a tiny part. Again, I felt the fear and loneliness, but it was more bearable this time because I understood it. My heart went out to God, for I began to realize his great sacrifice in pouring himself into this limited condition so all the lesser beings could live and flourish. From the core of my being I expressed appreciation and gave a blessing to the best of my ability, "I bless you my Lord. You are not alone, have never been alone and never will be alone. I am here, and your brothers await you and will rejoice at your presence."

Suddenly, it felt as if the universe itself shook and I sensed the voice of a familiar consciousness, the same as we had met in the Alpha Point, "I awaken again for an instant to give you thanks. You have helped more than you know. We shall meet again in fullness of joy at the end of time."

After hearing the Alpha Point, my consciousness returned to the void, looking back upon the universe. "Wow! That was something! How about you?" I said to the Ancient of Days. "Are you going to give God a blessing also?"

"I was there with you, lending my thoughts and support. You did well. It is rare for a human to have this opportunity, and this rarity makes the blessing all the more potent."

"So, how old of a child is the universe in its consciousness?" I asked.

"His consciousness corresponds to a three-year-old child," He said. "Now, you may wonder why this is so when you were told the universe is about half way through its evolution. The reason it is not further along in consciousness is because it has spent much of its life evolving through mineral, vegetable, animal and other types of consciousness lower than human to get to where he is now."

"His sacrifice is great," I said. "It is mind-boggling to see how low he descended to such a great depth so all of us could ascend higher. Can you tell me what will be the state of the universe when the central life matures?"

"Look and see."

I looked toward the universe and saw it begin to spin more and more quickly, and, as it rotated, it gained definition. First it became fairly flat, surrounded by rings, something like Saturn. Finally, time seemed to stop and I saw a universe, which had undergone great change. Again, I saw the number seven manifest, for at the center was a disc of light surrounded by seven beautiful rings, with the colors of the rainbow that danced about in various orbits until time came to a standstill. "This is the universe at maturity. It will have full self-consciousness and intelligence greater than the sum of its parts. Over many billions of years it will go from an elementary consciousness and form to the sublime. It will then be the all-powerful benevolent God, which the children within have always dreamed."

"And will it discover it is not alone?"

"Indeed. It will discover many friends; behold, again the great void."

I looked toward the void again and saw that our universe was in proximity to six other universes of similar, but still unique design, making seven when our universe is counted. I received the strong impression that they had an association beyond our current understanding; but, most important, from my point of view, the universe was no longer alone and was receiving great joy through communion with others like itself.

"Will our universe next move on to become the Universe of Eight?" I asked.

"You're getting ahead of yourself. We all have a long way to go before the Universe of Eight will manifest. Observe the end and rebirth of the universe."

Again, time seemed to move forward with extreme rapidity. The rings darted about so quickly that the universe looked like a great ball. I marveled as I saw it interplay within its group of six and then with other clusters of universes. Finally, I saw that they seemed to lose their energy, and at the center of our universe was a dark spot that grew in strength and power. I watched as it seemed to devour our universe, and as I watched, it dawned on me that this was a giant black hole. As I continued watching, I saw that our universe, as well as all others in view, were consumed until they were no more. All that was left was a void, blackness, and nothing else.

"What is to happen now?" I asked. "Is the universe completely gone?"

"No creation is ever lost to the mind of God," he said. "Descend again to the Alpha Point, and you will see that the seed of creation remains forever."

We descended again in size, but this time in an instant, and before us we saw the Alpha Point containing the Universe of Eleven. "This is amazing," I said. "You mean that all that is left of the entire universe is one tiny Alpha Point, millions of times smaller than a single atom?"

"That is all that is needed."

"So what happens now?" I asked.

"The Alpha Point will remain at rest, or pralaya, for as long as the universe was previously in manifestation. Then the universe will be reborn. Look and learn as we move ahead in time."

I looked with great interest and saw the beginning of what could only be called another Big Bang. An explosion of creation took place, and I saw the universe of three four, five, six and, finally, seven like our current universe come into manifestation. Then I saw our universe evolve and take shape again, but the shape and consciousness within seemed slightly different. Finally, it reached maturity again and obtained a beauty even greater than before.

My guide spoke again, "Look again as we speed up time many times over."

I looked and I saw the universe disappear again and then be reborn. Time seemed to speed up even more as I watched the universe die and be reborn several hundred times within what seemed like a couple minutes. Each time it matured it was more beautiful than before, and developed more complex associations with other universes and groups of universes. Finally, such a degree of perfection was achieved that there was no purpose in dying and being reborn, and all the universes remained without disintegration.

"Now what?" I asked.

"You are seeing into the far future, where there is nothing new to accomplish for the universes built upon the number seven. The lives, which occupy the universes, have received eternal life and need not die again in this creation. Now they must build a Universe of Eight."

"And how will that occur?" I asked.

"What you have seen so far is a virtual reality constructed by the Brotherhood of Light. We only know some basics of the Universe of Eight. Look and see its beginning."

Again, I looked and I saw our universe gather with its group, and the groups gather into greater groups until they created particles, which, in turn, gathered and created a great atom built on the Principle of Eight. Then, I was raised up and saw that a massive number of other universes were gathering to create other atoms. Finally, I was raised up to a greater height and saw a number of atoms (composed of Universes of Seven) that defied the imagination, creating a greater world and then a greater universe.

"That's as far as I can show you."

"That's far enough,' I said. "This is mind expanding beyond anything I have ever imagined. I need to ask a question, though. When the Universe of Eight is created, you and I will only be tiny specks, much smaller than an atom, in this greater universe. What is to happen to us?"

"Like the Alpha Point we encountered earlier, we will have achieved all that is possible, and there will be nothing else to learn. We will thus go to sleep in the Universe of Seven and seek to be reborn in the Universe of Eight. Our rebirth will be into a group life that we will share, and there we will again resume the struggle to achieve, to learn and to create, but on a scale we can only guess at in our current consciousness.

"This progress will continue for us until the Universe of Eight dies ands is reborn many times. Then we will progress to the Universe of Nine, to Ten, then Eleven and finally to Twelve, where the perfect circle of creation will manifest. At that point all things will have been gathered into one, and another great decision will be made as to the direction of the creative energies of God."

"This is the most fantastic knowledge that I could imagine receiving," I gasped.

"But there is more," he said. "I have only shown you creation on the physical plane. There are higher grades of matter and spirit which use different creative processes, but what you have seen will have to suffice for now."

"I have no complaints," I thought back. "What I have seen should satisfy the greatest of seekers. I felt satisfied and ready to return to do what is necessary to save my wife."

CHAPTER TWENTY-ONE
Life is Fair

As we began the return, the thought occurred to me that I might never get an opportunity like this again. "I have to ask one more question. Do we have time?"

"Remaining time is short, but perhaps...," the Ancient of Days mused. "What is your question?"

"Your mentioning a serpent connection with the constellations Hydra and Draco got me thinking. John said there was a great mystery connected with serpent and human evolution. The story of the talking serpent in the Garden of Eden makes it even more mysterious. Can you elaborate on this?"

"Indeed, this is a mystery over which the sages of the ages have pondered, and many volumes have been written. The answer has never been given, yet it is very simple, so simple even a child can understand. Observe the universe before us, full of stars and galaxies containing every imaginable life form of which you can conceive. As the lives progress from the lesser to the greater, there are many struggles for dominance. There is a survival of the fittest, which prevails until we arrive at the stage where intelligent upright figures begin to manifest. Eventually, a plethora of forms, competing for domination as self-conscious units, manifest on the various worlds. A number of variations appear and disappear but, in almost every case, the evolution of a world comes down to competition between two forms. These two forms are the serpent and the mammal human.

"What generally transpires on a developing world is the serpent race will, at first, have complete domination until the highest of humanity reaches a point of soul contact. After this occurs, a fierce competition ensues, which eventually results in the complete destruction of one race or the other. This doesn't occur all in one moment, but over a period of many thousands, sometimes millions of years. During this transition period one race will be almost completely exterminated, but then survives to eventually flourish and almost exterminate the other race. This war goes back and forth until one race dominates to the extinction of the other. Because the human race is the more spiritually sensitive, they are the victors in over 90% of the worlds."

"So, in the final victory, we humans exterminate the serpent race?" I asked nervously. "That doesn't sound right even if they were our enemies."

"That's not quite how it occurs," he said. "In the few cases where the serpents dominate; they will physically kill all the humans. They hunt them down until there is not one left to continue the race. It is different when the humans dominate. During the transition period they are forced to fight wars of self-defense, but when they reach a point of domination on a spiritual level, the life of the planet itself comes to their assistance and eliminates the serpent race. Because of their spiritual progression, they have earned the right to dominate the earth until the end of their evolution, unless..."

"Unless what?" I asked anxiously.

"Unless they revert to the lower serpent consciousness themselves and lose their rightful place. In this case, the serpent race is reborn, and, in their fierceness, they completely and cruelly eliminate the entire human race. On a small percentage of the planets we, therefore, have the situation where the serpents either completed their domination during the transition period, or the humans lost their right and the serpents were reborn and dominate."

"So, what happens when the serpents dominate with humans out of the way?"

"First, let me give you some background. In the course of natural evolution, the serpents complete their purpose and evolution about the time that humans reach spiritual domination. When it is their time to go, those who were serpents are then reborn into the human race. Most adapt and move on, but others tap into ancient memories and work with the dark brotherhood in a spiritual conspiracy with the goal of complete elimination of the human race and the re-establishment of the serpents. This is the dangerous situation the earth is in right now. The human race managed by a hair's breadth to dominate the serpents, but the serpents' hope is far from extinguished. Philo and his masters are hard at work with the dark plan to reverse the progress of the millennia and restore the ancient race in all its glory.

"Now to answer your original question: if you want an idea of what the world would be like with serpent domination, visualize what the world would be like if Hitler had won World War II and the Nazis had complete dominion. Even here, your imagination will not go far enough. The extermination of the Jews was only a foreshadowing of the next step, which would have been the extermination of the human race. Even Hitler did not realize that this final solution would eventually apply to his beloved master race. His true masters, the serpents, saw themselves as the true master race."

"But I have seen some dark brothers on the earth and they are in human form," I noted.

"But the masters above them are of the serpent race, and most of them are extra terrestrial."

"Do the dark brothers on the earth know the serpents' plan to exterminate the human race?" I asked.

"The rank and file disciples such as Philo do not know, but the initiated masters are aware."

"Why in the world would they cooperate in the extermination of their own kind?" I asked incredulously.

"They have been convinced that the serpent race is superior, with greater powers than humans, and are promised they will be reborn into this greater race when they gain domination."

"I can't imagine looking forward to becoming a serpent," I said.

"It does bother some of them when they first learn where their path leads, but most fully embrace it when the carrot of ultimate power is dangled before them. It is true that the serpent race does have some of what humans consider supernatural powers, but they lack the spiritual powers of the soul and spirit, which are all-inclusive and always dominate in the end."

"So, what would be the fate of life on earth if the serpents did gain domination?"

"Because their time has passed the serpents would be struggling against the natural stream of evolution. In most cases, what eventually happens is the highest of the serpents pick up on the current and sacrifice themselves for the re-creation of the human race. This results again in the dominion of the humanoids. This cycle may take as long as a million years and results in a delay in evolution that must be made up."

"You said *in most cases*. What about the other cases?" I asked.

"In rare cases the serpents dominate with such will and determination that the human race is not reborn. When this occurs, and the situation has crystallized, the Logos of the planet is forced to act, and the entire planet is destroyed with a foundation being laid for a future and better creation. Among all the creations of the universe there are failures now and then, but the creators learn from them and always start anew with greater wisdom than before. The principle to keep in mind is that evolution can only be blocked for so long; then a way is prepared for continued progress."

"Will humans eventually be replaced by a higher evolution then?"

"Yes, they will be replaced by those with androgynous bodies such as I possess. When this time comes, many years in the future, humans will resist the change just as the serpents did."

I forgot I was communicating with a being in a more advanced body than my own and should have been able to answer my own question. "Can I see a world where the serpents dominate?" I asked.

"Now there are many infant worlds where the serpents are living out their natural evolution. Then there are others, fewer in number, where both serpents and humans are competing for domination. Finally, there are just a few where the serpents have lived past their appointed time to dominate and eliminate the human race. There are three such planets in the constellation of Draco," he said. "This is an unusual concentration and they create a potent force. Look and you shall obtain an overall glimpse of one of the worlds."

I concentrated on seeing and gradually a vision of a planet similar to earth opened, except some very strange creatures populated it. Their appearance made me think of space aliens from a science fiction movie. They stood erect like humans, had no tails, but had a very leathery hard skin and large lizard eyes.

I found it strange that the leaders seemed to be larger and more physically powerful than the rank and file, sometimes reaching a height of ten to twelve feet. These leaders not only had to prove their physical prowess, but had to demonstrate their sexual virility on a periodic basis to maintain their station. Worst of all, they had to rule with a stern hand and refrain from any pity or sympathy for their subjects.

Volumes could be written on their way of life, but I could see many similarities to Nazism, especially their strong central authority.

On this world they didn't have any modern technology. Instead, the elite leaders, called overseers, obtained their comfort by being served by many slaves and wives. They also had knowledge of lower magic and used advanced forms of voodoo to control their subjects and instill fear.

In addition, they had their own peculiar forms of meditation that was quite effective. Some were proficient at leaving their bodies and meeting with other serpents from the other two worlds in that system. I saw that they were familiar with earth and sought for a foothold of power here, with the hope they could overthrow the human race and eventually incarnate here as serpent masters.

Another point of interest I viewed was the difference in the vibration of their bodies compared to humans. There was a limitation of vibration because their foundation DNA made it very difficult for them to sense the higher spiritual energies. This caused all but a few to put full attention on satisfying the self and physical and sexual needs to a degree we can only imagine.

The reason humans replace them in evolution is because our bodies are more suited to house the higher vibration that the serpents have great difficulty in picking up.

"Why do the serpents hold so strongly to their form when the human form is more advanced?" I asked.

"Because the serpent body is more attuned to sensation, the physical senses and pleasure," he said. "Many human teachers talk of humanity as being sensual, but they do not know what sensual is until they meet an advanced serpent. When serpent entities become aware that they will lose much of their physical sensation in return for higher emotional and spiritual sensation, many do not want to make the leap."

"Interesting," I said. "I have also heard various fringe teachings about serpents being among the human race as shape shifters. Some have reported seeing them even among our leadership in disguise. Is there anything to this?"

I could almost feel him smile as I felt the response, "There are no shape shifters among you, but when some report seeing certain people turn into serpents they are not completely wrong. Those who see such things are very sensitive and tune in to those who have incarnated as humans yet retain a high degree of serpent consciousness. Come. It is time for you to return. Even I cannot squeeze any more time into our encounter."

"I am assuming it is in the plan that we save my wife?"

"The important thing is that it is in your plan."

"I would assume that what happens is part of some larger plan?" I queried anxiously.

"The larger is always composed of many smaller branches. Saving your wife at this point is up to you. Have you given any thought as to how you're going to do it?"

"What!" I gasped. "All my thought went into passing this test. It now appears that, with your help, I have done that. I wasn't aware that any more thought was required. John was supposed to heal my wife after I completed the Third Key."

"Shortsightedness is a mistake most disciples continually make," he replied. "They use the power of thought to see up to a point and then no further. You imagined passing the test, but then what? John will heal her, but you must first save her from the Dark Brothers. How are you going to do this?"

"Me?" I gasped. "I don't have power to defeat them. I thought that you or John were going to do it."

"And why should we do for you what you can do for yourself?"

"But I can't do it myself. I am no master," I protested.

"And you thought you wrote the three parables with assistance, and yet you did it through your own natural power. Think. You wrote them because you are connected to the same source as John and I, not because anyone was looking over your shoulder assisting you. Remember the words of Jesus; *Anything is possible to him who believes."*

"So are you saying I have to use the faith that moves mountains to save my wife?"

"Yes."

"But I don't have the faith to move a mountain," I pleaded.

"You don't? What if I told you to command a mountain to move? Do you think it would?"

"Of course. *You* have the power to move a mountain."

"Then let me tell you something. You have the power to defeat and dominate the Dark Brothers according to your will. I have spoken it. Now, you must return. You have three seconds to obtain victory. Real time begins when you decide."

Before I could say anything I found myself in my home next to Elizabeth's body, surrounded by a coven of dark brothers. The dark master had the sword raised over Elizabeth's heart, ready to descend. To my left I saw my physical body bound in a chair. It then occurred to me that I was in my spiritual body and time was standing still. I looked at the clock. It looked as if the hands were right on midnight, but then the Ancient of Days told me that I had three seconds, that time would begin when I decided.

I felt grateful when I realized that time was slowed by the Ancient of Days giving me a period to reflect and decide how to defeat them. When I decided there would just be three seconds. *Wow! These masters like to put pressure on a guy*, I thought.

I strolled like a lion after his prey around the circle contemplating what to do.

Suddenly I felt what could only be described as fear and trembling and had a strong feeling to just flee. I gathered my thoughts and did all I could to override the fear but without complete success. Somehow I felt this fear needed to be contained before I could be successful. Then I recalled the feelings I had when I communicated with the universe and I realized this showdown with light and dark was creating in me the same feelings of insecurity that was felt by the universe itself.

It made me realize that our fears are a reflection of our infant universe, a lower self and our hopes, dreams and faith are a reflection of the Higher Self of the Universe. I knew I had to override my fears. I stood up and asked myself what a Master would do.

If our fears reflect the lower self of the universe, I reasoned, faith could reflect its Higher Self composed of entities such as the Ancient of Days, Christ and the much higher intelligences throughout space. The Ancient of Days told me that I had the power to dominate these guys, but how? That was the question.

"Think, think like a master, I commanded my mind. He said I could do it according to my will. I grew in confidence as his remembered words gave me hope. What had I to loose by having faith in his words just one more time? If I had his power at my disposal, what would I do? Of course, I would save my wife from the dagger over her heart, from Philo's hold over her body, and the recurring MS, but I'd also use that awesome power to teach these guys a lesson for trying to destroy us. Just maybe this was my one chance to give them some of their own medicine.

I visualized first one scenario and then another until I had arrived at one that felt the most likely to be successful. I stood quietly tuning into my soul for reassurance. I carefully approached my decision, knowing it would move me into real time. I finally knew what to do. It was now or never.

As I was about to will real time to resume another problem occurred to me as I looked on my body, which was gagged and bound. What good would it do to return to my body and use my last three seconds in a useless struggle to get free? Could I somehow use the power of faith to free myself? I felt that somehow I had to map out a plan for the next three seconds of real time. That plan would have to include freeing my body from bondage.

Then I recalled that John had, in the past, used his powers to teleport my body from one place to another. If, for a few seconds, I could use these higher powers myself then perhaps I could teleport my own body out of bondage and in a position to free my wife. I decided to place all my faith on the words of the Ancient of Days words which indicated that I could prevail and proceed.

I decided that the first step was to enter my body and then move it into the circle by the same teleportation process John used on me.

I made the final decision and real time began. I suddenly found myself bound and gagged looking toward the Dark Brotherhood ready to destroy my wife. A long second passed as I used all my will to quiet any fear or emotion. During the next second I willed myself to be transported next to the Dark Master. If nothing hap-

pened in the next second all would be lost. I tried not to think of
that possibility and visualized the Ancient of Days assisting me.

Suddenly, I was next to the Dark Master with the sword in
the process of descent into the body of my wife. What if I had
gone this far and only had normal powers? All still could be lost.
I had to act as if I had all power to succeed.

Before any of the Dark Ones knew what had happened I leapt
next to the Dark Master with the sword, grabbing his arm. The
whole group shrieked back in surprise, and the Dark Master was
so shocked at the unexpected attack he dropped the sword. Normally a death sentence to stare into a Dark Master's eyes, I felt the
power of the eye of the Ancient of Days and radiated divine light
right into the demon's dark head.

He screamed with a cacophonous sound that touched my very
soul. It revealed such tremendous pain that I almost felt sorry for
him. But now was not the time to be faint-hearted. I grabbed his
sword and plunged it into his heart. The whole group looked dev-
astated and I sensed that their only concern now was to save their
master's life. They tried to scream their agony, but no sound came
from them as they faded along with the sword, leaving only
Elizabeth's tortured body before me.

Philo was still possessing her as he cried, "What in the? You
son of a bitch! What have you done to my brothers?"

He apparently still thought he had power over me and grabbed
at me as he did before. This time was different, and I found myself
much stronger than he and grabbed him back. I held him firm while
being careful to not do any more damage to Elizabeth's body. I
looked into his frightened eyes and said, "You reap what you sow.
Go back and revel in that which is yours."

Immediately her body shook and a wispy smoke snaked out
of her head and dissipated. I saw that Elizabeth's eyes started to
flutter and she shook her head from side to side as consciousness
slowly returned. "Is that you, sweetie?"

"I think so," she hoarsely whispered. "Am I still alive?"

I knelt down and held her tight to my chest. "You feel me,
don't you? That means you are alive and all is well." I held her
even closer.

Her eyes immediately brightened, "You passed the test? How
could it be?"

"It be," I joked, somewhat bright-eyed myself.

"But how?" she asked. "Even though I tried to show faith in you, I had little hope."

"Well that show of faith was the little extra incentive I needed. I passed the test, but couldn't have done it without you." I didn't dare stand yet as the enormity of what had just occurred overwhelmed me. I dropped my head on hers and we clung to one another not speaking.

We both sensed a presence at the same time. Turning to the side and with great joy we beheld our friend, John. "Time for a group hug," he smiled. "Why don't you stand up this time?" He grabbed Elizabeth's hand and pulled her up. We all embraced for a blissful moment.

He then drew back and looked at Elizabeth, "You're a mess. You realize that, don't you?"

"You don't tell a woman she's a mess," she said, almost crying.

"But you have earned the right to undo the mess. This time you will be healed for good and there is nothing Philo can do to bring your illness back." He swept her up in his arms, held her shoulder high, and spoke some words in an ancient tongue. Instantly, her body began to glow until it looked as if John was carrying the sun in his arms. The glow continued for about ten seconds and then began to dim. After the light left, John put her down on her feet; but what surprised me more than the fact she had strength again to stand on her own, without a scratch or bruise - was the dress she now wore. Her attire was totally different than it was before.

"You look something like Little Bo Peep," I grinned.

She looked at herself with very perplexed eyes and then went to the mirror and stared at herself in a white frilly dress. "What kind of outfit is this?" she asked bewildered.

"I've kept it in my creation room for you," he said, looking slightly embarrassed. "I've saved it for this moment because I thought you would appreciate something cheerful."

"Well, I hope I don't hurt your feelings," she said, "but this just isn't me."

"It does have a cheerful look, though," I noted.

"That it does," she laughed. Then she looked at John and

said, "I'll tell you what. If I ever get depressed, I'll put on this dress and look in the mirror and remember this moment. It can't help but cheer me up."

"That's a deal," said John. "You must forgive my taste, for I haven't had much experience with women's clothes over the past 2000 years."

"Think nothing of it," she said. "I would have been happy to be clothed in rags in exchange for the strength I now have." She then briskly walked around the living room and ended with a few graceful leaps. "I feel just terrific," she beamed, "and as a bonus you seemed to have removed every scratch and bruise that Philo inflicted." She then looked toward me, "Now I just want to hear how you passed that test with only a few moments left. This seems unbelievable to me."

"And it's almost too much for me to believe myself," said John looking at me. "Would you mind if I shared your memories so I can get the full story?"

"Nothing would make me happier," I replied.

As John was about to touch me on the forehead, Elizabeth jumped in, "Hey! How about me? Is there any way I can get in on this?"

"I suppose I could see what I can do," he said. "It will tax my abilities to the limit to include you, and you may not see every-thing at once, but you'll get the general picture and Joseph can fill in the holes later."

He then put his right hand on my forehead and his left on Elizabeth's. Within a few seconds I felt a very soothing, loving feeling and sensed a familiar merging. I should be able to look into John's past, I thought, reflecting back to my experience on the sun. As soon as I had this thought I saw two doors. One was open and one was closed. I somehow immediately knew that behind the closed one were memories he did not want me to discover at this time, but the open door had memories that I could explore. I went through the open door and chose one of his past lives and reveled in the experience for what seemed like days. I cannot write about it at this time, but I felt like I understood John much better after this sharing. Suddenly, I returned to my normal consciousness.

"Wow! How long have I been gone?" I asked.

"Just a few seconds," smiled John. "I must admit that was

quite an experience you had. When you write about it, you will place in words what has never before been given to humanity."

Elizabeth shook her head like a dog shaking off water. "Yes, that was quite the experience alright and I don't know whether to kiss you or slap you."

"What do you mean?" I gasped. "Why would you want to slap me?"

She put her hands to her hips and let me have it, "Well, there I was in a tortured state, a sword hanging over my head with minutes to live and what are you doing? Gallivanting around the universe, enjoying yourself with the most fascinating tour guide of them all, you didn't seem to have a care in the world."

"Well, John said you'd have gaps that I would need to fill in. You must have missed the parts where I was thinking about you," I said sheepishly.

John put his arm around Elizabeth and said, "Actually, if all Joseph did during those last few moments was think about you, he wouldn't have completed the test and you would not be saved."

"Oh, I was just giving him a bad time. It's in the female nature," she said, giving me a hug of acceptance."

"That's a relief," said John. "You know, I think the mystery of the female psyche is the last piece of the universal puzzle I will understand."

"You and me both," I said agreeing.

"Then I guess us females are ahead of you because we understand each other," she said feigning a tone of superiority.

"I think we'll quit while we are ahead in this conversation," said John. "Meanwhile, Joseph and I are late for a meeting. Please excuse us for a few minutes."

John grabbed my hand and immediately Elizabeth, the house and everything in it began to fade. We stood before the group of Masters that I previously encountered.

John looked the group over for a few moments and spoke, "Is there any doubt that this disciple has completed the test and passed the Third Key - even beyond what was expected?"

There was silence.

"Is there any reason why he should not give out the Keys of Knowledge?"

Silence again.

"Is there any reason why we should not throw our full support behind the books that he shall write?"

After a period of silence the Master wearing the silver cord stepped forward and spoke, "I was the one who insisted on this extreme test, and I must admit I did not expect the Ancient of Days to step in and assist. Without this assistance he would have failed."

"But without an exercise of faith he would not have been assisted," said John. "Surely you do not question the wisdom of the Planetary Logos?"

"I am sure he has his reasons," was the humble reply. "Even so, I still have reservations about supporting fiction as we have previously supported truth."

"We would be supporting true teachings with some fiction as a vehicle," said John.

"But even we do not foresee all the repercussions of such a move."

"Does anyone else feel the same way?" asked John.

Two more stepped forward.

Afterwards, the Master with the gold cord, radiating multi colors from his robe stepped forward and spoke. "Our brother has passed the test and has earned the honor of presenting the Keys of Knowledge to the world. Of this there can be no dispute. We are at a crossroads of the ages, and some changes are in order. Some of the old ways are no longer effective, and we must try the new.

"Joseph will write some books teaching truth enhanced by fiction," he continued, "but he will write many other words with no fiction, teaching spiritual principles in plain language that all seekers will understand. The books in story format have the best chance of attracting initial success, but because we are not united in supporting it, only the more spiritually sensitive will be, at first, drawn to its truth.

"The work will eventually succeed for truth always finds a way. Because of the karma of humanity we are limited in our direct assistance. We must now turn the work over to John, Joseph and others who will come to create the point of tension needed to reach the general consciousness of humanity. When the spiritual energy is built up to the point where the Keys reach many who are not disciples, our unity of purpose will be strengthened and the spiritual flow to humanity will increase."

He then raised his right hand to us and said, "Go in peace."

Instantly, we were back in the house. I touched myself in several places to make sure I was real. I looked at John, "Was that head Master who I think he was?"

"He was indeed," John smiled.

I looked over my shoulder and saw Elizabeth coming down the stairs. I saw she was no longer wearing John's dress. "What happened to your pretty white dress?" I asked. "You looked so cute in it."

"It's in a safe place," she smiled. "I felt like something a little more casual. Hope you don't mind John."

"No problem."

"I've got some hot tea waiting if you want some," she volunteered.

"Sounds great," I said. "That is unless John brought some more Dom Pérignon."

"Sorry, not today," he said as we sat down at the table. "That is not to say that you do not deserve a good toast."

"Actually, a good hot drink will hit the spot with me," I said. "You must answer a question for me though. When I plunged the sword into the dark master they all disappeared. What happened to them? I assume we do not have the good fortune to be rid of them forever."

"No such luck," said John. "Your surprise attack on their master forced them to immediately withdraw to save his life. They returned to their lair and fed him with enough of their own energies to restore his life force. They lost out in two ways. First, they did not gain the vital energy they sought through the sacrifice of Elizabeth's life and, second, the group, as a whole, was drained of energy in order to save their master's life. They will be weakened for some time now; that is until they restore their vital force with new victims."

"So, does that mean they will not be bothering us for a while?" asked Elizabeth.

John chuckled, "I think they'll be nervous about taking on you two again, even after they are restored to health."

"I hope you're right," I said, sipping a cup of tea. "I have a feeling, though, that Philo is so stark raving mad at me that it will override his fear."

"Fortunately, he is pretty much out of commission on the physical plane for some time. The worst he can do is to seek to get to you through possessing the bodies of others, but you have learned to detect him. There's not much chance he can fool you through a medium. Now that Elizabeth is healed, she will be strong enough to resist him indefinitely. You have the dark brothers direct interference under control; now you must tackle the job of putting the teachings in writing and promoting them to the world."

"Why do I feel that could be a bigger job than defeating the dark brothers?"

"Because it probably will be," he said.

Elizabeth pulled up a chair and joined us. "So when do we start the next key?" she asked.

"Good question," said John. "The next key is different from the rest in that it will take a number of years to interpret. In fact, you will have covered a number of other keys by the time you get the fourth one completed."

"That sounds intriguing," I said. "Are you going to give us a hint or something?"

"Indeed," he nodded. "And a major hint it is. The clues are in the last book of the Bible. What do you suppose that is?"

"I suppose that would be the Apocalypse, commonly called the Revelation of John. The John there would, of course, be you.

"I am flattered they have called it that, but it has been wrongly named. For the correct name of the book, read the first five words."

I grabbed a King James Bible and turned to the last book. "Here it is. The first five words are: *The Revelation of Jesus Christ.*"

"Now the book itself says it is *The Revelation of Jesus Christ*, yet they have titled it *The Revelation of John*. Why do you suppose they did this?"

"*The Revelation of John* seems like the logical choice," I said. "After all, it was a revelation to you.

"That is where the mistake has been made that has bothered me for 2000 years, for a Key of Knowledge is buried in those first five words, and no one has seen it correctly. To help you understand, I want you to look up the word *Revelation* in your concordance."

I retrieved my Strong's Concordance, found the word and said. "It looks like it was translated from the Greek word

APOKALUPSIS. I take it the English *Apocalypse* came from this."
  Correct," he said.

"APOKALUPSIS is translated in a variety of ways," John said, "including, *revelation, be revealed, to lighten, manifestation, coming and appearing*. It is derived from the Greek APOKALUPTO which means *to take off the cover*. This is the reason some have translated the word as *unveiling or unfolding*. These words are closer to the original intended meaning, but the word *revelation* is not too far off either.

"The reason *unveiling* is better is that it pins down the meaning more accurately. If the book were called *The Revelation of Jesus Christ* it could be fulfilled by a short glimpse of the image of Christ; but *unveiling* implies that layers of meaning are being revealed. Now the question that unlocks the Key is this: Where are the writings that reveal, unfold or unveil the mystery, which is Christ?"

"Like I said, there does not seem to be anything in the book that explains much about Christ," I replied. "Most of it is dire predictions of the future."

"Are they predictions of the future, or are they symbols representing something more important," he said, "like the mystery of how the Christ unfolds within us? Perhaps the core meaning has been completely overlooked all these years."

"Are you telling me that apparent predictions such as a comet hitting the earth, green grass burning up and the waters of the earth being poisoned are not predictions, but contain hidden teachings about Christ manifesting in us?" Elizabeth and I were stunned.

"Yes, that is what I am saying. It is true that, now and then, events have occurred, and will occur, that seem to give credibility to the black and white predictions of the book, but the predictions are merely a vehicle for the real message. You see, if I had clearly written the meaning of the revelation and explained the unfolding of Christ consciousness as it develops in the disciple, the entire work would have been destroyed by ignorant authorities. Instead, the true teaching is encrypted in a spectacular vision of the future that so captivated the imaginations of the church, they couldn't reject it and decided to include it as scripture."

Suddenly, a light turned on in my head. "No wonder you support the books I am to write containing truth with fiction. The entire Book of Revelation is fiction that veils true principles."

"That is an interesting point," he said looking impressed.

"And it would have helped our case if you had brought up this point to the Masters," I added.

"You may be right," he smiled. "I never really thought of my book as being fiction because it is not in regular story form and I was concentrating on revealing the truth while writing it. I guess in a way; it's not much different than The Immortal series you are writing."

"So, if we look at this from another angle, the books will not be teaching in an approach much different from the past."

"Good point," he said. "I'll have to bring it up in the next conclave. Now to your assignment: Simply put, the Fourth Key is the Unveiling of Jesus Christ and the mystery is waiting to be seen through my book, The Apocalypse, also called the Book of Revelation. Your assignment is to study the book and its symbols while tuning into my mind through the Oneness Principle. Then, when you feel you are ready and the time is right, you will write a treatise giving the core meaning of the book. You will explain the true meaning of the mystery of *Christ in us, the hope of glory*, as the scripture says.

"When you have finished this you will have completed the Fourth Key. It will be years from now before you finish this project and, in the meantime, you will receive other keys. You are not to feel rushed in completing this project. You will know when the time is right to move forward. In the meantime, study the book, contemplate the meaning of symbols, and practice tuning into my mind through the Oneness Principle. If you faithfully do this, you will write the interpretation very much like I would if I were to do it."

"It seems like it would be easier and more accurate if you were to just write it and give it to me to publish."

John gave me a chastising look that communicated more than words. "Okay," I conceded. "You guys do not want to do for us what we can do for ourselves. I get it."

"I hope so," he said. "A teaching will always be more powerful and long lasting if it comes from a regular human who has struggled to achieve it. It took the Masters a long while to completely realize this, but now it has become their prime directive."

"I can understand the reasoning," I said, "but I can also relate to the inclination on both sides to side step it. Humans are lazy and just want things done for them. I can imagine the Masters getting impatient sometimes with the slow progress in working with us, and just wishing they could do the work for us."

"You understand correctly," he said. "Now I am short on time and must leave. Unfortunately, I have several duties to which I must attend. Any questions before I go?"

"Yes," I said. "Since it will be years before I complete the Fourth Key, when will we start working on the Fifth Key?"

"I will return soon and we will continue with the other Keys. In the meantime, read over the story of Moses and ask yourself why he was not allowed to enter into the Promised Land. The Fifth Key reveals the mystery."

He rose up, ready to leave, saying, "Thank you for your graciousness and congratulations for passing the test. I do not know who is more thrilled by it, you or me."

Elizabeth ran to him and embraced him tightly, "Oh, John, thank you so much for all you have done. Thank you for keeping your word and healing me! It feels so good to have my strength back and to not worry about becoming ill again. Will you say the Song of the 144,000 with us before you go?"

"It will be my pleasure," he said. We then held hands and said the Song, or perhaps I should say *sang* the Song. It did indeed seem as if we were raised up and joined a choir of angels rejoicing in spirit, light and love over the lower nature.

We took the next couple days off and just kicked back, relaxed and enjoyed each other's company. It was nice to live as two normal people, even if for only a short time. Then I received a phone call that reminded me that our life was not going to be so normal.

On the other side was a gravelly sounding voice, "Is this Joseph Dewey?"

"Yes."

"Forgive me for calling. I'm Doctor Leonard from Los Angeles and I received your number from your friend Lance."

"Yes," what can I do for you?" I asked.

"I'm calling because of Lance's friend Philo. Do you know of him?"

"Yes, he was up here a couple months ago with Lance and stayed with us a short while. What about him?"

"As you may know, he's been in a coma for some time. But the odd thing is that every now and then he comes out of it into semi-consciousness; and when this happens he is always shouting your name and cursing you. Several times it's gotten pretty intense, but then he seemed to settle back into his coma that is, until a couple days ago. He came back with an intensity that we have never seen before, shouting your name, cursing you and violently flinging his body around, even injuring two attendants. We've shot him full of tranquilizers, strapped him down tight, and still he rages on."

"Sounds like a sad case," I said.

"It is," he returned. "Several doctors besides me are curious as to how someone several states away could so affect one who is usually comatose. We've asked Lance about your relationship with Philo and he is also mystified, for he said you only met once. He said you didn't get on that well, but nothing extraordinary transpired. Is this correct?"

I paused a moment, realizing that he may want to put me away if I put the wrong slant on this. "Lance is speaking correctly," I said. "Philo came up once to visit with Lance, and while here, he tried to steal from me. I told him that I did not want to see him again."

"Have you been here to visit him in the hospital?"

"No. I haven't been to LA for a few years."

"Any ideas as to why he feels such intense emotion toward you?"

"I may have something," I said. "If you talk to Lance about Philo, you'll find that he sees himself as a New Age guru with superhuman powers. He thinks he can astral travel, or leave his body, and visit me. He's probably been having dreams of encounters with me, and thinks I have done some hocus pocus to strip him of his powers that left him in a coma. Outside of that guess, I can't tell you much."

"We have interviewed several of his friends and they do say he claims supernatural powers. Perhaps we are just dealing with an out-of-control delusion here. We have no other choice than to keep him heavily sedated, something we have never done with a coma patient."

"I'd keep him well strapped down also," I said. "You don't want any more of your people injured."

"Indeed," he said. "Thank you for your help."

After I hung up, I related the conversation to Elizabeth.

She laughed with delight and said, "You know, a lot of people are saying that life is not fair, and when I was sick I almost bought into it. But now that I am healed and I see that Philo is getting his just due, I am changing my mind. Life is fair. Life is more than fair. Life is great!"

"Yes," I agreed. "Life is indeed great. A part of me wishes this moment could last forever."

I sat back in my chair as Elizabeth came over and sat on my lap, giving me a hug. I wondered though about the next challenge to our peace. Ironically, I was almost looking forward to it.